SOIL—PLANT RELATIONSHIPS

SOIL–PLANT

NEW YORK . JOHN WILEY & SONS, INC.

London • Chapman & Hall, Limited

RELATIONSHIPS

C. A. BLACK

Department of Agronomy
Iowa State College
Ames, Iowa

PREFACE

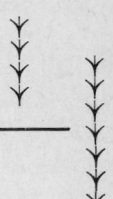

   This book covers some of the more important soil-plant relationships with emphasis throughout on soil as a substrate for plant growth. A special attempt is made to set forth the pertinent facts and ideas about soil properties and soil behavior as a basis for understanding but to minimize attention to technical details. Most of the concepts are illustrated by examples from specific locations. Except for purposes of illustration, however, no attempt is made to interpret the principles in terms of practice in a given geographical region, since frequently the proper application must take into account the particular combination of conditions in the area under consideration.

   The principal scientific problems in the area of soil-plant relationships are those of measurement and integration. The basic conditions that affect the growth of plants must be measured, and the measurements then must be integrated in the proper manner to obtain an index to the responses of plants. For the present, the major concern is measurement, and an accompanying objective of this text is to provide the student with a critical evaluation of knowledge of these problems as they are viewed at the moment by the author.

   The functions of soil in respect to the growth of higher plants are to supply the necessary mineral nutrients, water, and oxygen and to provide the environment for the elaboration of the root system that absorbs these substances and anchors the aerial parts. Some thought was given to the possibility of treating the subject matter of soil-plant relationships according to an outline in which these functions would appear as chapter headings. Although this approach has been used in part, it has not been followed exclusively. The soil properties involved are not associated uniquely with the basic requirements of plants. Also certain inhibitory factors are associated with the same soil properties that are involved in meeting the basic requirements. Hence it appeared to be more economical of space and more in accord with the natural state of affairs to discuss part of the subject matter from the standpoint of soil properties.

The subject matter is covered by the author in a course taught at Iowa State College. The level of presentation is intended to be suitable for students who already have attained some knowledge of soils, plant physiology, and the basic sciences at the undergraduate level. Review papers are cited wherever applicable since these are the most useful source material to a student who wishes to pursue further any particular subject. Other literature citations are included primarily for the purpose of giving credit for material cited.

The author wishes to acknowledge his indebtedness to Dr. W. H. Pierre for encouragement and counsel during the early phases of the manuscript preparation and to Dr. A. D. Scott for his willingness to discuss problems of soil chemistry on which advice was needed. Special thanks are due Dr. N. C. Brady and associates for the opportunity to spend a semester as a visiting professor at Cornell University. The last two chapters of the book were written there.

C. A. BLACK

June 1957

CONTENTS

1
Soil Composition   1

2
Soil Water   39

3
Soil Aeration   88

4
Exchangeable Bases   102

5
Soil Acidity   128

6
Soil Salinity and Alkalinity   159

7
Nitrogen   179

8
Phosphorus   248

9
Potassium   287

Index   325

1. SOIL COMPOSITION

This first chapter deals with the composition of the soil framework or solid phase as viewed from different standpoints. The subject matter provides both a brief review of much basic material and an insight into the value of the various characterizations of soil composition for evaluating soil as a substrate for plant growth.

MECHANICAL COMPOSITION

Soils have been described for many years in terms of the proportions of particles of different sizes that they contain. This basis of characterizing soils developed because particle size is an obvious characteristic and because particle size is related to soil behavior and plant response. The effects of particle size for the most part are indirect in nature, because particle size of soils is not one of the primary factors that affect plant growth. Indeed particle size per se has no known direct effect other than that of the mechanical impediment offered by large stones that deflect the passage of roots or prevent the vertical emergence and growth of the aerial parts.

Although the nature and properties of coarse and fine soil particles differ considerably, there is no sharp, natural division of any kind at any particular particle size. For purposes of experimentation and classification, however, some arbitrary boundaries have been established. The size limits used in the United States system and in the international system are indicated in Fig. 1 together with a brief description of the nature and properties of the soil "separates" or size fractions.

The mechanical composition of a soil is the weight percentage of the mineral matter that occurs in each of two or more specified size fractions. Ordinarily the soil is separated into at least three size frac-

1

United States system	Diameter of particles, mm.	International system	Diameter of particles, mm.	Approximate number of particles per gram*	Approximate surface area, cm.² per gram*	Visibility of individual particles	Physical character	Mineralogical composition
Very coarse sand	2.0–1.0	Coarse sand	2.0–0.2	5.4×10^2	21	Visible to naked eye	Loose and single-grained; not sticky or plastic	Mainly quartz with some rock fragments
Coarse sand	1.0–0.5							
Medium sand	0.5–0.25							
Fine sand	0.25–0.1	Fine sand	0.2–0.02	5.4×10^5	210	Visible to naked eye	Loose and single-grained; not sticky or plastic	Mainly quartz and feldspar with some ferromagnesians
Very fine sand	0.1–0.05							
Silt	0.05–0.002	Silt	0.02–0.002	5.4×10^8	2,100	Visible under microscope	Smooth and floury; only slightly cohesive	Mainly quartz and feldspar with some ferromagnesians, mica, and clay minerals
Clay	0.002–0.000	Clay	0.002–0.000	7.2×10^{11}	23,000	Invisible under microscope except in upper range; many particles resolved by electron microscope	Sticky and plastic when moist; hard and cohesive when dry	Mainly clay minerals with some quartz

* Based on average diameter and a density of 2.65 gm. per cm.³

Fig. 1. The soil separates and their properties.

tions, namely, sand, silt, and clay. The process by which the mechanical composition is measured is known as mechanical analysis. The numerous methods of mechanical analysis are based on the fact that the rate of fall of soil particles through water increases with the diameter of the particles or on some combination of this property with the use of sieves for separating coarse particles.

The relative proportions of sand, silt, and clay in the soil determine what is called the soil class, texture, or textural grade. There is, obviously, an infinite number of textural grades. For practical purposes, however, certain arbitrary divisions have been made, and descriptive names have been applied to the several classes denoted. Figure 2 shows the classification of soils into textural grades used in the United States, and it may be used to determine the name of the soil class when one has at hand the results of a mechanical analysis. In soil survey work the soil class is estimated in the field by the feel of the wet soil when rubbed between finger and thumb. Each soil class has particular characteristics that aid in distinguishing it from others. As may

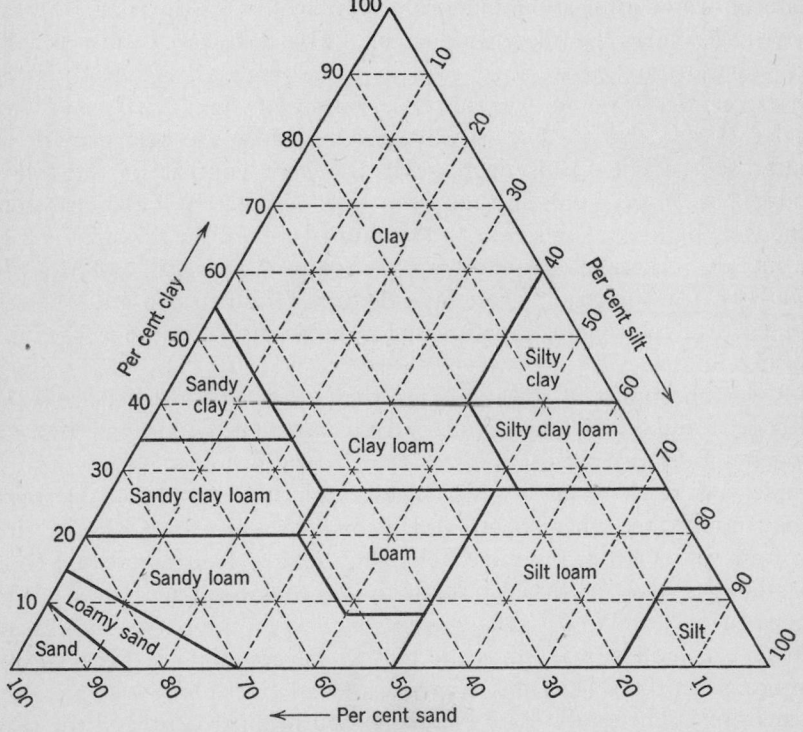

Fig. 2. Guide for textural classification of soils. (Alexander, 1952).

be inferred from the relatively large range in mechanical compositions classified as "clay" in Fig. 2, the characteristics of clay are dominant over those of sand and silt in determining the properties of the soil as a whole.

That plant growth is related in some way to the mechanical composition of soils has been recognized for many years. A bulletin on the subject of adaptation of crops to different soil textures was published before 1900 by Whitney (1896) of the United States Bureau of Soils. Whitney accounted for the observed soil texture effects in terms of the effect of soil texture on available water supply.

The supply of water to plants usually is greater in moderately fine-textured than in coarse-textured soils in humid regions such as the eastern United States where Whitney's observations were made. The reason for this is that the water-holding capacity increases as the texture becomes finer, and usually the rainfall is sufficient to fill soils of all textures to capacity at intervals. When the rainfall is not sufficient to fill all the soils to capacity, however, the higher water-holding capacity of the finer-textured soils may not be the deciding factor. Rate of water infiltration and protection against evaporation by deep penetration may be more important. Coarse-textured soils usually are superior to fine-textured soils in these respects. Probably these characteristics account for the observation of Yankovitch and Berthelot (1948) that in Tunisia olive trees achieve the best growth on sandy soils. The yields decrease if the clay content of the soil is above 8 to 10 per cent, and the crop fails completely if the clay content is as high as 25 per cent. The annual rainfall in this area is 8 to 12 inches. Another example was reported by Volk, Bell, and McCubbin (1947) in Florida. These investigators found that in a dry season the yield of cabbage on experimental plots decreased as the soil texture became finer.

A second important soil condition that varies with the texture is the nitrogen supply. Under similar environmental conditions the nitrogen supply usually increases as the texture becomes finer. An example was reported by Wilsie, Black, and Aandahl (1944) in Iowa. They noted that where hemp and soybeans were grown side by side on four soil types in the same field, the yield of hemp increased from 0.7 ton per acre on a sandy loam to 2.6 tons on a silty clay. The hemp plants exhibited nitrogen deficiency symptoms, the severity of which became less marked as the texture became finer. The yield of soybeans, on the other hand, was affected relatively little by variations in texture. The sandy loam yielded 21 bushels per acre, and the silty clay yielded 23 bushels per acre. The yields on all four soils were within the range from 19 to 25 bushels. The behavior of the soybean crop may be attributed to its leguminous nature, by virtue of which it was substantially independent of the supply of nitrogen in the soil. The rainfall in this season was sufficient to supply an ample amount of water to the plants on soils of all textures. The same investigators measured the yields of hemp on two soil types on both sides of an old crop boundary that crossed both types. Both sides of the field were planted to corn the year preceding the hemp, but during the 3 years preceding the corn, alfalfa had been produced on one side and a corn-oats rotation had been followed on the other. Prior to the alfalfa crop, the field had been handled as a unit. Table 1 shows that the effect of the alfalfa in increasing the yield of hemp was considerably greater on the sandy loam, in which the native supply of nitrogen was relatively low, than on the loam, in which the native supply of nitrogen was relatively high.

Table 1.   Yield of Hemp Following Two Different Cropping Systems on Sandy Loam and Loam Soils in the Same Field in Iowa

(Wilsie, Black, and Aandahl, 1944)

Soil Class	Cropping System	Yield of Dry, Retted Straw per Acre, ton
Sandy loam	Corn-oats	0.6
	Alfalfa	4.2
Loam	Corn-oats	5.0
	Alfalfa	6.1

STRUCTURE

As viewed from another standpoint, soils are composed of structural units that bear the same relation to soil as concrete blocks to a wall of such blocks. The overall structure of a soil is a resultant of the arrangement and bonding of individual soil particles into structural units and the arrangement and bonding of these units. The individual particles in a structural unit are attached more strongly to each other than to adjacent particles, which may or may not be part of another structural unit. Grouping of particles into structural units occurs in all soils; however, the strength of the bonds, the size and shape of the units, and the proportion of the soil particles involved in the units differ considerably among soils.

Formation

Little is known about structure formation; however, two distinct phases of the process may be recognized. The first, the development of interparticle bonds, confers the stability; the second, the separation of structural units from each other, confers the size and shape characteristic of individual units.

With respect to bond development, the generalization may be made that strong interparticle bonds form much more readily in the presence than in the absence of clay. If clay particles are present, structural units of moderate stability may be formed simply by allowing a dispersed mixture of particles to dry. The reason for this behavior is not clear. The hypothesis may be suggested, however, that as the particles approach each other more and more closely during removal of water, the separate particles become bound together by the same forces that cause the individual lattice layers within particles to cling together. As verification for this view, there is evidence that originally suspended clay particles that have settled from suspension on the bottom of a container are to some extent oriented with respect to each other. Freezing may have an effect similar to drying, since, if freezing occurs slowly, ice crystals form in the larger pore spaces at the expense of the water in the surrounding region.

The most stable interparticle bonds result from intergrowths of one kind or another. The enduring effect of organic matter on soil structure is probably the result of an intergrowth of comparatively stable residues of organic matter decomposition that are combined chemically with the surfaces of the mineral particles. In addition to the enduring effect, the rapid decomposition of fresh organic matter has a marked transient effect that probably results from production of mucilaginous material and fungal hyphae. Intergrowths of mineral matter may occur also. Oxides or hydrous oxides of iron, hydrous oxides of aluminum, silica, calcium carbonate, and calcium sulfate are possibilities. Iron compounds are thought to be of major importance in certain soils of warm, humid regions, and in the B horizon of podzol soils.

The explanation for the separation of structural units from each other must of necessity be even more vague than the explanation for the nature of the interparticle bonds. Disrupting effects of root growth, ice formation, shrinkage during drying, and compression of air entrapped when entering water seals outer pores have been suggested as possibilities.

A more detailed discussion and literature review of the subject of structure formation is given by Stallings (1952) and Baver (1956).

Characterization

Qualitative. Structural units of soils may be said to be platelike, prismlike, blocklike, or spheroidal, with variations of each (Soil Survey Staff, 1951). In platelike units, the particles are arranged around a plane, which usually is horizontal. Platelike structural units often are well developed in the A_2 horizon of virgin gray-brown podzolic soils. In prismlike units, the particles are arranged around a vertical line. The units have relatively plane vertical surfaces. Prismlike structural units commonly are well developed in the B horizon of chestnut soils and in the B horizon of solonetz soils. In blocklike units, the individual particles are arranged around a point. The surfaces of the structural units are fitted to those of adjacent units. Blocklike structural units often are well developed in the B horizon of fine-textured, gray-brown podzolic soils. In spheroidal units, the particles are arranged around a point, but the surfaces of the structural units show little accommodation to the shape of adjacent units. Spheroidal units often are well developed in the A horizon of chernozem soils. Prismlike units usually are the largest, followed in order of decreasing size by blocklike, platelike, and spheroidal units. These terms are used widely in soil survey work, where the soil profile characteristics are judged from observations made in the field.

Quantitative. A complete quantitative characterization of soil structure would involve evaluation of the size and shape of the structural units, the strength of the interparticle bonds within and between units, and the size distribution and continuity of pore spaces within and between units. The structure of the soil as a whole involves a summation of these characteristics in the soil profile. Soil structure is, therefore, a complex phenomenon that cannot be characterized precisely by a single physical measurement. Quantitative methods in use at present evaluate only a portion of the overall phenomenon.

Probably the most widely used measurement of soil structure is the so-called aggregate analysis procedure that was developed by Tiulin and modified by Yoder (1936). In this procedure, a sample of air-dry soil is placed in a nest of sieves, which is immersed in water. The sieves are gently raised and lowered mechanically for 30 minutes to bring about a separation of the different size fractions. The soil material left on the individual sieves then is dried and weighed. The size fractions reported often include 5 to 2 mm., 2 to 1 mm., 1 to 0.5 mm., 0.5 to 0.25 mm., 0.25 to 0.1 mm., and <0.1 mm. diameter. In some cases the results are expressed as a single figure by reporting the percentage of the soil material in size fractions larger than, say, 0.25 mm. diameter or by some scheme of weighting the percentages of the different size fractions. The exact weighting employed is arbitrary, but it is done in such a way that the result will reflect common experience that aggregates of coarse-sand size are more favorable for most agricultural purposes than are aggregates of smaller size. Since some of the material that remains on individual sieves may be present as individual particles rather than as aggregates, a mechanical analysis sometimes is made as a means of "correcting" the aggregate analysis.

The aggregate analysis procedure evaluates, in part, the size distribution of the structural units (and perhaps also the size distribution of relatively coarse individual particles) and, in part, the stability of the units under the treatments employed. One of the questions still under debate is whether the soil sample should be field-moist, air-dry, or in some other condition. The results depend on the condition employed.

Numerous other techniques have been employed to give information on soil structure. The so-called falling-drop technique gives a measure of the stability of structural units to raindrop impact. Measurements of bulk density and pore space give an indication of differences in structure among soils of similar textures. For soils of similar texture, low bulk density and high pore space are taken as an indication of favorable structure. More useful information is given by measurements of pore-size distribution. The pore-size distribution may be estimated from a microscopic examination of thin sections of soil or from the quantity of water removed from an initially saturated sample of soil with successive increments of tension applied to the soil. Permeability of the soil to water or air is another measure of soil structure. Permeability is determined, in part, by the size distribution and, in part, by the continuity of the pores. The difference obtained between the permeability found by air and that found by water has been used as still another index of soil structure. This measurement gives an indication of the swelling and disintegration of structural units that occur upon wetting with water. Penetrometer tests represent quite a different sort of measurement. A soil penetrometer is an instrument for recording the force required to push a blunt-pointed probe into the soil. Other conditions being equal, soils with good structure for most agricultural plants are penetrated more easily than soils with poor structure.

Effect of soil treatments

In general, the structure of soils deteriorates with cropping. The results of aggregate analyses by Sokolovsky (1933), Paschall et al. (1935), Puhr and Olson (1937), and others may be cited in this connection. Although the deterioration is associated with a decrease in content of soil organic matter, the latter probably is not the sole cause. The passage of implements through and over the soil and the impact of raindrops on the bare soil no doubt are responsible in part.

When comparisons are made between crops within soils that have

STRUCTURE   9

been cultivated for some time, the usual observation is that the structure is better under close-growing, noncultivated crops than under
row crops. The results of an experiment of Browning et al. (1948),
in Table 2, may be cited as an example.

Table 2.   Aggregate Analysis of a Silt Loam Soil under Different
Cropping Treatments in Iowa
(Browning et al., 1948)

Crop	Proportion of Soil in Aggregates >0.25 mm. Diameter, %
Continuous corn	33
Corn in corn-oats-clover rotation	42
Oats in corn-oats-clover rotation	51
Clover in corn-oats-clover rotation	57
Continuous alfalfa	60
Continuous bluegrass	62

Applications of decomposable organic matter, such as crop residues
and manure, improve the structure. Synthetic organic soil aggregants
have a much more pronounced effect per unit weight than do the foregoing materials. The synthetic soil aggregants are long-chain molecules that apparently combine with mineral particles and form bridges
between them. Cost, undoubtedly, is the major deterrent to widespread usage of these substances. Application of certain inorganic
substances, such as silicones and sodium and potassium silicate, likewise results in marked improvement of soil structure. These substances have not found practical application for agricultural purposes,
partly because of deleterious effects on plants in the case of the silicates,
and partly because of cost.

Effect on plant growth

Many experiments have been reported in which particular soil treatments or management practices have resulted in an improvement in
soil structure and an increase in crop yield. Data of Rynasiewicz
(1945) in Table 3 may be cited as an example. The correlation between aggregates >0.5 mm. diameter and onion yields is 0.99. Despite
the relatively high positive value of the correlation coefficient, however, one may inquire to what extent the differences in onion yields
were caused by the aggregation of the soil and to what extent they
were caused by other conditions associated with the crop rotation.
In other words, the existence of a direct cause-and-effect relationship
between soil aggregation and onion yields may be questioned, since
the variations in both are attributable to crop rotations. Crop ro-

Table 3.   Aggregation of a Very Fine Sandy Loam Soil, and Yield of Onions
Obtained with Different Crop Rotations in Rhode Island
(Rynasiewicz, 1945)

Crop Rotation	Proportion of Soil in Aggregates >0.5 mm. Diameter, %	Yield of Onions per Acre, bu.
Onions, mangels, mangels	22	157
Onions, buckwheat, buckwheat	23	218
Onions, corn, corn	26	249
Onions, redtop, redtop	37	487

tations may affect plant growth in a variety of ways besides the structural changes they bring about. Experiments in which modifications of soil structure are produced by treatments that may have independent effects on plants are not entirely suitable as a source of evidence for the importance of soil structure to plant growth.

Synthetic soil aggregants provide a more suitable means of investigating the importance of soil structure to plant growth. According to present information, some of these chemicals are capable of making profound changes in aggregation with only small direct effects on the microbiological population and nutrient status of soils. If chemicals having such properties are applied to soils to improve aggregation, the changes in crop yield that result may be attributed to structure with greater certainty than previously was possible. Experiments with soil aggregants have produced various results. Increases in yield sometimes have been large, as in work of Alderfer (1954) in Pennsylvania, where lima beans yielded 1.7 tons per acre without a soil aggregant and 3.1 tons with a soil aggregant, an increase of 82 per cent. In other instances, yields have been decreased. Haise, Jensen, and Alessi (1955) found this to be true in an experiment with sugar beets in North Dakota, where the yield of the control was 12.6 tons per acre, and the yield with 500 lb. of soil aggregant per acre was 10.2 tons, a decrease of 19 per cent. Evidently, therefore, soil structure does not invariably limit crop yields. Reliable predictions cannot yet be made as to the extent to which yields will be limited by soil structure in individual instances. Experiments of Martin et al. (1952) on fine-textured soils with poor visual structure showed that soil aggregants produced various results. A marked increase in both aggregation and crop yield occurred in some instances; in others, the aggregation increased but the crop yield did not. Evidently it cannot be assumed that crop yield is limited by soil structure simply because a soil appears to have poor structure. According to Quastel's (1954) review of experimental results, soil aggregants often cause an improvement in crops early in the season even though final yields are not increased. There is some indication that the importance of soil structure, as a limiting factor in plant growth, increases with density of the plant population (Hely, Bonnier, and Manil, 1954) and fertility level of the soil (J. Runkles, unpublished data, Iowa Agricultural Experiment Station).

Once it has been decided that differences in plant growth observed in a particular situation are attributable primarily to differences in structure, the next question is the manner in which the effects on plant growth have been brought about. Soil structure may affect plant growth in a variety of ways, some direct and some indirect.

Direct effects. Changes in soil structure may be said to have a direct effect on plant growth whenever differences in expansion of plant parts can be attributed to differences in mechanical impediment offered by the soils under consideration. Deciding whether or not observed differences in expansion of plant parts are attributable to differences in mechanical impediment is seldom an easy matter. Nevertheless, a few instances can be cited in which direct effects undoubtedly are present and apparently are primarily responsible for the effects produced.

The first case of direct effects of structure has to do with emergence of seedlings in crusted soils. There is little doubt that the bending of seedlings that sometimes occurs when they reach a dry crust from beneath is a direct result of the mechanical impediment offered by the crust. Work on synthetic soil aggregants (Quastel, 1954) suggests that one of the major benefits from application of such substances to soils that produce surface crusts is the resulting increase in seedling emergence.

A second, fairly clear direct effect is the restriction of root development that may occur in hard surface soils. Taubenhaus, Ezekiel, and Rea (1931) reported cases of "root strangulation" of cotton in clay soils compacted by rain or irrigation and then hardened by extended hot, dry weather. The normal tap root failed to develop. Instead, a constricted zone about 0.3 to 0.4 mm. in diameter and 25 mm. in length developed in the root in the hardest layer of soil, located just below the surface. The portion of the tap root found in the less compact soil beneath was more nearly normal in size. Such malformed plants often died during the season, apparently when the rate of water movement through the restricted part became insufficient to meet plant requirements.

A third possible direct effect is the failure of roots to expand normally in compacted or fine-textured zones below the soil surface. In

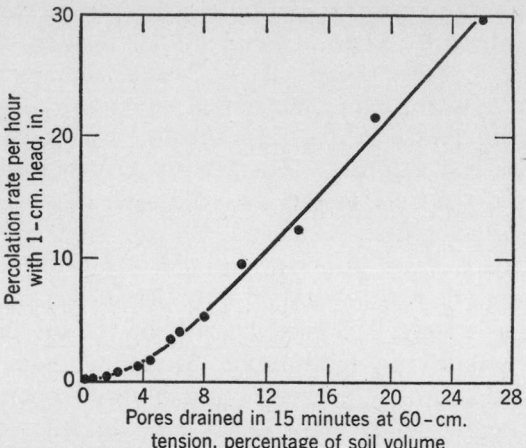

Fig. 3. Rate of percolation of water versus pores drained in 15 minutes at 60-cm. tension in undisturbed cores from different horizons of soils from Virginia, North Carolina, South Carolina, and Georgia. (Each point represents the average of from 16 to 65 measurements). (Peele, 1950.)

many cases indirect effects may be important, which will be shown later. One instance will be noted, however, in which the effect appears to be direct. Jean and Weaver (1924) compared the root system produced by sugar beets on comparable plots of irrigated and nonirrigated soil in 2 years differing in rainfall. In the year with the higher rainfall, the beets on both plots produced a relatively straight taproot, and the branch roots were of smaller diameter than the main taproot. The same was true of beets on the irrigated soil in the year with the lower rainfall. The soil of the nonirrigated plots, however, was too dry for the best growth of the plants. The taproot followed a zigzag course downward through the soil and often divided into several branches of similar diameter. The peculiar behavior of the roots under these conditions probably resulted directly from the mechanical impediment offered by the relatively dry soil. More evidence is required, however, before local differences in water availability can be eliminated as a possible causal factor.

Indirect effects. Soil structure may have important indirect effects on plants through its influence on air and water relationships of soils. In general these effects must be inferred because of the lack of experimental verification of the causal relationships in particular instances where structural changes have been made.

Structural modifications most easily effected in soils result in changes in volume percentage of large or "noncapillary" pores. These pores are of major importance in determining the rate of saturated water flow through the soil. Data of Peele (1950) may be cited as an example. Figure 3 shows the results of Peele's laboratory tests of the rate of water flow through undisturbed cores of a large number of samples from different horizons of soils from Virginia, North Carolina, South Carolina, and Georgia. The rate of saturated water flow evidently is related not only to the rate of drainage of excess water but also to aeration and erosion.

The importance of soil structure in relation to infiltration of water is basically the same as for saturated flow within the soil. Infiltration is mentioned separately, however, because of the special significance of structural stability to infiltration. Structural units that are not strongly bonded internally disintegrate readily under bombardment by raindrops. The fine soil particles released are filtered out of the water as it enters the soil, thereby closing the large pores and reducing the subsequent rate of infiltration. The effect is illustrated by the results of an experiment of Lowdermilk (1930) in Fig. 4. The rate of water infiltration into saturated columns of a sandy loam soil remained essentially constant with time as long as clear water was applied, but dropped sharply upon application of muddy water. Runoff and erosion, of course, are increased as a result of disintegration of surface

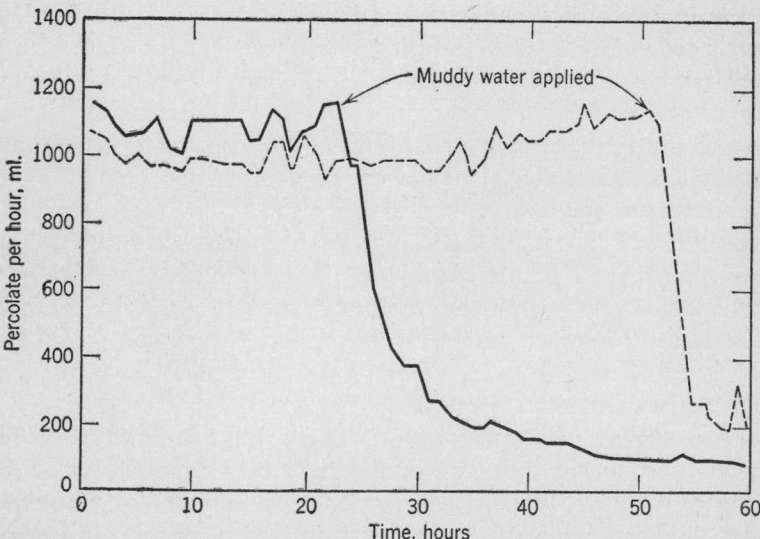

Fig. 4. Rate of percolation of water through two columns of a sandy loam soil to which clear water was applied initially and muddy water was applied after 24 or 51 hours. (Lowdermilk, 1930.)

structure. Experiments demonstrating the action of soil aggregants in increasing infiltration and decreasing erosion have been reviewed by Quastel (1954). Mulches of organic materials have a similar effect. The mechanism by which they act, however, is not the same as that of the soil aggregants. Although organic mulches may improve the structure of the immediate surface of the soil, they act primarily by breaking the fall of raindrops. Literature on this subject has been reviewed by Stallings (1950).

Finally, the indirect effect of structure on root penetration may be noted. Many instances have been reported of limited penetration of roots into subsoil layers having poor structure. In some such instances the effect may be direct. In others it may be largely indirect, as in unpublished observations of J. C. Russel in Iraq. Russel noted that roots of alfalfa, barley, and wheat grown under irrigation on a certain alluvial silty clay soil fail to penetrate below a depth of about 18 inches. No hard layer can be found in this soil at the depth where root penetration ceases. The cause of the root behavior apparently is poor aeration, which is associated with the compacted condition of the soil. The soil has a moisture equivalent of 28 per cent, but pore space of only 25 per cent, so that after irrigation the soil is saturated and poorly aerated. The native plant, *Prosopis steptheniana*, which can endure waterlogging, produces roots that penetrate several times as deep as those of alfalfa, barley, and wheat. Instances in which particular soil layers exhibit properties similar to those of the soil described above have been reported by Woodruff (1940) and Veihmeyer and Hendrickson (1946). The matter of aeration will be considered in more detail in a subsequent chapter.

MINERALOGICAL COMPOSITION

From the mineralogical standpoint, the inorganic portion of the soil solid phase is composed of minerals, the primary source of which is igneous rocks. As shown in Table 4, a total of 92 per cent by weight of the igneous rocks is composed of only a few types of minerals. The remaining 8 per cent is composed of a large variety of accessory minerals, each present in small proportion. According to Jeffries (1947), 25 per cent of the surface of the earth is underlain by igneous rocks. The remaining 75 per cent is underlain by sedimentary rocks, the average composition of which is shown in Table 4. An average mineralogical composition of soils has not been worked out, but if such were done, the values for the various minerals probably would bear greater similarity to the average for sedimentary than for igneous rocks. The reason for this is that igneous rocks undergo alteration

Table 4. Average Mineralogical Composition of Igneous and Sedimentary Rocks

	Proportion of Mineral Present	
Mineral Group	Igneous Rocks, % (Clarke, 1924)	Sedimentary Rocks, % (Jeffries, 1947)
Feldspar	59	7
Amphibole	17	. . .
Quartz	12	38
Mica	4	20
Carbonates	. . .	20
Clay	. . .	9
Limonite	. . .	3
Accessory	8	3

by weathering, whether the igneous rocks are altered to soil in place or after transportation and consolidation into sedimentary rocks.

Sand and silt fractions

Usually the mineralogical composition of the sand and silt fractions is considered separately from that of the clay fraction. This subdivision is largely a matter of tradition, which developed from experimental necessity. The petrographic microscope is the most useful instrument for determining the mineralogical composition of the sand and silt fractions, but it is not suitable for identifying single grains of clay size. At one time only the sand and silt fractions could be studied because no instruments suitable for clay identification were available.

McCaughey and Fry (1913) made a mineralogical examination of the sand and silt fractions of twenty-five soils obtained from locations scattered widely over the United States and reported their results in the terms shown in Table 5. The data in this table illustrate the fact that although many minerals may be identified in the sand and silt fractions of soils, only a few species commonly are found in abundance. The data indicate also that relatively minor constituents of the original igneous rocks may become important soil minerals by virtue of their resistance to weathering. The outstanding example is quartz, which, despite its occurrence to the extent of only 12 per cent by weight of the igneous rocks, was the only mineral found in all soils and abundant in all soils. The same principle is indicated in Table 4 by the change in ratio of feldspar to quartz between igneous and sedimentary rocks.

The mineralogical composition of soil particles changes with the size. In general the proportion of primary minerals decreases and the proportion of secondary minerals increases as the particle size becomes smaller. The mineralogical composition changes rapidly in

Table 5. Occurrence and Abundance of Certain Minerals in the Sand and Silt
Fractions of Twenty-five Soils
(McCaughey and Fry, 1913)

Mineral	Number of Soils Present	Number of Soils Abundant	Mineral	Number of Soils Present	Number of Soils Abundant
Quartz	25	25	Zircon	22	1
Orthoclase	20	14	Tourmaline	21	1
Hornblende	23	12	Magnetite	6	1
Microcline	20	10	Ilmenite	2	1
Epidote	24	8	Calcite	2	1
Biotite	21	8	Sericite	1	1
Muscovite	20	6	Hematite	1	1
Plagioclase	13	5	Rutile	17	0
Andesine	6	4	Apatite	12	0
Oligoclase	7	3	Fluorite	4	0
Chlorite	21	2	Titanite	2	0
Garnet	10	2	Hypersthene	2	0
Sillimanite	10	2	Phlogopite	1	0
Pyroxene	6	2	Serpentine	1	0
Albite	5	2	Actinolite	1	0
Labradorite	3	2	Iddingsite	1	0
Augite	2	2	Staurolite	1	0

the size range near the boundary between silt and clay.   For example,
Truog et al. (1937) found that feldspar was abundant in the 0.01 to
0.005 mm. diameter size fraction of four of five samples of soil from
eastern United States.   In the 0.003 to 0.002 mm. diameter size fraction, however, only a trace of feldspar was found in four samples and
none was detected in the fifth.   In samples of three soils of England,
Marshall (1935) found mainly feldspar, mica, and quartz in the silt
fraction (0.02 to 0.002 mm.), mainly quartz, clay minerals, and intermediate material in the 0.002 to 0.001 mm. fraction, and mainly clay
minerals in the 0.001 to 0.0005 mm. fraction.   These mineralogical
changes with particle size constitute some justification for the placement of the silt-clay size boundary at 0.002 mm.

Differences in intensity and time of weathering are reflected in soil
mineralogical composition.   Coffey (1912) grouped the twenty-five
soils studied by McCaughey and Fry (1913) into three groups, according to their location in arid, prairie, or timbered-humid regions, and
obtained the data of Table 6.   These results show that the weight
percentage of the sand and silt fractions composed of minerals other
than quartz decreased in the order arid>prairie>timbered-humid.
Over equal intervals of time, alteration of parent minerals by weathering would be expected to be least in the first and greatest in the last
of these regions.   The significance of the classification of minerals into

Table 6.   Average Mineralogical and Chemical Composition of Soils
from Different Regions
(Coffey, 1912)

	Minerals Other Than Quartz in Indicated Soil Fraction		Composition of Soils		
Region	Sand, %	Silt, %	Calcium, %	Magnesium, %	Potassium, %
Arid	37	39	1.9	0.7	0.6
Prairie	20	29	0.8	0.3	0.4
Timbered-humid	8	12	0.3	0.2	0.3

quartz and minerals other than quartz lies in the fact that quartz may
be considered as a relatively inert residue of weathering that will
furnish no plant nutrients upon solution. The minerals other than
quartz, on the other hand, include species that contain such nutrients
as calcium, magnesium, and potassium. On decomposition of the
mineral, these nutrients are liberated in soluble form and may be used
by plants. The difference between the two mineral groups in regard
to these nutrients is indicated in Table 6 by the quantities of calcium,
magnesium, and potassium present in the same three categories of soils.
The content of these nutrients varies directly with the content of
minerals other than quartz.

The data of Nichols (1939) may be cited as a further indication of
the soil fertility implications of the mineralogical nature of soils.
Table 7 shows that in the group of three soils of Australia examined,

Table 7.   Mineralogy, Maturity, and Fertility of Soils in the Mount
Gellibrand Area, Western Australia
(Nichols, 1939)

	Average Content of Minerals in the Fine Sand		
	Brown Loam, %	Black Clay, %	Gray Loam, %
Rock fragments	7.6	0.3	Trace
Augite	12.3	1.0	Trace
Plagioclase	19.3	8.7	3.9
Olivine	2.2	0.8	0.5
Iron oxide	8.4	1.7	1.2
Quartz	50.3	80.8	93.7
Relative fertility	High	Medium	Low
Maturity	Immature	Intermediate	Mature
Topography	On slope	Foot of slope	Plain

the fertility of the soil increases with the percentage of minerals other
than quartz in the fine sand fraction.

Some progress has been made in evaluating different types of potassium-bearing minerals as sources of potassium for plant growth. Various lines of evidence indicate that mica is superior to potassium feldspar in this respect. This work will be discussed in more detail in the chapter on potassium. Work on the relative decomposition rates of a variety of minerals was reviewed by Jackson and Sherman (1953).

There is no doubt that through weathering, plant nutrients contained in minerals of the sand and silt fractions are released gradually in soluble form that can be used by plants. With sufficient experimental work on the problem, an empirical method probably could be devised for estimating the total amount of individual mineral nutrients released per year. The procedure would need to take into account the mineralogical composition of the sand and silt fractions, and the environmental factors that affect the weathering rate. The process of evaluating a soil by such a procedure, however, would be exceedingly laborious. Moreover, as a technique for assessing the nutrient status of the soil, the procedure still would be inadequate because it takes no account of the clay fraction, the importance of which cannot be evaluated on the basis of mineralogical composition alone. At present mineralogical studies of the sand and silt fractions appear to be of greatest value in research on problems of soil genesis and classification.

Clay fraction

Although the sand, silt, and clay fractions of the soil all result directly or indirectly from the weathering of igneous rocks, there is a significant difference between the processes leading to the formation of sand and silt on the one hand, and clay on the other. Chemical processes of weathering are much more important in the formation of clay than in the formation of sand and silt. Whereas the sand and silt fractions by and large represent residual, unweathered material, much of the clay fraction is composed of new minerals that were not present when the weathering processes began. Some of the new minerals are alteration products of the minerals found originally in the sand and silt fractions; others are entirely new and are synthesized from the dissolved weathering products.

Since the chemical processes leading to the formation of clay in the soil take place in water solutions, the degree of weathering (hence the amount of clay formed) would be expected to increase with the effective amount of water supplied to the soil. In confirmation of this prediction, Jenny and Leonard (1934) found that at constant annual temperature, the clay content of the soil increased with annual rainfall in their traverse from eastern Colorado through Kansas and Missouri

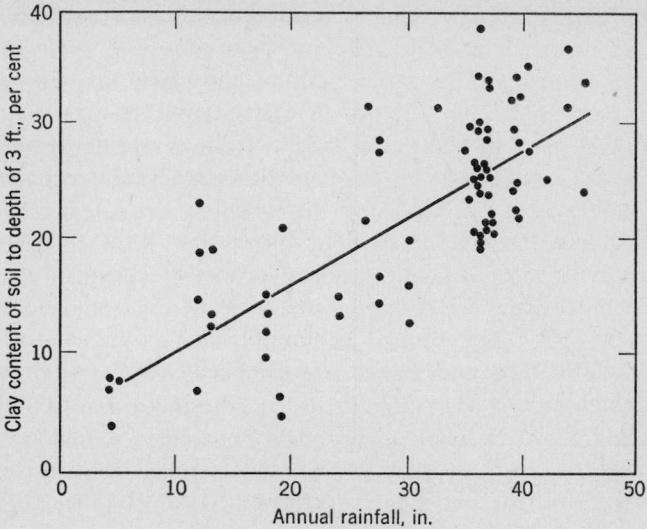

Fig. 5.   Clay content of soils versus annual rainfall along the 52° to 56° F. isotherm in Colorado, Kansas, and Missouri.   (Jenny and Leonard, 1934.)

(Fig. 5).   How much higher the clay content would have become had it been possible to extend the traverse to areas of progressively higher rainfall is not known.   The data of Craig and Halais (1934) suggest that under some conditions the clay content might pass through a maximum and then decrease again.   Their results in Table 8 show

Table 8.   Mechanical Composition of Soils of Mauritius Developed
with Different Annual Rainfall
(Craig and Halais, 1934)

Average Annual Rainfall, in.	Stones and Gravel (200–2 mm. Diameter), %	Sand and Silt, %	Clay ($<2\mu$ Diameter), %
25–50	8	27	73
50–75	4	33	67
75–100	5	44	56
100–125	5	51	49
125–150	2	55	45

that on the island of Mauritius the clay content decreased with increasing rainfall.   These results do not mean that chemical weathering became less severe as the rainfall or the water content of the soil increased.   Under the conditions of intense weathering that occur in tropical Mauritius, much of the sand and silt in the soils consists of

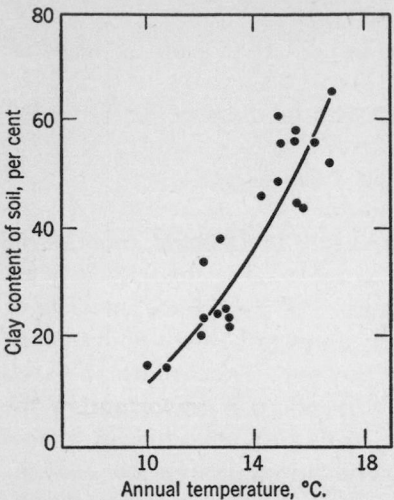

Fig. 6. Clay content of soils versus annual temperature at constant water supply expressed as NS quotient = 400. (Jenny, 1935.)

concretions that result from the alterations of other soil constituents. The sand and silt fractions are, therefore, not "residual" as, presumably, is the case in the soils Jenny and Leonard dealt with, but "synthesized."

Since clay is the result of chemical processes acting on the coarser materials in the soil, and since the temperature coefficient of the rate of chemical reactions generally falls in the range of 1.4 to 7 for each increase of 10° C., the clay content of soils would be expected to increase with temperature. That such is the case is indicated by the data of Jenny (1935) in Fig. 6. Jenny found that in soils derived from basic rocks in the eastern United States the clay content increased about 7 per cent with each degree centigrade increase in mean annual temperature.

Because of the small size of clay particles, little could be done in the early days to investigate the nature of the components present. When X-ray diffraction methods were applied to soil clays by Ross (1927), however, crystalline minerals were found to be present. The current view is that the clay fraction is composed mainly of secondary minerals. In temperate and cold regions these minerals are mostly crystalline silicates along with smaller amounts of nonsilicate minerals. Some soils may contain important amounts of amorphous silicates. In tropical regions the dominant minerals may be free oxides and hydrous oxides of iron and aluminum. Quartz is the only primary mineral commonly present in large quantities in the clay fraction of soils. Where present, quartz is most abundant in the coarse clay. According to Hendricks and Alexander (1939) the principal minerals of the clay fraction may be classified as follows:

1. Silicates.
   a. Kaolins.
   b. Montmorillonites.
   c. Hydrous micas or illites.
2. Nonsilicates.

   a. Quartz and amorphous silica (SiO_2).
   b. Free oxides and hydrous oxides of iron, such as hematite (Fe_2O_3) and goethite [$FeO(OH)$].
   c. Hydrous oxides of aluminum, such as diaspore [$AlO(OH)$] and gibbsite [$Al(OH)_3$].
   d. Calcium carbonate ($CaCO_3$).

A schematic representation of the structure of kaolinite, montmorillonite, and illite will be found in the chapter on exchangeable bases.

The main connection between the nature of the silicate minerals of clays and the nature of the parent rock seems to be between the content of magnesium and potassium in the two. According to Grim (1953, pp. 342–343), the supply of magnesium is important in the formation of montmorillonite, and the supply of potassium in formation of illite. If magnesium and potassium are present in low concentration in the rock or are removed rapidly during weathering, the tendency is for formation of kaolinite. Since the rate of removal of magnesium and potassium will be determined by the environmental conditions, the latter will modify the effect of the parent material. In fact, Hosking (1940) found that the same parent rock gave rise to soils containing kaolinite under one set of conditions and to soils containing montmorillonite under other conditions. Conversely, Humbert and Marshall (1943) found that parent rocks of different composition gave rise to soils having the same clay mineral composition when the soils were developed under similar environmental conditions.

In general, illite and montmorillonite are the dominant silicate mineral types in the clay fraction of soils of dry regions and cold regions, and kaolinite is dominant in warm, humid regions (Grim, 1953, pp. 340–341; Winters and Simonson, 1951). Kaolinite, therefore, appears to be more stable than are the montmorillonite and illite minerals under conditions of strong weathering. Kaolinite, however, is not the end product of weathering. Tanada (1951) found that in soils of Hawaii, where weathering is intense, the percentage of the clay fraction composed of kaolinite decreased with increasing annual rainfall. In extreme cases the soil may be composed mainly of resistant oxides. Bennett and Allison (1928, p. 73) reported, for example, that the 0- to 26-inch layer of a highly weathered soil from Cuba contained 63 per cent Fe_2O_3 and 18 per cent Al_2O_3.

There are numerous exceptions to the generalizations of the preceding paragraph which are based on "average" conditions. One cause of exceptions is the nonuniformity of the time and conditions of weathering to which materials now found in soils in adjacent locations have been exposed. In soils of Iowa, for example, Peterson (1946) found that kaolinite typically is either absent or present in only small amount. All soils showing this characteristic have developed from glacial drift or loess deposited during Pleistocene geological time. In contrast, kaolinite is the dominant clay mineral in the Gosport soil. This soil has developed on recently exposed sedimentary deposits that were laid down originally during the much earlier Pennsylvanian geological age, when conditions were favorable for formation of kaolinite. Kaolinite is dominant in the parent material as well as in the soil. Apparently, therefore, the Gosport soil merely inherits a characteristic already present in parent material that was formed under environmental conditions different from those found at present.

Jackson, Tyler, et al. (1948) made an attempt to integrate the problem of the mineralogical nature of the clay fraction of soils. They placed the various important minerals in a weathering sequence according to the rate at which they were thought to disappear if they were present in clay size in the soil. Arranged in order from most easily weathered to most difficultly weathered, the type members of their thirteen weathering stages are gypsum, calcite, hornblende, biotite, albite, quartz, illite, mica-intermediate, montmorillonite, kaolinite, gibbsite, hematite, and anatase. (Jackson and Sherman [1953]

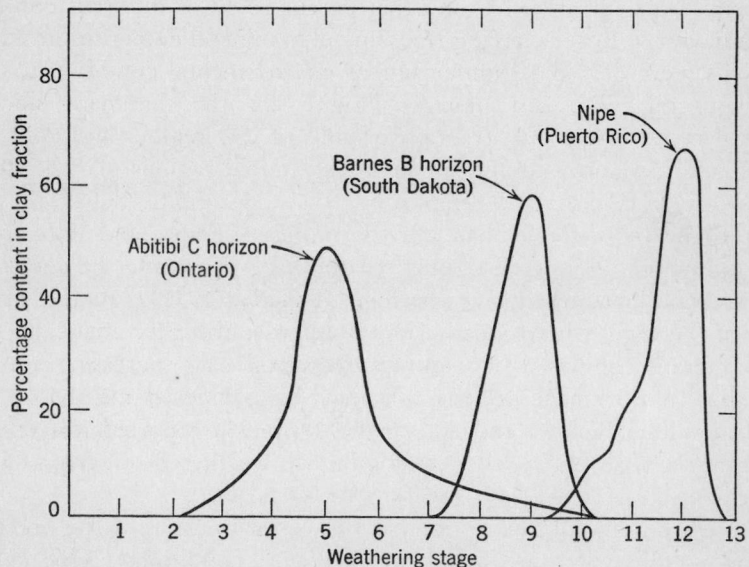

Fig. 7. Percentage content of minerals in clay fraction of three soils versus weathering stage of minerals. (Jackson, Tyler, et al., 1948.)

modified this terminology slightly by describing "mica-intermediate" as interstratified 2:1 layer silicates and vermiculite.) The thesis of Jackson, Tyler, et al. (1948) is that usually from three to five minerals of the weathering sequence are found in the clay of a given soil horizon. When the percentage content of the minerals at each weathering stage is plotted against the weathering stage, the distribution curve obtained is dominated by one or two members of the weathering sequence, with the percentages of the other minerals decreasing with the distance in either direction from the dominant mineral. The nature of the dominant mineral may be used to characterize the weathering stage of the clay. Examples of the distribution curves obtained with three soils are shown in Fig. 7.

The significance of clay mineralogy to plant growth will not be discussed here except to state that the clay is the most reactive inorganic portion of the solid phase of the soil. The nature of the minerals present therein has some bearing on the availability of most, if not all, of the nutrients that plants derive from soils. The importance of the clay fraction will be considered in more detail in connection with topics to be treated subsequently.

CHEMICAL COMPOSITION

Chemically, soils are composed of a variety of elements present in different proportions. The proportions differ according to the nature of the parent rock material and the changes brought about by weathering and accumulation of organic matter. As would be expected from the mineralogical changes associated with weathering, some elements are lost more readily than others. The difference in susceptibility of various elements to loss by weathering is illustrated by the comparative chemical composition of the lithosphere and of river water shown in Table 9. The amount of $Al_2O_3 + Fe_2O_3$ is set

Table 9. Comparative Chemical Composition of the Lithosphere and of River Water, with the Amount of $Al_2O_3 + Fe_2O_3$ Set at Unity in Each Case

(Robinson and Holmes, 1924)

	SiO$_2$	Al$_2$O$_3$ + Fe$_2$O$_3$	CaO	MgO	K$_2$O	Na$_2$O
Lithosphere	2.81	1.00	0.21	0.18	0.44	0.16
River water	13.4	1.00	30.3	7.81	2.72	11.7

at unity in each case, and the content of each of the other constituents is expressed as a fraction or multiple of the amount of $Al_2O_3 + Fe_2O_3$. Of all the constituents considered, the sum of $Al_2O_3 + Fe_2O_3$ evidently suffers the least percentage of loss by weathering. This inference is in agreement with the weathering sequence of Jackson, Tyler, et al. (1948) in which gibbsite $[Al(OH)_3]$ and hematite (Fe_2O_3) are listed as types of the most resistant minerals except for anatase (TiO_2). Silica, which occurs in the lithosphere to the extent of 2.8 times the amount of $Al_2O_3 + Fe_2O_3$, is present in river water to the extent of 13.4 times the amount of $Al_2O_3 + Fe_2O_3$. The bases, calcium, sodium, magnesium, and potassium, which occur in the lithosphere in amounts smaller than that of $Al_2O_3 + Fe_2O_3$, occur in river water in amounts much greater than that of $Al_2O_3 + Fe_2O_3$. The relative resistance of the bases to loss increases in the order given above.

The chemical composition of igneous rocks and various soils is given in Table 10; only a few points about these analyses will be men-

Table 10.   Chemical Composition of Igneous Rocks[1] and Soils[2]

Content of Constituents by Weight

Constituent	Igneous Rocks, % (Average)	Barnes Loam, % (South Dakota)	Caribou Loam, % (Maine)	Cecil Sandy Clay Loam, % (North Carolina)	Columbiana Clay, % (Costa Rica)
SiO_2	59.1	69.3	57.5	74.7	19.8
Al_2O_3	15.3	11.4	7.8	12.3	37.1
Fe_2O_3	7.3	3.8	2.5	4.9	15.6
TiO_2	1.0	0.5	0.7	1.3	2.0
MnO	0.1	0.2	0.2	0.3	0.3
CaO	5.1	1.6	1.2	0.2	0.2
MgO	3.5	0.9	0.6	<0.1	0.5
K_2O	3.1	1.8	0.9	0.6	0.1
Na_2O	3.8	1.1	1.0	0.2	0.2
P_2O_5	0.3	0.2	0.2	0.2	0.3
SO_3	0.1	0.1	0.3	...	0.2
Ignition loss	1.2[4]	9.5	27.2	7.1	24.1
Organic matter[3]	...	6.0	25.3	2.4	6.0
Nitrogen[3]	...	...	0.9	...	...

[1] Clarke (1924).

[2] Byers, Alexander, and Holmes (1935). The soil analyses are of the surface horizon, which had a thickness of 9 inches in the Barnes soil, ¾ inch in the Caribou soil, 6 inches in the Cecil soil, and 10 inches in the Columbiana soil.

[3] Included in ignition loss. The nitrogen percentage is included in the organic matter percentage.

[4] Includes the H_2O and CO_2 reported in the analyses.

tioned. First, SiO_2 is the most abundant constituent in igneous rocks and in all but the Columbiana soil, which is much more strongly weathered than the other soils listed in the table. Second, the CaO, MgO, Na_2O, and K_2O percentages are much lower in the soils than in igneous rocks, indicating the preferential removal of these constituents by weathering. Third, the soils contain organic matter and nitrogen. Unaltered igneous rocks do not contain organic matter, but according to Ingols and Navarre (1952) they may contain nitrogen to the extent of 80 p.p.m. The nitrogen in igneous rocks is ammoniacal, whereas in soils it is mostly organic. Fourth, the ignition loss is much greater in the soils than in igneous rocks because of the presence in the soils of organic matter and additional water of hydration and constitution.

The various soil separates differ in chemical composition, as would be predicted from the fact that they differ in mineralogical composition. Failyer, Smith, and Wade (1908) analyzed separates of a number of soils for calcium, magnesium, potassium, and phosphorus and found that with all these elements in most soils the percentage content was highest in the clay fraction and lowest in the sand fraction. The difference in composition among separates was most pronounced with respect to phosphorus and magnesium.

Knowledge of the total amount of individual nutrients in soils is of only limited value in predicting the adequacy of supply of nutrients for plant growth. The reason for this situation is that the availability, or effective amount, of a plant nutrient in soil is less than the total and usually is poorly correlated with the total. In evaluating the nutrient status of soils, therefore, the purpose of the chemical methods employed usually is to estimate the availability, or effective amount, of individual nutrients and not the total amount. Data of Andharia, Stanford, and Schaller (1953) may be cited as an example. These investigators determined the correlations between corn yields and soil nitrogen in a crop rotation experiment in Iowa in which nitrogen supply was an important limiting factor. They obtained a correlation coefficient of 0.64 between corn yields and total soil nitrogen and a correlation coefficient of 0.78 between corn yields and the nitrate nitrogen produced during a 3-week incubation of soil samples in the laboratory. The nitrate produced in this way represented only a small fraction of the total soil nitrogen, but to judge from the correlation coefficients, it was a better estimate of nitrogen availability than was the total nitrogen.

Measurements of the total content of plant nutrients in soils are seldom made in soil fertility studies, except in the measurement of changes in the soil that may occur during the course of long-time field experiments. Total analysis has its greatest application in connection with research in soil mineralogy and soil genesis and classification.

ORGANIC FRACTION

The organic fraction of soils represents less than 5 per cent of the total soil weight in most instances but may represent a much higher proportion. The total organic matter of soils consists of living organisms of various types, together with their decaying residues. The bulk of the organic matter falls within the category of decaying residues. Russell and Russell (1950, p. 192) estimated that living microbial cells account for only 1 to 2 per cent of the total weight of organic matter.

The organic matter of soils is derived directly or indirectly from plant tissue. The major portion of mature plant tissue may be classified into three types of compounds, namely, polysaccharides, lignin, and protein.

The polysaccharide group is the most abundant in plant material and includes such compounds as cellulose and hemicellulose, which are condensed ring compounds containing carbon, hydrogen, and oxygen. Cellulose alone usually accounts for about half the dry weight of plant tissue. Plant polysaccharides are decomposed readily by microbiological action, hemicellulose disappearing more rapidly than cellulose; however, many soil microorganisms synthesize polysaccharides of the same or different types, so that polysaccharides do not disappear entirely as decomposition proceeds.

That polysaccharides are present in soil organic matter is indicated by the identification of polysaccharide components in hydrolysates. The relatively rapid decomposition of polysaccharides, together with the results of polysaccharide analyses on soils, indicates that the proportionate content of polysaccharides is lower in the organic matter of soils than of plants. The exact figure is in doubt, however, because as yet the analytical methods are not entirely adequate.

Like the polysaccharides, lignin is composed of carbon, hydrogen, and oxygen in ring structures condensed into large molecules. The lignin rings, however, are in part or entirely aromatic, whereas those of the polysaccharides are not. The lignin of plant materials decomposes less readily than the polysaccharides; hence the proportion of lignin in the total organic matter increases as decomposition proceeds. Soil microorganisms apparently do not produce lignin, but some of them produce substances that are similar to it. Lignin is soluble in alkali, is reprecipitated by the addition of acid, is relatively resistant to hydrolysis by strong mineral acid, contains methoxyl and phenolic hydroxyl groups, and is attacked readily by mild oxidizing agents.

These properties are shared by a part of the organic matter of soils, from which fact it is presumed that soils contain lignin. Certain other properties of lignin from plant materials are not shared by soil organic matter, which suggests that soil organic matter either does not contain lignin or contains a modified form. The latter is the more likely since there is evidence that as decomposition proceeds, the structure of lignin is modified in minor respects without loss of the integrity of the main part of the molecule.

The proteins are aggregates of amino acids that are joined by means of the nitrogen-bearing amino group. Although proteins are attacked readily by microorganisms, they may appear to be resistant to decomposition, because if enough energy-supplying material (such as polysaccharide) accompanies the protein, the microorganisms merely use the nitrogen released to synthesize proteins of their own. Thus the total protein, inferred from organic nitrogen measurements, may remain constant for a time. By the time the stage of decomposition has reached that of the soil organic matter, however, the properties of the nitrogen-bearing fraction have been altered, and at this stage there is some question about the extent to which the nitrogen-bearing substances in soil can be classified as protein. This subject will be discussed in more detail in the chapter on nitrogen.

Soils contain various other types of organic compounds in small quantities, and of these the phosphorus-bearing compounds have received most attention. Reviews of the properties of soil organic matter have been published by Norman (1943), Bremner (1951, 1954), and Broadbent (1953). These papers should be consulted for further details and references to the literature.

The organic fraction of soils may affect plant growth indirectly through its properties of binding soil particles together into structural units and holding cations in exchangeable form. The former property was discussed earlier in this chapter and the latter will be discussed in a separate chapter. On decomposition, soil organic matter releases nitrogen, phosphorus, and sulfur in forms available to plants. The nitrogen and phosphorus effects will be discussed in some detail in the chapters on the respective elements. Other indirect effects may be attributed to the carbon dioxide released during organic matter decomposition. These effects will be noted in several chapters in connection with the condition or process they affect.

The extent to which soil organic matter per se affects plants is a question of long standing. Early in the present century Whitney (1909) thought that such effects were of major importance and went so far as to propose what might be called the "organic toxin" theory of soil fertility. His view was that aside from water, the most important soil factor limiting plant growth was organic toxic material excreted from plants or produced from plant residues during microbial decomposition. The beneficial effects of fertilizers were supposed to result from an increase in the rate of toxin decomposition associated with their presence. Soils were thought to have an ample supply of nutrients for plant growth. Whitney's hypothesis about plant nutrients was found to be incorrect, and the organic toxin idea fell into disrepute from association with the incorrect idea and from lack of evidence. More recently, evidence has been obtained to support the organic toxin idea in a limited way. Work on this subject was summarized by Bonner (1950). The only well-authenticated toxicities are those of chemicals produced by plants and excreted from the roots (cinnamic acid from guayule) or washed from the leaves into the soil (absinthin from wormwood, 3-acetyl-6-methoxy benzaldehyde from brittlebush). The effects are specific. That is to say, the chemicals are toxic to some plants but not to others. Probably toxic effects of this type would disappear shortly after removal of the source of the toxin because of decomposition of the toxic principle by the soil microorganisms. The production of organic plant toxins by microorganisms acting on plant residues or soil organic matter remains to be demonstrated. The existence of such toxins is not unlikely, however, in view of recent developments of knowledge regarding production of antibiotic substances by microorganisms isolated from soils.

Various claims of special beneficial effects of soil organic matter on plants have been advanced from time to time. One such claim that was the subject of much scientific work was the observation of Bottomley (1914) that plants in water cultures grew better when he added an extract of "bacterized peat" than when he supplied only inorganic nutrients. Bottomley thought that the presence of certain organic substances in the root medium was essential for normal plant growth. He gave these hypothetical substances the name "auximones" (Bottomley, 1917). In Bottomley's original experiments the plants in solution cultures without added organic matter grew for a time but later withered and died, whereas the plants that received the organic extract continued to grow. In the light of present knowledge that plants can be grown satisfactorily in solution cultures containing inorganic salts only, it appears that at least part of the beneficial effect of the organic extract resulted from the presence in the organic extract of some mineral substance required by plants, or from the interaction of the organic extract with the mineral substances already present in the solution to increase their effectiveness or to decrease their toxicity.

Bottomley published a number of papers on the subject, and later Clark and co-workers took up the problem and carried it further. Clark and Roller (1931) succeeded in growing duckweed plants through many generations in solution cultures containing only inorganic salts. These results indicate that duckweed plants, at least, do not require an external source of organic matter in excess of that excreted by the plants themselves. Even this may be incidental. Clark and Roller found that when they added sources of organic matter to the nutrient solutions, the growth rate of the duckweed was not increased under sterile conditions, but it was increased if the added organic matter was not sterilized or if it was sterilized and then reinoculated. The favorable effects of the organic matter were thus associated with microbial activity, and not with the organic matter per se. Substances produced from the added organic matter during its decomposition by the microorganisms presumably were responsible for the favorable effect.

More recent evidence suggests that the unexplained favorable effect of organic matter and microorganisms observed in the work of Clark and Roller may have resulted from vitamins and hormones produced by the microorganisms. Under certain cultural conditions, microorganisms may produce these substances in excess of their requirements and may excrete part of the material into the surrounding medium. The presence of vitamins and hormones in soil has been demonstrated; also plants have been found to absorb certain vitamins and hormones which are added to the soil or solution in which the plants are growing. Under special conditions one or more of these substances may actually be required. For example, excised root tissue of certain plants cultured in solution media containing the appropriate mineral salts and sugar soon stops growing if vitamin B_1 is not added to the solution. Plants, like animals, require vitamins and hormones. Intact higher plants, however, are autotrophic organisms and generally are considered to be capable of synthesizing all the vitamins and hormones needed for their own development. The vitamin and hormone requirements of portions of the plant that may not produce these substances are met by translocation from other organs. Whether or not the small quantities of vitamins and hormones that presumably are absorbed by plants from soils have any beneficial effect is not known. Additions of such substances to soil cultures or solution cultures sometimes have produced increases in plant growth. Definitely positive effects in field experiments, however, have not been obtained. For reviews of the literature on this subject the papers of Bonner (1937) and Schmidt (1951) and the book by Audus (1953) should be consulted.

Antibiotic substances produced in soils by microorganisms may affect plant growth in various ways, one of which is the suppression of plant pathogens. Full proof of such action is not available, but there is little doubt that it exists under some circumstances. A brief review of this subject was published by Evans and Gottlieb (1955).

It is clear that the organic fraction of soils affects plant growth indirectly in a variety of ways. Direct effects appear to be important in individual instances, but it is uncertain whether such effects are of general significance. Because the organic fraction affects plant growth in several different ways and because the relationship between the various effects is not fixed but variable, the significance of the soil organic fraction cannot be estimated from any single measurement. Even the precise measurement of the total amount of organic matter in soil is difficult and at present perhaps impossible. Most investigators are content to measure the content of organic carbon and to use this as an index of the content of organic matter (the conventional assumption being that soil organic matter contains 58 per cent carbon). An alternative measurement sometimes employed is the content of total nitrogen (since soil organic matter appears to contain about 5 to 6 per cent nitrogen in many instances). Despite the incomplete understanding of the exact nature and magnitude of the individual effects of organic matter, the overall effect seems to be favorable. In consequence there is rather general agreement that the content of organic matter is a useful characteristic for judging the suitability of soils for plant growth. For example, a positive correlation between the content of nitrogen in soils and the yield of corn was noted in the Missouri (Jenny, 1933; Klemme and Coleman, 1939) and Ohio (Salter and Green, 1933) soil fertility experimental fields. Jenny (1933) and Hamner (1935) noted that the value of land in Missouri increased with increasing content of nitrogen in the soil.

SOIL PROFILE

From what sometimes is called the morphological standpoint, soils are composed of a series of layers of varying degrees of distinctness. These layers are approximately parallel with the soil surface and are called "horizons." Collectively, the horizons make up what is called the soil "profile." Figure 8 gives a diagram of a hypothetical soil profile having all the principal horizons, together with some generaliza-

The A_0 and A_{00} horizons are composed of organic matter, and rest on the A_1 horizon of unplowed soils. They are found on most unburned soils under forest vegetation and usually are absent from soils developed under grasses.

The A horizon is the zone of maximum biological activity in the mineral portion of the soil. In dry regions the A horizon is a zone in which organic matter accumulates. The same is true in humid regions where, in addition, it frequently has a clay content lower than that of the B horizon as a result of weathering and transportation of clay by water.

The B horizon includes the lower layers that have been influenced strongly by the factors of soil formation. In soils developing on fresh geological formations no B horizon may be discernible. The same may be true occasionally in mature soils found in dry regions. Usually the B horizon is differentiated from the A horizon above and the C horizon below by color. In addition there may be differences in structure, in content of clay, iron, aluminum, and organic matter, or a combination of both. In dry regions the B horizon frequently is distinguished from the A horizon by structure; the B horizon has a blocky or prismatic structure that is not shared by the A and C horizons. Also the organic matter content is lower in the B than in the A horizon. In cool, humid regions the B horizon is a zone of accumulation of clay, sesquioxides, and organic matter moved downward in varying proportions from the A horizon. In warm, humid regions the B horizon often is relatively thick and high in content of clay and sesquioxides, showing but little evidence of accumulation from the A horizon.

The C horizon is a layer of unconsolidated material that is affected relatively little by the action of organisms. The C horizon is presumed to represent the parent material, i.e., the type of material from which at least part of the overlying horizons have developed.

The D layer is any stratum that is essentially unaffected by organisms acting in the overlying horizons and at the same time is different from the material from which the overlying layers were formed. The D horizon is not a part of the soil profile, but it may be of significance to the overlying soil, as when the D horizon consists of consolidated rock.

A_{00}	
A_0	
A_1	
A_2	
A_3	
B_1	
B_2	
B_3	
C	C_{ca}
	C_{cs}
	G
D	

The A_{00} horizon consists of relatively fresh plant residues, generally of the past year.

The A_0 horizon consists of partly decomposed or matted plant residues.

The A_1 horizon is dark colored, and has a relatively high content of organic matter mixed with the mineral matter. Usually it is relatively thin in soils developed under forest vegetation and thick in soils developed under grasses. Availability of plant nutrients is relatively high as a result of the surface deposition of plant residues and the activities of the soil population.

The A_2 horizon is lighter in color than the A_1 horizon and usually is lighter in color than the underlying horizon. It is the region of maximum loss of clay, iron, aluminum, or all three. This horizon usually is absent from or weakly developed in soils of dry regions but may be strongly developed in soils of humid regions, particularly those occurring in cool climates under forest vegetation.

The A and B horizons merge through the transitional A_3 and B_1 horizons. If the B horizon is absent, the A_3 is transitional to the C horizon.

The B_2 horizon is the layer in which the maximum "B" properties are found.

The B_3 horizon is transitional to the C horizon.

The C_{ca} and C_{cs} horizons are layers of accumulated calcium carbonate and calcium sulfate found characteristically in some soils of dry regions. Commonly the C_{cs} horizon is below the C_{ca} horizon. Sometimes these accumulations are found in horizons other than the C, in which case the symbol is changed from C to B or A, as the case may be, and the subscripts remain the same.

The G horizon is a layer of intense reduction. It is characterized by the presence of ferrous iron and by a gray to olive color that commonly changes to brown on exposure to air.

Fig. 8. Diagram of a hypothetical soil profile having all the principal horizons. (Adapted from the Soil Survey Manual: Soil Survey Staff, 1951.)

tions about the nature of the different horizons. Individual soils have one or more of these horizons but do not contain all of them.

A soil profile is the resultant of all the factors involved in its formation. These may be listed as climate, organisms, topography, parent material, and time. An infinite variety of soil profiles may be produced by variations in these five factors. Certain kinds of differences in soil profiles may occur within a space of a few feet, depending on local factors. For example, the thickness of the A_1 horizon may decrease as the topography becomes steeper; or the depth to the C_{ca} horizon may increase as the soil becomes more sandy. Other kinds of differences, attributable primarily to climatic factors, are found in profiles that usually are separated widely. For example, climate is primarily responsible for the difference between the gray sierozem soils of Wyoming and the black chernozen soils of North Dakota.

Following is a profile description of a specific soil type, Cecil sandy loam, taken from the *Soil Survey Manual* (Soil Survey Staff, 1951, p. 473). Cecil sandy loam occurs extensively in the Piedmont area in southeastern United States.

A_{00} A thin layer of leaves and pine needles.

A_1 0 to 2 inches, brownish-gray very friable sandy loam with fine weak crumb structure; strongly acid. 1 to 4 inches thick.

A_2 2 to 8 inches, weak-yellow to light yellowish-brown nearly loose or very friable sandy loam; strongly acid. 4 to 10 inches thick.

B_1 8 to 10 inches, weak reddish-brown to strong-brown friable heavy sandy loam or light sandy clay loam with medium granular structure; strongly acid. 2 to 4 inches thick.

B_2 10 to 38 inches, moderate to strong reddish-brown clay that is plastic when wet, very firm when moist, and very hard when dry. The clay has a medium moderately blocky structure and contains some white sand grains and small mica flakes; strongly acid. 20 to 36 inches thick.

B_3 38 to 60 inches, light to moderate reddish-brown clay loam with mottles or splotches of yellow; firm to friable when moist. The soil contains enough small mica flakes to make it feel slick when rubbed through the fingers; it has a weak coarse blocky structure and is strongly acid. 10 to 30 inches thick.

C   60 inches +, mottled or splotched redish-brown, yellowish-brown, light-gray, and black friable disintegrated rock material in which there is usually much mica; strongly acid. 20 to 60 inches thick.

Plant roots may not be found in all the horizons of a soil profile, but usually they are in contact with more than the surface horizon. Characterization of a soil as a substrate for plant growth thus requires an examination not only of the surface horizon but also of the portion of the soil that lies below. Obviously a characterization that gives the vertical variation of soil properties that affect plant growth would be superior to a characterization based on the properties of a single horizon. Soil profile characterizations of the desired type no doubt can be approached as time goes by. Such characterizations, however, will require special measurements. They cannot be made merely by recording what meets the eye because for the most part the soil properties that affect plant growth cannot be seen. A profile description of the type illustrated above thus gives only an inferential insight into the properties of a soil as a substrate for plant growth.

Three different approaches have been used for estimating the response of plants from measurements of soil profile characteristics. In the first type, measurements are made of one or more features that are thought to be salient in controlling differences in plant response among the group of soils in question. Each feature is measured in a selected soil layer or horizon, which is not necessarily the same for the different features. This approach represents an extension of the usual procedure of expressing plant response in terms of a single soil property, measurements of which have been made in the plowed layer or surface horizons only. Coile and co-workers used this approach to estimate the suitability of different soils for growing pine trees in southeastern United States. On the basis of observations (Coile, 1948) indicating that the most important soil features affecting tree growth in that area are growing space for the roots, aeration, and water availability, the soil measurements employed were the thickness of the A horizon in inches (x_1) and the difference between the moisture and xylene equivalents of the B horizon, expressed as a water percentage on the dry-weight basis (x_2). The former of these measurements provides an index of root space and water availability, and the latter an index of aeration. As an example of the type of relationship developed, the equation of Coile and Schumacher (1953) for loblolly pine is

$$\log y = 2.02 - 0.40/x_1 - 0.0084\ x_2 - 0.020/x_2$$

where y is the "site index" or height in feet of the average dominant tree in a stand 50 years of age. The standard error of estimate for this equation, which is based on measurements made at 123 locations, is only 11 per cent. The relatively small experimental error indicates that the abridged type of evaluation employed in this instance provided a remarkably good prediction of the suitability of individual soil profiles as a substrate for loblolly pine.

In the second approach to the prediction of plant response from soil profile characteristics, the values for a given property are summed over all depth increments from the surface downward to a depth approximately that of root penetration. The measurements made at the different depths are treated as if they were strictly additive. This procedure differs from the first in that the measurements are made in all parts of the profile occupied by roots and not just in selected parts.

G. R. Clarke (1951) used the foregoing approach for relating the texture profile to plant yield. He made all yield measurements in a single field having extremely heterogeneous soil. After harvesting the wheat from each of a number of 25-square-foot quadrats scattered over the field, he dug a pit in the center of each quadrat and estimated the texture and thickness of each distinct horizon above a depth of 30 inches or above the gley horizon, whichever was the more shallow (the 30-inch depth was selected on the basis of observations that few visible roots occurred below that depth). The profile texture value V was determined by multiplying the thickness of each horizon in inches D by an arbitrary texture value T, and summing these products. Clarke's values of T ranged from 8, for soil containing less than 30 per cent silt plus clay, to 20, for soils containing 45 to 55 per cent silt plus clay, to 5, for soils containing more than 80 per cent silt plus clay. Figure 9 shows a plot of the yields of wheat against the profile texture value. The relatively small scatter of points around the re-

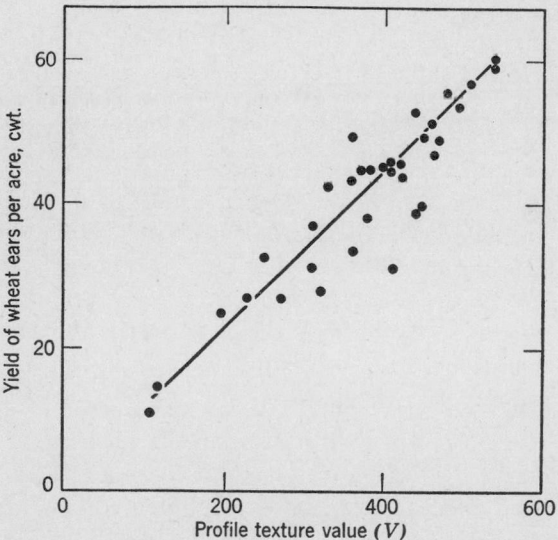

Fig. 9.   Yield of wheat on areas in a field having heterogeneous soil versus the profile texture values of the soil.   (Clarke, 1951.)

gression line is evidence of the satisfactory nature of the procedure for predicting the yields.

Taylor (1952, 1952a) proposed a way of evaluating the supply of water in the soil profile for plant growth. In his work a figure for the seasonal water supply was obtained by combining periodic measurements of the supply at different depths. He related his integrated values of water supply to the yields of crops in irrigation experiments. Taylor's procedure is based on the same general idea as that of Clarke (1951) but is much more complex in detail because of the changes in water content of the soil throughout the season.

The third approach to the prediction of plant response from soil profile characteristics is similar to the second in that the values for a given property are summed over all depth increments from the surface downward to a depth approximately that of root penetration. The third approach differs from the second in that the measurements made at the different depths are not assumed to be additive; that is, the significance of a given value to plants is permitted to vary with the depth at which it occurs.

Black (1955) proposed a way of using the third approach to estimate the total availability of individual nutrients in soil profiles from laboratory measurements on one or more forms of the nutrient in samples from different layers in the profile. In brief, the procedure amounts to finding by statistical methods the relationship between laboratory measurements on the individual layers in each of a group of soils and measurements of the total availability of the nutrient derived from field measurements of plant responses to fertilization with the nutrient on these same soils. The procedure has been applied to potassium with some success in a cooperative project carried out by a group of investigators in the north central states.

Each of the three approaches to the problem of predicting plant responses from soil profile measurements has its limitations. In the first, the measurement made on one part of the profile is used to provide an index to the property in question for the profile as a whole. The success of this approach thus depends on the existence of a high degree of correlation between the quantity or intensity measured in the selected soil layer or horizon and the total effective quantity or intensity in the soil profile. The second involves the assumption that the significance to plants of a given quantity or intensity of a particular factor measured in individual soil layers is independent of location in the profile. The third involves the assumption that the relative significance to plants of a given quantity or intensity of a particular factor among the individual soil layers is independent of the soil in which the measurements are made. Because of these limitations, the accuracy of predictions made from a given equation (such as that of Coile and Schumacher [1953] given above) decreases as the range of soil conditions increases.

Beyond the foregoing limitations, which apply to the techniques, it should be noted that the soil properties employed in the specific applications cited are of divergent types. The water content of the soil, employed by Taylor (1952, 1952a), is a characterization involving one of the primary factors of plant growth. The texture of the soil profile, employed by Clarke (1951), is a secondary factor. Soil texture probably has little or no direct effect of its own but is associated with plant responses in an indirect manner through its correlation with primary factors of plant growth (such as, water, oxygen, and mineral nutrients). Whereas a better prediction of plant responses sometimes may be provided in local situations by measurements of a single secondary factor (such as texture) than a single primary factor (such as water), progress toward general applications lies in the direction of the primary factors and their integration.

LITERATURE CITED

Alderfer, R. B. (1954) Physical condition of the soil affects fertilizer utilization. Better Crops with Plant Food 38, No. 10:24, 44—45.

Alexander, Lyle T. (1952) The physical nature of soil. Agronomy 2:1—23.

Andharia, R. M., G. Stanford, and F. W. Schaller. (1953) Nitrogen status of Marshall silt loam as influenced by different crop rotations. Soil Sci. Soc. America Proc, 17:247—251.

Audus, L. J. (1953) Plant Growth Substances. Interscience Publishers, New York.

Baver, L. D. (1956) Soil Physics. Third edition. John Wiley and Sons, New York.

Bennett, Hugh H., and Allison, Robert V. (1928) Soils of Cuba. Tropical Plant Research Foundation, Washington, D. C.

Black, C. A. (1955) Evaluation of nutrient availability in soils, and prediction of yield response to fertilization. Iowa State College Jour. Sci. 30:1—11.

Bonner, James. (1937) The rôle of vitamins in plant development. Bot. Rev. 3:616—640.

Bonner, James. (1950) The role of toxic substances in the interactions of higher plants. Bot. Rev. 16:51—65.

Bottomley, W. B. (1914) The significance of certain food substances for plant growth. Ann. Bot. 28:531—540.

Bottomley, W. B. (1917) A bacterial test for plant food accessories (auximones). Royal Soc. London Proc. 89B:102—108.

Bremner, J. M. (1951) A review of recent work on soil organic matter. Part I. Jour. Soil Sci. 2:67—82.

Bremner, J. M. (1954) A review of recent work on soil organic matter. II. Jour. Soil Sci. 5:214—232.

Broadbent, F. E.   (1953)   The soil organic fraction.   Adv. Agron. 5:153–183.

Browning, G. M., R. A. Norton, A. G. McCall, and F. G. Bell.   (1948)   Investigation in erosion control and the reclamation of eroded land at the Missouri Valley Loess Conservation Experiment Station, Clarinda, Iowa, 1931–42.   U. S. Dept. Agr. Tech. Bul. 959.

Byers, Horace G., Lyle T. Alexander, and R. S. Holmes.   (1935)   The composition and constitution of the colloids of certain of the great groups of soils.   U. S. Dept. Agr. Tech. Bul. 484.

Clark, Norman Ashwell, and Emery M. Roller.   (1931)   The stimulation of lemna major by organic matter under sterile and non-sterile conditions.   Soil Sci. 31:299–309.

Clarke, Frank Wigglesworth.   (1924)   The data of geochemistry.   U. S. Geol. Survey Bul. 770, 5th Ed.

Clarke, G. R.   (1951)   The evaluation of soils and the definition of quality classes from studies of the physical properties of the soil profile in the field.   Jour. Soil Sci. 2:50–60.

Coffey, George Nelson.   (1912)   A study of the soils of the United States.   U. S. Dept. Agr., Bur. Soils Bul. 85.

Coile, Theodore S.   (1948)   Relation of soil characteristics to site index of loblolly and shortleaf pines in the lower Piedmont region of North Carolina.   Duke Univ. School of Forestry Bul. 13.

Coile, T. S., and F. X. Schumacher.   (1953)   Relation of soil properties to site index of loblolly and shortleaf pines in the Piedmont region of the Carolinas, Georgia, and Alabama.   Jour. Forestry 51:739–744.

Craig, N., and P. Halais.   (1934)   Influence of maturity and rainfall on the properties of lateritic soils in Mauritius.   Empire Jour. Exptl. Agr. 2:349–358.

Evans, Elfed, and David Gottlieb.   (1955)   Gliotoxin in soils.   Soil Sci. 80:295–301.

Failyer, G. H., J. G. Smith, and H. R. Wade.   (1908)   The mineral composition of soil particles.   U. S. Dept. Agr., Bur. Soils Bul. 54.

Grim, Ralph E.   (1953)   Clay Mineralogy.   McGraw-Hill Book Co., Inc., New York.

Haise, Howard R., L. R. Jensen, and Joseph Alessi.   (1955)   The effect of synthetic soil conditioners on soil structure and production of sugar beets.   Soil Sci. Soc. America Proc. 19:17–19.

Hamner, Conrad H.   (1935)   Factors affecting land values in Missouri.   Missouri Agr. Exp. Sta. Res. Bul. 229.

Hely, Frank W., Charles Bonnier, and Paul Manil.   (1954)   Investigations concerning nodulation and growth of lucerne seedlings in a loess soil artificially aggregated to various levels.   Plant and Soil 5:121–131.

Hendricks, Sterling B., and Lyle T. Alexander.   (1939)   Minerals present in soil colloids: I.   Descriptions and methods for identification.   Soil Sci. 48:257–271.

Hosking, J. S.   (1940)   The soil clay mineralogy of some Australian soils developed on granitic and basaltic parent material.   Jour. Council Sci. Indus. Res.   (Australia) 13:206–216.

Humbert, R. P., and C. E. Marshall.   (1943)   Mineralogical and chemical studies of soil formation from acid and basic igneous rocks in Missouri.   Missouri Agr. Exp. Sta. Res. Bul. 359.

Ingols, Robert S., and Alfred T. Navarre.   (1952)   "Polluted" water from the leaching of igneous rock.   Science 116:595–596.

Jackson, M. L., and G. Donald Sherman.   (1953)   Chemical weathering of minerals in soils.   Adv. Agron. 5:219–318.

Jackson, M. L., S. A. Tyler, A. L. Willis, G. A. Bourbeau, and R. P. Pennington. (1948) Weathering sequence of clay-size minerals in soils and sediments. I. Fundamental generalizations. **Jour. Phys. Col. Chem.** 52:1237–1260.

Jean, Frank C., and John E. Weaver. (1924) Root behavior and crop yield under irrigation. **Carnegie Inst. Washington Publ.** 357.

Jeffries, Charles D. (1947) The mineralogical approach to some soil problems. **Soil Sci.** 63:315–320.

Jenny, Hans (1933) Soil fertility losses under Missouri conditions. **Missouri Agr. Exp. Sta. Bul.** 324.

Jenny, Hans. (1935) The clay content of the soil as related to climatic factors, particularly temperature. **Soil Sci.** 40:111–128.

Jenny, Hans, and Chester D. Leonard. (1934) Functional relationships between soil properties and rainfall. **Soil Sci.** 38:363–381.

Klemme, A. W., and O. T. Coleman. (1939) Evaluating annual changes in soil productivity. **Missouri Agr. Exp. Sta. Bul.** 405.

Lowdermilk, W. C. (1930) Influence of forest litter on run-off, percolation, and erosion. **Jour. Forestry** 28:474–491.

Marshall, C. E. (1935) Mineralogical methods for the study of silts and clays. **Zeitschr. f. Krist.** 90A:8–34.

Martin, W. P., G. S. Taylor, J. C. Engibous, and E. Burnett. (1952) Soil and crop responses from field applications of soil conditioners. **Soil Sci.** 73:455–471.

McCaughey, W. J., and William H. Fry. (1913) The microscopic determination of soil-forming minerals. **U. S. Dept. Agr., Bur. Soils Bul.** 91.

Nichols, Ann. (1939) Some applications of mineralogy to soil studies. **Jour. Australian Inst. Agr. Sci.** 5:218–221.

Norman, A. G. (1943) Soil organic matter: I. Problems in the chemistry of soil organic matter. **Soil Sci. Soc. America Proc.** (1942) 7:7–15.

Paschall, A. H., R. T. A. Burke, and L. D. Baver. (1935) Aggregation studies on the Muskingum, Chester and Lansdale silt loams. **Amer. Soil Survey Assoc. Bul.** 16:44–45.

Peele, T. C. (1950) Relation of percolation rates through saturated soil cores to volume of pores drained in 15 and 30 minutes under 60 centimeters tension. **Soil Sci. Soc. America Proc.** (1949) 14:359–361.

Peterson, J. B. (1946) Relation of parent material and environment to the clay minerals in Iowa soils. **Soil Sci.** 61:465–475.

Puhr, Leo F., and Oscar Olson. (1937) A preliminary study of the effect of cultivation on certain chemical and physical properties of some South Dakota soils. **South Dakota Agr. Exp. Sta. Bul.** 314.

Quastel, J. H. (1954) Soil conditioners. **Ann. Rev. Plant Physiol.** 5:75–92.

Robinson, W. O., and R. S. Holmes. (1924) The chemical composition of soil colloids. **U. S. Dept. Agr. Dept. Bul.** 1311.

Ross, C. S. (1927) The mineralogy of clays. **First Int. Congr. Soil Sci., Proc. Commission V,** 4:555–561.

Russell, E. John, and E. Walter Russell. (1950) **Soil Conditions and Plant Growth.** Longmans, Green and Co., London.

Rynasiewicz, Joseph. (1945) Soil aggregation and onion yields. **Soil Sci.** 60:387–395.

Salter, Robt. M., and T. C. Green. (1933) Factors affecting the accumulation and loss of nitrogen and organic carbon in cropped soils. **Jour. Amer. Soc. Agron.** 25:622–630.

Schmidt, E. L.   (1951)   Soil microorganisms and plant growth substances. I. Historical. **Soil Sci.** 71:129—140.

Soil Survey Staff.   (1951)   Soil survey manual. **U. S. Dept. Agr. Handbook 18.**

Sokolovsky, A. N.   (1933)   The problem of soil structure. **Int. Soc. Soil Sci., Trans. First Commission, Soviet Section, A,** 1:34—110.

Stallings, J. H.   (1950)   Keep crop residues on surface of ground. **Better Crops with Plant Food 34,** No. 8:9—16, 48—49.

Stallings, J. H.   (1952)   Soil aggregate formation. **U. S. Dept. Agr. SCS-TP—10.**

Tanada, T.   (1951)   Certain properties of the inorganic colloidal fraction of Hawaiian soils. **Jour. Soil Sci.** 2:83—96.

Taubenhaus, J. J., W. N. Ezekiel, and H. E. Rea.   (1931)   Strangulation of cotton roots. **Plant Physiol.** 6:161—166.

Taylor, Sterling A.   (1952)   Estimating the integrated soil moisture tension in the root zone of growing crops. **Soil Sci.** 73:331—339.

Taylor, Sterling A.   (1952a)   Use of mean soil moisture tension to evaluate the effect of soil moisture on crop yields. **Soil Sci.** 74:217—226.

Truog, E., J. R. Taylor, Jr., R. W. Pearson, M. E. Weeks, and R. W. Simonson.   (1937)   Procedure for special type of mechanical and mineralogical soil analysis. **Soil Sci. Soc. America Proc.** (1936) 1:101—112.

Veihmeyer, F. J., and A. H. Hendrickson.   (1946)   Soil density as a factor in determining the permanent wilting percentage. **Soil Sci.** 62:451—456.

Volk, G. M., C. E. Bell, and E. N. McCubbin.   (1947)   The significance and maintenance of nitrate nitrogen in Bladen fine sandy loam in the production of cabbage. **Florida Agr. Exp. Sta. Bul. 430.**

Whitney, Milton.   (1896)   Texture of some important soil formations. **U. S. Dept. Agr. Bur. Soils Bul. 5.**

Whitney, Milton.   (1909)   Soil fertility. **U. S. Dept. Agr. Farmers' Bul. 257.**

Wilsie, C. P., C. A. Black, and A. R. Aandahl.   (1944)   Hemp production experiments: cultural practices and soil requirements. **Iowa Agr. Exp. Sta. Bul. P63.**

Winters, Eric, and Roy W. Simonson.   (1951)   The subsoil. **Adv. Agron.** 3:1—92.

Woodruff, C. M.   (1940)   Soil moisture and plant growth in relation to pF. **Soil Sci. Soc. America Proc.** 5:36—41.

Yankovitch, L., and P. Berthelot.   (1948)   Enracinement de l'olivier et des autres arbres fruitiers dans le sud de la Tunisie. **Compt. rend. acad. agr.** 34:774—776.

Yoder, Robert E.   (1936)   A direct method of aggregate analysis of soils and a study of the physical nature of erosion losses. **Jour. Amer. Soc. Agron.** 28:337—351.

2. SOIL WATER ———————————

As a factor limiting plant growth over the land surface of the earth, water probably is foremost in importance. Vast areas produce only limited yields of crops because of water deficiency. For this reason behavior of water in soils and the response of plants to the various conditions that obtain are of particular practical importance.

The problems connected with retention of water by soils and movement of water in soils constitute a major segment of the field of soil physics. The physical behavior of the soil-water system forms the basis for much of the subject matter of this chapter. The principal objective of this chapter, however, is to point out the significance of the physical behavior to plant growth rather than to treat the properties of the soil-water system as such. Another treatment of this same subject will be found in a paper by Richards and Wadleigh (1952).

FREE ENERGY

The behavior of water in soils and plants has been discussed and described in terms of many different concepts. The terminology for soils and for plants is usually different. In the most basic of all concepts, the energy concept, however, the terminology is the same for both soils and plants. Ultimately, the retention of water by soil and the movement of water from place to place in soil, from soil to plant, and through plant to atmosphere, are explainable on the basis of energy changes. The direction of water movement is from regions of high to regions of low free energy. Absolute values of free energy cannot be determined, but differences can be measured and expressed as indicated below.

Basic concept

The concept of free energy may be explained by reference to the following system. If a vertical column of dry soil is placed in contact with free water at the bottom, water will move upward into the soil spontaneously because the free energy of the water in which the column of soil is placed is greater than that of water in the soil. If such a column of soil is allowed to come to equilibrium with free water at the bottom, without movement of soluble materials and without loss of water by evaporation from the surface of the column, the percentage content of water in the soil will decrease with increasing height.

Let us consider now the energy changes involved in moving unit mass of water from the height h_0 at the free-water surface to its condition in the soil at the height h_1. The process may be broken down into two steps, namely, (a) lifting free water through the distance $(h_1 - h_0)$, as a result of which it gains free energy, and (b) adding the free water to dry soil at the height h_1, as a result of which it loses free energy. If the units of quantity and height are the gram and the centimeter, respectively, the increase in free energy resulting from lifting 1 gram of free water to the height h_1 is $(h_1 - h_0)$ gram-centimeters, (980.7) $(h_1 - h_0)$ dyne-centimeters, or (980.7) $(h_1 - h_0)$ ergs. If the gram of free water at the height h_1 is now added to the quantity of dry soil that will result in the water percentage found at equilibrium in the soil column at that height, free energy will be lost. The quantity of free energy lost will be numerically equal to the quantity gained by raising the free water to the height h_1. That this is true is evident from the law of conservation of energy, and the fact that the soil-water system thus produced is in equilibrium with the soil-water system in the soil column.

If the moistened soil containing the gram of water is now lowered to h_0, the gram of water will lose (980.7) $(h_1 - h_0)$ ergs of free energy, as a result of which it will contain (980.7) $(h_1 - h_0)$ ergs less free energy than a gram of free water at the height h_0. This is the same loss of free energy that would result if a gram of water were added at the height h_0 to the quantity of dry soil that would result in the water percentage found at equilibrium in the soil column at the height h_1. The change of free energy of water between the two states may be defined as the maximum available work that can be accomplished by the process of adding the free water to the dry soil under conditions of constant temperature and pressure. That any work could be accomplished by the process of adding free water to dry soil at the same height is difficult to conceive. It has just been noted, however, that the loss of free energy in this process is exactly the same as the loss of free energy when a gram of water, in soil at the height h_1 in equilibrium with a free-water surface, is lowered to the height h_0 of the free-water surface. Clearly the work that can be accomplished by this latter process approaches, as a maximum, the work of raising a gram of water from the height h_0 to the height h_1.

Application of the free-energy concept is not limited to the conditions for which it has been described above; it may be applied to water in an isolated sample of soil or to water at a specific location in a soil that is not in equilibrium with a free-water surface. Under these circumstances the height $(h_1 - h_0)$ is purely hypothetical and represents the height above a free-water surface at which the soil sample would be found if the equilibrium conditions described above were to prevail.

The difference in free energy between unit mass of soil water at some particular height h_1 and unit mass of free water at some height h_0 is the resultant of several components which may be listed as follows, according to Edlefsen and Anderson (1943): (1) the force field emanating from soil particles, (2) hydrostatic pressure, (3) osmotic pressure, (4) external (atmospheric) pressure, and (5) surface tension. Evidently the relative importance of the various components will vary from place to place in the soil water. At equilibrium, however, the values of the individual components will be adjusted in such a way that their sum is constant at all points throughout the water.

If the change in free energy is calculated per unit mass of water, it is known as a change in specific free energy. Strictly speaking, specific free energy should be expressed in terms of free energy per unit mass, that is, dynes $\times$ cm. per gram or ergs per gram. In research on water relationships of soils and plants, however, specific free energy usually is expressed in units of pressure, such as atmospheres or centimeters of water. Multiplication of specific free energy in dyne-centimeters per gram by density in grams per cubic centimeter gives specific free energy in units of pressure, namely, dynes per square centimeter. Since 1 standard atmosphere $= 1.013 \times 10^6$ dynes per square centimeter, and since the specific volume of water at $25° = 1.003$ cm.^{3} per gram, a pressure of 1 standard atmosphere corresponds to a specific free energy of $(1.013 \times 10^6 \text{ dynes/cm.}^2) \times (1.003 \text{ cm.}^3/\text{g.}) = 1.016 \times 10^6$ ergs/g. at $25°$ C. Similarly, the pressure exerted by a 1-cm. column of water is 977.8 dynes/cm.^{2} at $25°$ C., which corresponds to a specific free energy of (977.8 dynes/cm.^{2}) $\times$ (1.003 cm.^{3}/g.) = 980.7 ergs/g.   At 25° C., 1 standard atmosphere corresponds to 1036.0 cm. or 34.0 feet of water.

Measurement

The difference in specific free energy between soil water and free water may be calculated from suitable measurements of the status of water in some phase in equilibrium with soil water.   This approach is based on the principle that at equilibrium the specific free energy of a substance is the same in two or more phases in contact with each other.   For example, vapor-pressure data can be used to calculate the value of Δf for soil water on the basis that the specific free energy of water vapor in equilibrium with soil water is the same as the specific free energy of the soil water.   This technique has been applied successfully to relatively dry soils, but it is of little or no value in soils containing enough water to support plant growth.   The atmosphere in equilibrium with soil water is almost saturated with water vapor (more than 98 per cent relative humidity) in soils moist enough to support plant growth.   Instruments capable of making precise measurements in the range between 98 and 100 per cent relative humidity have not been perfected.

Measurements of the freezing-point depression with a Beckmann thermometer or a resistance thermometer are more sensitive than measurements of vapor pressure for finding the free energy of soil water in the range of water content suitable for plant growth.   Measurements of freezing-point depression are most useful in soils that are relatively dry or saline.   In moist, nonsaline soils the freezing-point depression is so small that the measurements have a low degree of precision.

The so-called tensiometers of Gardner et al. (1922) are useful for making measurements in relatively moist, nonsaline soils in which the sensitivity of the vapor-pressure and freezing-point-depression measurements is inadequate.   A tensiometer is a fired, porous, clay vessel that is filled with water and attached to a manometer or a vacuum gauge.   The clay vessel is placed in the soil, where contact between the water in the vessel and in the soil is established through the porous clay walls.   If the porous clay vessel is placed in a soil that is moist, but not flooded, and if the initial pressure reading on the manometer is zero, water will flow from the interior of the vessel through the pores in the wall and into the soil until equilibrium is established. The removal of water from the tensiometer will cause the height of the liquid in the manometer to fall, indicating that a negative pressure or tension has been placed on the water in the tensiometer. The tension is proportional to the difference between the initial and final heights of water in the manometer. The tension reflects all the free energy components on page 41 except the osmotic component. The tension of the soil water is not influenced by dissolved substances except as these substances may alter the surface tension and density of the water and the hydration and arrangement of particles in the solid phase. In humid regions where generally the salt content of the soil is low, the osmotic effects of dissolved substances are relatively small, and the tension data may be used as an approximate measure of specific free-energy differences. Since tensiometers fail to operate at tensions greater than about 0.85 atmosphere, measurements are limited automatically to that part of the soil-water range where osmotic effects cause the least error.[1] In arid regions, where in some instances the salt content of the soil is appreciable, a measurement of soil water tension may give a considerable underestimate of the difference in specific free energy between soil water, with its content of solutes, and free, pure water, containing no dissolved materials. To deal with this difficulty, Wadleigh (1946) and others have calculated the osmotic component of the specific free energy from freezing-point-depression measurements made on the displaced soil solution and have added this component to the component calculated from the water tension, measured independently on the original soil. The sum of these two components represents the Δf value of the soil water (or the total soil moisture stress, in the terminology of Wadleigh and others) if the reference level and temperature are the same as those of the soil water.

Equations for making free-energy calculations from various types of measurements will be found in the monograph by Edlefsen and Anderson (1943) on the thermodynamics of soil water.

Effect of water content of soil

When the difference in specific free energy between soil water and free water is plotted as a function of the water percentage in a particular soil during either drying or wetting, a smooth curve results. The water content that corresponds to a particular specific free-energy level differs between soils, being greater in fine-textured soils than in coarse-textured soils, as illustrated by the data of Russell (1940) in Fig. 1. Figure 1 illustrates also the similarity of the specific free-

[1] Tensions up to 180 atmospheres (Richards, 1949) have been produced in Richards' (1947) "pressure-membrane" apparatus, but this apparatus is not suited to direct measurement of soil-water tension.

energy level of water between soils at the hygroscopic coefficient, the permanent wilting point, or the moisture equivalent.

The value obtained for water content at a given specific free-energy level depends on whether the soil is being wetted or dried. This behavior is illustrated in Fig. 2. Apparently there are two causes of the difference between wetting and drying curves. First, the tension at which a given soil pore will be drained during drying is determined by the diameter of the largest bounding neck in contact with air, but the tension at which the drained pore will fill with water during wetting is determined by the maximum diameter of the pore itself. Second, the soil particles may undergo some incompletely reversible

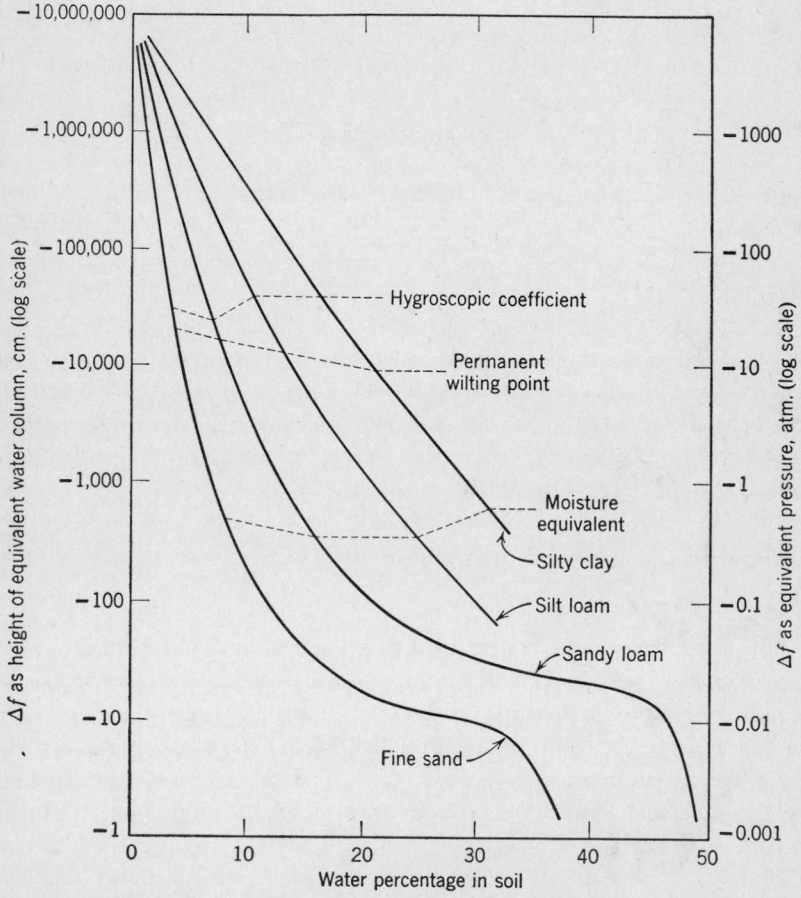

Fig. 1. Specific free energy of water in four soils at different water percentages obtained by various desorption techniques. (Russell, 1940.)

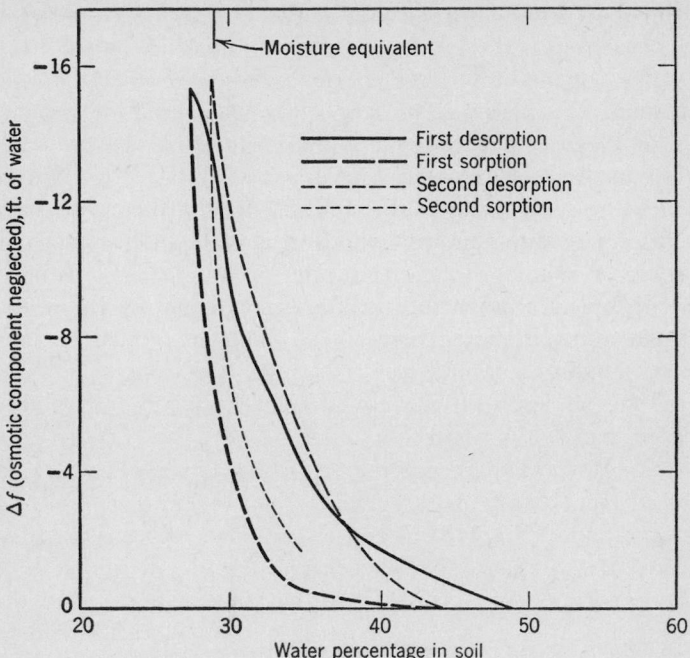

Fig. 2. Water sorption and desorption curves for a silt loam soil. (Richards, 1941.)

rearrangement to a closer packing as the soil shrinks during drying, with the result that in the presence of a given quantity of water the soil occupies a smaller volume during wetting than during the preceding drying. Evidently, therefore, there is no unique free-energy, soil-water curve for a given soil.

MOVEMENT

Pore-size effects

The rate of flow of water in both saturated and unsaturated soils is approximately proportional to the potential gradient (Darcy's law), which may be expressed in centimeters of water, atmospheres, or other terms, as desired. The proportionality factor decreases with decreasing water content of a given soil, a peculiarity that may be explained by the fact that the flow of water takes place through pores differing in size and irregular in shape.

Perhaps the simplest model for discussion is a bundle of capillary tubes differing in radius. The rate of flow of water through capillary tubes decreases rapidly as the bore becomes smaller, being proportional to the fourth power of the internal radius. Thus if the rate of flow through a capillary tube having a radius of 1 mm. is taken arbitrarily as unity, the rate of flow through the number of smaller tubes sufficient to give the same cross-sectional area will be 0.01 if the radius is 0.1 mm. and 0.0001 if the radius is 0.01 mm. The cause of this behavior lies in the hydrogen bonding between the wall of the tube and the adjacent layer of water molecules and among the water molecules themselves. The water molecules adjacent to the solid surface appear to be essentially stationary.

Although soils are not strictly analogous to capillary tubes, the only essential difference is one of form where water movement is concerned. Hydrogen bonding among water molecules and between water molecules and the porous solid through which the water moves occurs in soils as well as in capillary tubes.

The rate of movement of free or gravitational water through a well-drained soil usually is far greater than the rate of movement of the water retained by the soil against gravity. The relatively rapid movement of water that takes place in saturated soils subjected to the force of gravity occurs mainly through the large pores in the soil. When the large pores have been emptied of water, the subsequent movement is much slower, for three reasons. First, the proportion of the cross-sectional area filled with water is decreased. Second, only the smaller pores are involved in conducting the water; the rate of movement in such pores is low, in accordance with the capillary-tube principle. Third, the continuity of the pores may be poor. Figure 3 shows the capillary conductivity[2] of several soils for water at different soil-water tensions. In three of the soils the rate of flow of water decreased rapidly with increasing tension, being essentially zero at tensions in excess of 100 cm. of water. In one soil, Greenville loam, the rate of flow decreased only gradually with increasing tension. At tensions where water conductivity in the other soils was practically nil, water flow in Greenville loam still continued at a substantial rate. Presumably the greater water conductivity of the Greenville loam at tensions above 100 cm. resulted from the presence of pores not drained under a tension of 100 cm. but drained under a tension of 600 cm. of water, from greater continuity of the small pores, or both.

The slow movement of water in relatively dry soils does not violate the principles of the energy concept of soil water developed in pre-

[2] Capillary conductivity is defined here as the grams of water that flow per second through a plane of 1-sq.-cm. area placed perpendicular to the direction of flow, where the pressure differences is 1 dyne per square centimeter per centimeter of distance in the direction of flow.

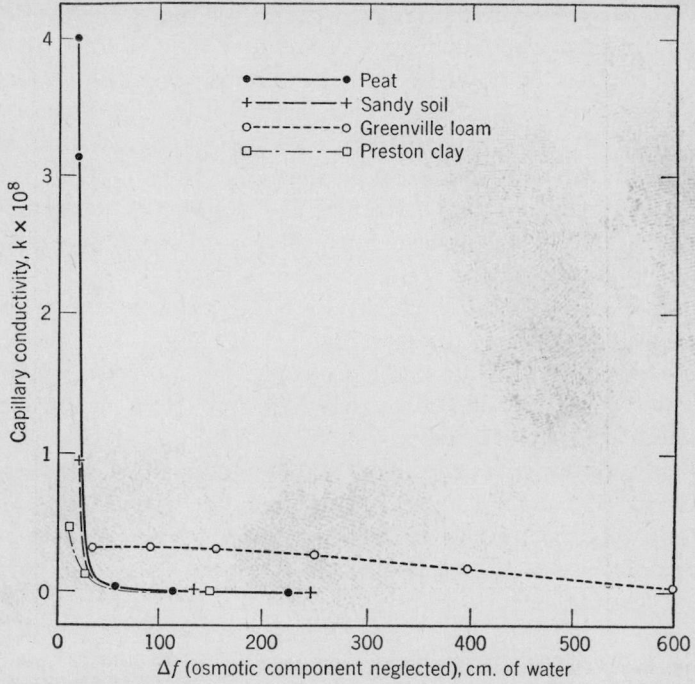

Fig. 3. Capillary conductivity of soils versus specific free energy of soil water. (Richards, 1936; Wilson and Richards, 1938.)

ceding sections. The energy concept deals only with initial and final states. In other words, it predicts the direction of flow, but not the rate.

Field capacity

Soils have the property of retaining water in a metastable condition against the downward pull of gravity over periods of time so long that for practical purposes the condition is permanent. During entry of water into a dry soil the water moves downward in a "front," across which the water content changes in a short distance from that of the moistened soil to the initial water content of the dry soil. When water intake ceases, penetration of the front continues, but usually its movement has almost ceased within 2 or 3 days. The water content of the moistened portion of the soil, after the excess water has drained away and the rate of downward movement has decreased materially, is defined by Veihmeyer and Hendrickson (1950) as the field capacity.

The phenomenon of field capacity is illustrated by Figs. 4 and 5.

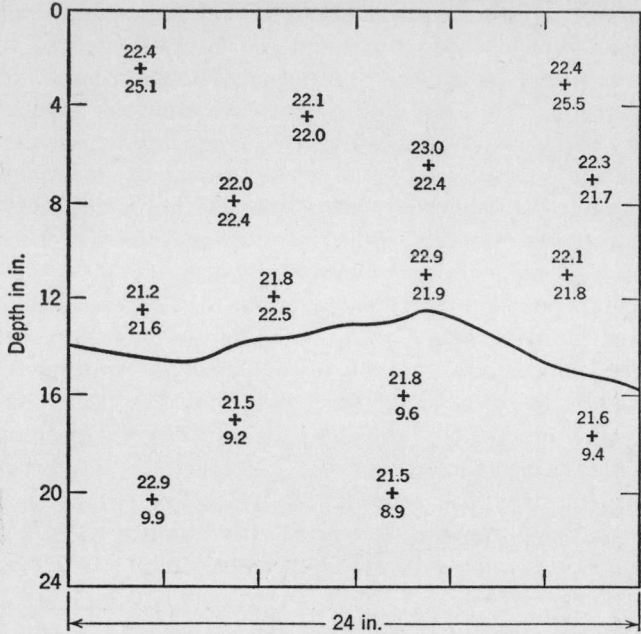

Fig. 4. Vertical distribution of water in Yolo loam soil in the field 48 hours after a rainfall of 2.15 in. (The cross + indicates the point from which the sample was taken, the figure above the cross represents the moisture equivalent of the sample, the figure below the cross represents the water percentage of the sample, and the approximately horizontal line through the soil represents the boundary between moistened soil above and unmoistened soil below.) (Veihmeyer, 1927.)

Figure 4 shows the distribution of water content and moisture equivalent[3] values in a 2-foot-square vertical cross section of soil 2 days after a rain. In the upper or moist part of the cross-section the water content of all soil samples was approximately that of the moisture equivalent. In the dry soil beneath, the water content was about 40

[3] The moisture equivalent is the percentage content of water that remains in a soil after the saturated soil has been subjected for 30 minutes under specific conditions to a centrifugal force equivalent to 1000 times gravity to remove part of the water. Laboratory measurements of moisture equivalent often are employed to estimate the field capacity of the soil. In a number of soil samples from South Carolina, Peele and Beale (1950) obtained a correlation coefficient of 0.98 between the field capacity and the moisture equivalent. The field capacity (y) could be estimated from the moisture equivalent (x) by the empirical equation

$$y = 0.86x \times 2.6$$

For unknown reasons, however, the soil water tension at the field capacity is much lower than that at the moisture equivalent.

per cent of the moisture equivalent. Figure 5 shows the results of an experiment in which a 2-foot column of soil moistened to the field capacity was stored for a period of 144 days between two 2-foot columns of dry soil. No evaporation loss was permitted. During storage the dry soil accumulated water at the expense of the moist soil, but no detectable increase in water content of the dry soil occurred at distances greater than about 14 inches from the initial boundary. The direction of water movement thus was in agreement with theory, but the rate of movement was exceedingly slow.

The phenomenon of field capacity in soil can be explained on two bases. First, the free-energy gradients in the soil water decrease with increasing time after addition of water. Second, continued downward movement of water after free water has disappeared from the soil surface involves penetration of water into dry soil at the expense of water contained in the moist soil. The water conductivity is limited in both the moist soil and the dry soil. The effects of size and continuity of soil pores discussed in the preceding section will bring about a decrease in rate of water movement out of moist soil as the

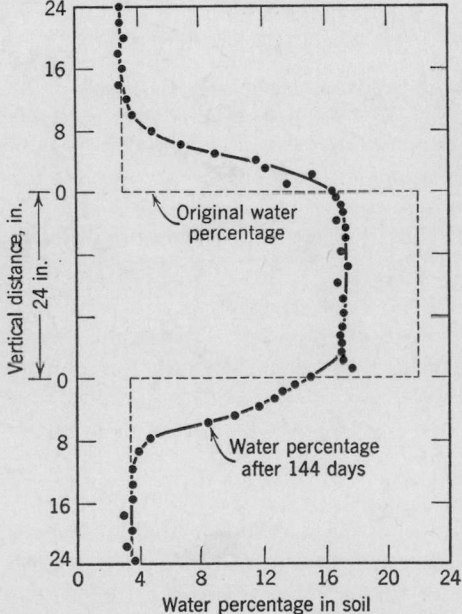

Fig. 5. Upward and downward movement of water during 144 days in a 6-ft. column of clay loam soil, the upper and lower 2 ft. of which originally contained relatively dry soil and the center 2 ft. of which originally contained soil moistened to the field capacity. (Veihmeyer, 1927.)

water content decreases. At the boundary between the dry and moist soil, the same effects limit the rate of movement into the dry soil. Thus, because the water in the moist portion of the soil is under tension and occurs only in the smaller pores, water in the liquid phase can move into only the small pores in the adjacent dry soil. The extent of movement into these pores diminishes as the continuity between them decreases.

Not all soils display the phenomenon of field capacity to the same extent. Water moves downward more rapidly in some soils than in others. Presumably the difference between soils in this respect is caused by differences in the arrangement and size distribution of pores. The water content at field capacity would be expected to remain more nearly constant over a period of time in well-aggregated, fine-textured soils in which the pore spaces consist of large pores between aggregates and small pores within aggregates than in soils that have gradually decreasing pore sizes. Of the soils shown in Fig. 3, the water content at field capacity probably would remain more nearly constant over a period of time in the sandy soil, the peat, and Preston clay than it would in the Greenville loam.

The foregoing considerations have dealt with the condition of moist soil overlying dry soil. Near the level of free water in the soil, moist soil overlies soil that is still more moist. Although the Veihmeyer and Hendrickson (1950) definition of field capacity does not exclude this condition, the water content of soil near the free-water level after the excess has drained away, and downward movement has decreased materially, may be substantially greater than that found in moistened soil in contact with dry soil beneath (see Fig. 1).

VAPOR LOSS

Evaporation

The rate of evaporation from bare, moist soil is essentially the same as that from an adjacent free-water surface with the same temperature and exposure. After a surface layer of dry soil is formed, however, the rate of evaporation from soil is much reduced (Penman, 1941). Experiments of Burov (1951) indicate that in the presence of a dry surface layer of soil, much of the water lost by evaporation evaporates below the surface of the soil and diffuses as a vapor to the surface.

As a result of the relatively slow rate of evaporation from soil having a dry surface layer, water remains for a long time in fallow soil that is originally moist throughout. Veihmeyer (1927) in California conducted an experiment in which a 4-foot column of soil contained in a

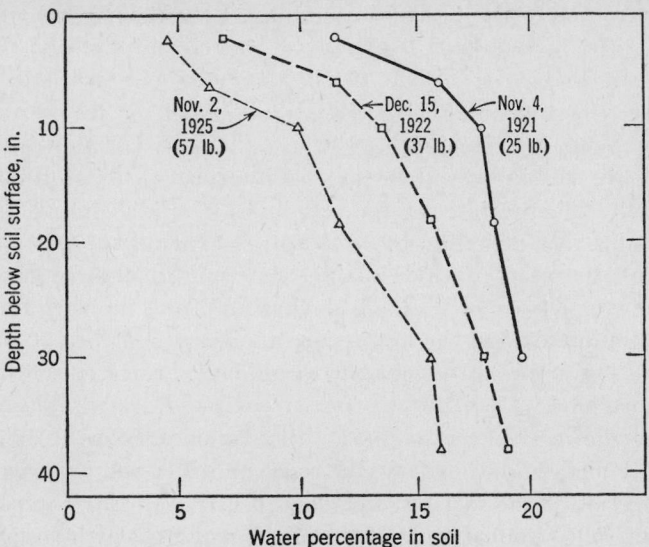

Fig. 6. Water percentage at different depths in 1000 lb. of bare, uncultivated, clay loam soil in a tank 4 ft. in depth at different times after application of 200 lb. of water on August 17, 1921. The figures in parentheses below the dates indicate the total number of pounds of water lost by exaporation from August 17, 1921, to the respective dates. (Veihmeyer, 1927.)

tank with a closed bottom was moistened with water to about the moisture equivalent and allowed to stand out-of-doors in a fallow condition for a period of 4 years. No rain was allowed to fall on the soil during the entire period. The tank was weighed at intervals to determine the total water loss, and samples were taken at different depths to determine the vertical distribution of water in the soil. The results in Fig. 6 show that during the entire 4-year period, the loss amounted to only one-fourth the amount of water added. Nearly half the total loss occurred in the first 3 months. Water was lost rapidly from the surface but slowly from the greater depths.

The long persistence of water stored in the soil is basic to the success of the alternate crop, fallow system of agriculture used widely in semiarid regions. Nevertheless, the efficiency of a summer fallow in conserving water for subsequent crop use usually is rather poor. At North Platte, Nebraska, Zook and Weakly (1950) found that on the average only 27 per cent of the precipitation received during the 12.5-month fallow period was present in the soil at the time the next crop was planted. Aside from runoff, the cause of such low efficiency is evaporation. At Adelaide, Australia, Butler and Prescott (1955) noted that in any month, the loss of water by evaporation from bare fallow was equal to approximately half the sum of the rainfall and the available water stored in the surface 2 feet of soil.

In areas where summer fallowing is practiced for water accumulation, much of the precipitation usually occurs as light rains that moisten only the surface of the soil. Little water storage results from such rains. The greatest storage per inch of rainfall results from the heavier rains that penetrate more deeply. Hopkins (1940) estimated that under the weather conditions in May and June at Swift Current, Saskatchewan, 34 per cent of a 1-day rainfall of 1 inch would be lost by evaporation during the following 10 days, but that 70 per cent would be lost if the same amount of rain was received in five daily showers, each of 0.2 inch.

Despite the efficiency of a surface dry layer of soil as a mulch, considerable benefit may be derived from a mulch of crop residues or other material on the surface of the soil. For example, in experiments of Krantz (1949) on adequately fertilized soils in North Carolina, average acre yields of unmulched and mulched corn were 60 and 81 bushels, respectively, under droughty conditions, and 100 and 106 bushels, respectively, under conditions of normal to above normal rainfall. The greater benefit was derived from the mulch, therefore, when the water supply was critical.

Organic mulches act in several ways to increase the supply of water in the soil. First, they commonly increase the infiltration of water into the soil on land where runoff occurs, and this effect is probably more important than any other on such soils. Second, they shade the soil, and the soil temperature immediately under a mulch is therefore lower during the heat of the day than is the temperature at a comparable depth in a bare soil. In one of the experiments of Krantz (1949), the average soil temperature at the ½-inch depth on two sunny afternoons was 118° F. in unmulched soil and 81° F. in soil covered with a mulch of 3 tons of straw per acre. The air temperature was about 95° F. in both cases. The lower temperature in mulched soil decreases the rate of evaporation, because both the amount of water vapor in the soil air and the rate of diffusion decrease with the temperature. Third, a surface mulch acts as a wind break, in effect increasing the distance through which the water vapor must diffuse between the soil water and the free atmosphere above the soil. Because of the reduction in vapor-pressure gradient, the evaporation is reduced. J. C. Russel (1940) determined the evaporation during a 9-hour period from columns of soil originally at the field capacity and found that where evaporation from bare, exposed soil (0.187 inch) was taken as 100, the relative losses were 64 where the soil was shaded, 47 where the soil was shaded and protected from wind by a cardboard collar to give a 9-inch column of still air over the soil, 27 where the soil was protected by a straw mulch (about 1.5 inches thick) of 4 tons per acre, and 9 where the soil was mulched with a 1.5-inch layer of air-dry soil from a fine, cloddy seedbed. He found also that the value of an organic mulch in controlling evaporation was greatest when the surface of the soil was moist and that it decreased rapidly as the surface of the soil became dry. A surface layer of dry soil was much more effective in reducing evaporation than was an organic mulch of equal thickness.

Evapotranspiration

Water is the major constituent of plants during growth and development. In addition, water is lost by transpiration in amounts far greater than those found within the plant. Several hundreds of pounds of water may be lost by transpiration during the production of a single pound of dry matter.

Transpiration is of major importance as a route of loss of soil water. Usually the rate of loss of water from soil is much greater if a crop is growing than if the soil is bare. Veihmeyer (1927) reported an extreme sample. In his experiment, tanks of soil 4 feet in depth were watered on August 17, and then were allowed to stand undisturbed out-of-doors without any additional water. The tanks were covered during rains. Twenty-five pounds of water had been lost by evaporation by November 4. On this date one tank was planted to vetch. From November 4 to June 30, when the vetch was mature, the loss of water from this tank amounted to 85 lb. During the same period the loss from the tank kept bare was only 10 lb. The loss by transpiration from the vetch and evaporation from the soil surface thus was 8.5 times as great as evaporation from the surface of the bare soil not planted to vetch. This example is extreme, because the surface of the bare soil was dry during the period of measurement and because the vetch in the planted tank was exposed to conditions of greater potential evaporation (because of greater solar radiation, greater wind movement, and lower relative humidity) than would be the case with an equal area in a field of vetch.

In the example given in the preceding paragraph the difference between the loss of water from the bare soil and the planted soil does not represent the loss of water by transpiration from the planted soil. The reason is that the evaporation from the soil under the vetch undoubtedly differed from the evaporation from the bare soil. Because

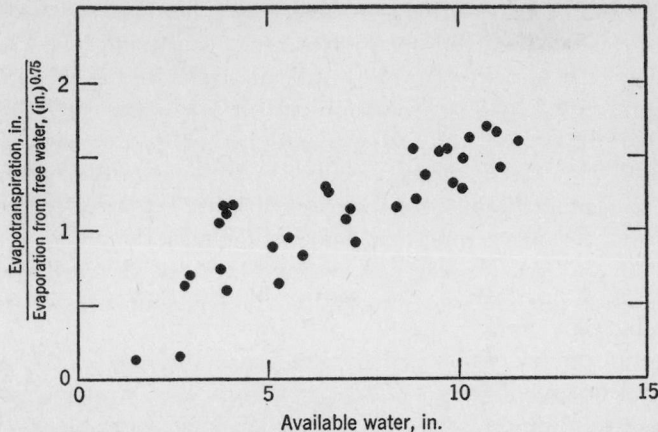

Fig. 7.   (Evapotranspiration from permanent pasture) / (evaporation from free water)$^{0.75}$ versus available water in soil at Adelaide, Australia.   (Butler and Prescott, 1955.)

of the experimental difficulty of determining the proportionate loss of water by evaporation and transpiration and because the total loss is of greatest practical importance, most measurements are of total loss. The total loss of water by evaporation and transpiration may be termed evapotranspiration.

Considerable effort is being expended currently on the problem of predicting evapotranspiration from meteorological measurements. The principal, practical objective of this work is to provide a simple way to combine meteorological and soil measurements to provide a prediction of the time when specific crops should be irrigated on specific soils. A general discussion of the problems involved was published by Schofield (1952). Detailed consideration of this work is beyond the scope of this chapter. Attention may be called, however, to the work of Penman (1948, 1949), since it bears on the effect of edaphic factors on efficiency of water use. Penman determined the evapotranspiration from small areas of short-cut grass, fertilized and unfertilized, lying within a larger area of grass. The fertilized grass yielded more than twice as much as the unfertilized grass, but the evapotranspiration was essentially the same. Similar results were obtained when the depth of the ground-water level was varied within certain limits. In one season, increasing the depth of the ground-water level from 10 to 16 inches below the soil surface increased the yield of grass 44 per cent and increased the evapotranspiration only 7 per cent. In another season, increasing the depth of the ground-water level from 16 to 24 inches increased the yield of grass 30 per cent and

decreased the evapotranspiration 5 per cent.   On the basis of these results Penman suggested that as long as soils remain moist and well covered by growing vegetation, the evapotranspiration is controlled by
environmental conditions, and is independent of the nature and yield
of the vegetation.

The problem becomes more complex when there is only a partial
canopy of vegetation and when evapotranspiration is decreased by depletion of water from the surface portion of the soil or by inactivity
of the vegetative cover, as during maturation of a grain crop.   Under
these circumstances, the specific nature of the plant and the soil must
be taken into account.

Evapotranspiration is limited by the supply of water in the soil in
widespread areas.   Figure 7 shows an instance in Australia in which
the evapotranspiration from permanent pasture land increased with
the available water supplied by natural rainfall.   Under these conditions, yield of dry matter increases with the evapotranspiration.   Both

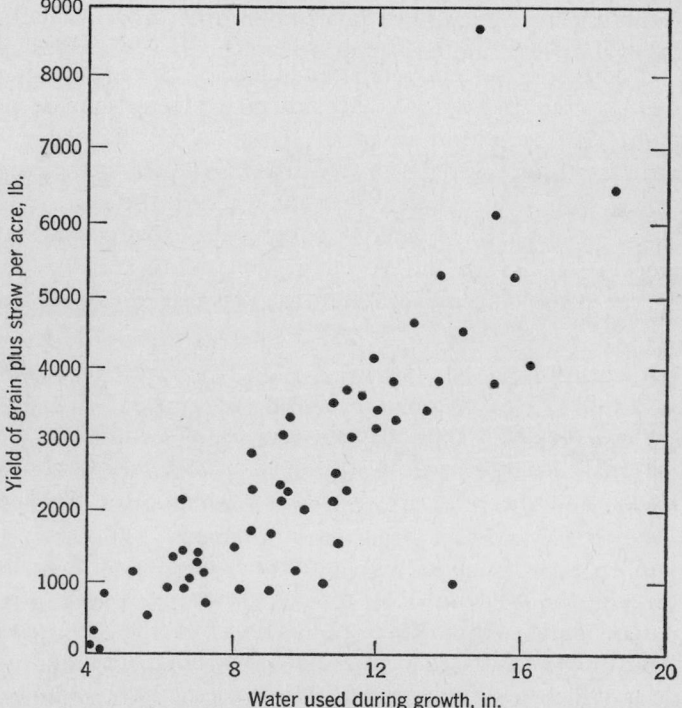

Fig. 8.   Yield of grain and straw of wheat versus inches of water used during the
growing season at eleven locations in the northern Great Plains in the period from 1909
to 1919.   (Cole and Mathews, 1923.)

yield of dry matter and evapotranspiration increase with the supply of water in the soil. Data of Cole and Mathews (1923) for spring wheat in the Great Plains region may be cited as an example. Figure 8 shows the yield of grain and straw plotted against the inches of water used during the growing season. The yield increased approximately linearly with the water use, indicating that the range in the water supply in the soils was below that required for the limiting conditions of Penman (1948), under which yield of dry matter is independent of water use. Similar results were obtained by Staple and Lehane (1954) in southern Saskatchewan.

AVAILABILITY TO PLANTS

Free-energy relationships

The particular value of the free-energy concept, as applied to the water relationships of soils and plants, is the fact that it permits the separation of processes that occur spontaneously from those that do not. A process will take place spontaneously only if it results in liberation of free energy (Δf is negative). If the change in free energy is zero, the system is in equilibrium. If the change in free energy is positive, the process will not take place spontaneously but will require the expenditure of energy from an outside source. Thus, for a plant to absorb water from the soil, the water in the plant must have a lower specific free energy than the water in the soil.

Water in plants has free-energy components analogous to those in the water in soils. The difference in specific free energy between water in the plant (f_p) and water in the soil (f_s) thus may be represented by

$$f_p - f_s = (o_p - o_s) + (a_p - a_s) + (h_p - h_s) + (e_p - e_s) + (t_p - t_s)$$

where o, a, h, e, and t represent specific osmotic, adsorptive, hydrostatic, external (atmospheric) pressure, and surface tension components, respectively, and the subscripts p and s represent the plant and soil phases, respectively.

Specific free energy has two important limitations as a means of characterizing the behavior of water for present purposes. First, free energy deals only with the difference between the static conditions represented by the initial and final or equilibrium states, and not with the rate at which a process occurs between the two. Movement of water in soils and absorption of water by plants are dynamic processes in which equilibrium conditions do not prevail. Second, specific free energy is an intensity factor. It has nothing to say about quantity.

Thus the water in two soils may have exactly the same specific free energy even though the quantity of water that may be used by plants is several times greater in one soil than in the other.

Effect of water content of soil

The quantity of water held by soils in the range between the field capacity and the permanent wilting point is said to represent the available water capacity of a soil (where "available water" means water that is subject to utilization by plants in support of growth). The reasons for the placement of these limits are that at the permanent wilting point, the soil water has such low availability (that is, its rate of absorption by plants is so low) that it cannot support plant growth; and water in excess of the field capacity usually drains from the soil so rapidly that little of it can be absorbed by plants. Where drainage is impeded and water in excess of the field capacity remains in the soil, however, plants may absorb a substantial amount of water that is outside the conventional available water capacity. Under such conditions the availability of the water sometimes is reduced by poor aeration. These points are agreed upon rather generally. For some years, however, the question of the availability of the water to plants in the range between the field capacity and the permanent wilting point has been a subject of controversy. One group of investigators argues that plants either do or do not have available water. That is to say, as long as the water content of the soil is in excess of the permanent wilting point, the quantity and quality of the water are unimportant. Another group of investigators argues that the transition from the available to the unavailable state is gradual and that the plant response may be affected to a measurable degree by this transition before the water content of the soil has been reduced to the permanent wilting point. Literature on this subject was reviewed by Kramer (1944), Veihmeyer and Hendrickson (1950), Wadleigh and Richards (1951), and Kelley (1954).

For clarification the problem may be separated into three parts. The first concerns the changes in the free energy of water in soil and plant as the water content of the soil is reduced. It will be recalled from the preceding section that soil water enters the plant on the free-energy gradient, $\Delta f = f_p - f_s$. The free energy of soil water in non-saline soils decreases from approximately zero at saturation to -15 atmospheres at the permanent wilting point.[4] This change tends to decrease the rate of entry of water into plant roots, as indicated by

[4] Richards and Wadleigh (1952) summarized the data of a number of investigators and found that for a group of 199 soils, the water percentage (y) in the soil at the per-

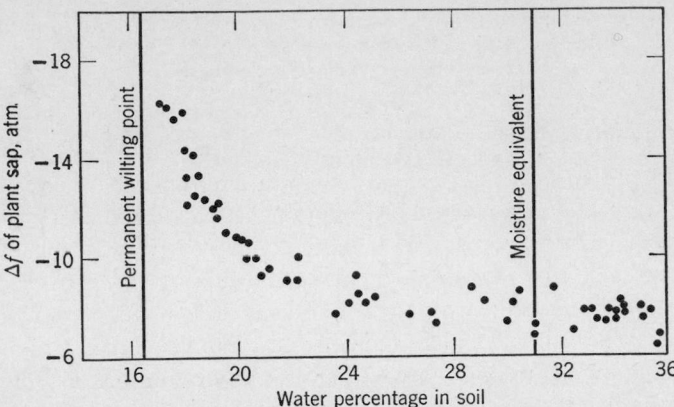

Fig. 9.   Specific free energy of water in sap expressed from sunflower plants in soil at different water percentages.   (Furr and Reeve, 1945.)

work of Hayward and Spurr (1944) on the relationship between the free energy of water in solutions and the rate of uptake of water by corn roots in experiments of short duration.   Over a longer period of time, however, plants supplied continuously with water at a reduced free energy level undergo internal adjustments, such as loss of water, that decrease the specific free energy of water in the plant and tend to maintain a specific-free-energy gradient favoring continued entry of water into the root.   This behavior is illustrated in Fig. 9, which shows the specific free energy of water in sap expressed from sun-flower plants plotted against the water content of the soil at the time the measurements were made.   As the water content of the soil decreased from the moisture equivalent toward the permanent wilting point, the specific free energy of water in the plant sap decreased. Thus as the soil dries, both f_s and f_p may be expected to decrease.

The second part of the problem concerns the effect of variations of f_s and f_p on the plant response.   Only a few examples chosen to illustrate different types of plant responses will be cited in this connection.

Davis (1940) grew corn plants in soil cultures in the greenhouse and measured the rate at which the plants increased in height at dif-

---

manent wilting point was related to the water percentage (x) in the soil when Δf was —15 atmospheres by the empirical equation

$$y = 0.96x + 0.85$$

In this work the osmotic component of the free energy was neglected since Richards' (1947) pressure membrane apparatus was used in making the laboratory measurements.

Table 1.   Rate of Increase in Height of Corn Plants in Soil
at Different Water Percentages
(Davis, 1940)

Water Content of Soil, %*	Number of Observations	Rate of Increase in Height per Hour, mm.
9–12	26	1.4
12–15	15	2.4
15–18	15	3.0
18–21	10	5.0
21–24	8	5.1

* Permanent wilting point = 6.8 per cent.

ferent water percentages in the soil.   As shown in Table 1, he found that the rate of growth increased with the water content of the soil. Since all the measurements were made at soil-water percentages above the permanent wilting point, and since commonly the water content of the soil at field capacity is about 1.8 times the content at the permanent wilting point, the soil evidently failed to supply water rapidly enough to maintain the same growth rate at all water contents between the field capacity and the permanent wilting point.   In connection with this work it may be noted that Davis did not attempt to "maintain" the water content of the soil within the ranges indicated.   Instead, he made the measurements of growth rate during short time intervals while the soil was drying out.   Each time he watered the soil he added enough water to bring it back to the field capacity or above. If smaller amounts of water are used, the upper part of the soil is wetted to field capacity, and the lower part remains dry.

Schneider and Childers (1941) determined the rates of transpiration and carbon dioxide assimilation of two apple trees grown in soil, the control tree being watered continually, and the test tree being allowed to dry until appearance of the first sign of wilting.   The results in Fig. 10 show that the rates of transpiration and carbon dioxide assimilation in the test tree dropped markedly below those of the control tree during the drying period before wilting occurred.

Evidently the rates of growth, transpiration, and carbon dioxide assimilation are decreased as the soil-water content decreases from the field capacity toward the permanent wilting point.   Generally, growth (in the sense of an increase in volume of the plant) essentially ceases some time before the permanent wilting point is reached.   Carbon dioxide assimilation usually becomes negative at about the permanent wilting point.   Transpiration (in the sense of water loss from the plant), however, continues even beyond the permanent wilting point.

Other evidence shows that the yield of plants may be affected by

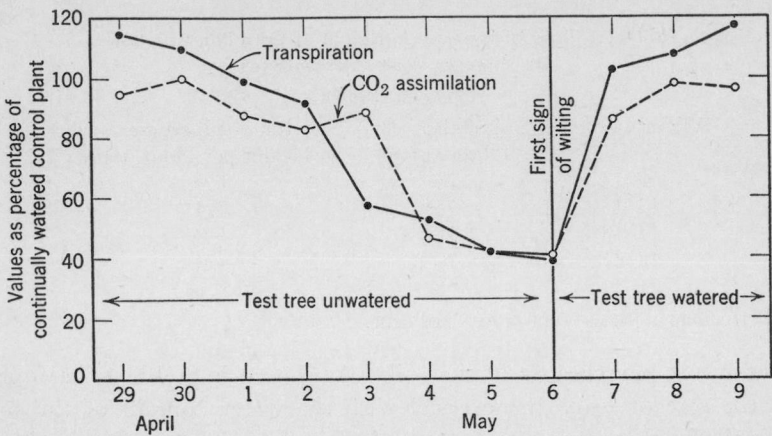

Fig. 10.   Transpiration and CO_2 assimilation per hour per 100 cm.^{2} of leaf surface of a McIntosh apple tree that was left unwatered from April 28 to May 6 as percentages of values for a comparable tree that was watered continually.   (Schneider and Childers, 1941.)

deficiency of water even though the soil is not allowed to dry to the permanent wilting point.   The experiment of Wadleigh, Gauch, and Magistad (1946) with guayule (see Fig. 14) may be cited as an example.

In view of the evidence that plants are affected by water deficiency before the soil has dried to the permanent wilting point, one may inquire how the opposing view could reasonably be held.   This is the third part of the problem.   The answer appears to be that the individuals concerned are not talking about the same thing.   Perhaps the basic difficulty is failure to agree on how changes in availability of soil water should be measured and on the experimental conditions under which the measurements are to be made.

Where plants are grown in soil, the most direct way to investigate changes in availability of water is to plot the rate of loss of water from the soil against the water content of the soil.   Over short periods of time in a constant aerial environment and with a complete canopy of vegetation the rate of water loss should remain the same as long as the availability is unchanged.   (Figure 7 shows an example of an adaptation of this approach to field experimentation.   If the availability had remained the same with different supplies of water in the soil, the points in the figure would lie on a horizontal line instead of decreasing as the available water content of the soil became smaller.)

Alternatively, indirect effects of water supply on the plant may be employed as an indication of differences in availability.   These in-

Table 2. Response of Cotton to Different Applications of Irrigation
Water in California

(Adams, Veihmeyer, and Brown, 1942)

Water Applied, in.	Plant Height, %	Index of Water Availability (maximum = 100%)	
		Yield of Above-Ground Parts of Plants	
		Total Minus Seed Cotton, %	Seed Cotton, %
13	73	51	90
25	91	81	96
43	100	100	100

direct effects differ considerably in sensitivity to water deficiency. Table 2 shows an example taken from a field experiment on irrigation of cotton. From the scientific standpoint the choice between such criteria is based upon the ratio of the sensitivity of the response to the experimental errors of measurement. From the practical standpoint the choice may be made on some other basis, such as the utilitarian value of the responses. Of the responses shown in Table 2, the yield of the vegetative parts of the plant and the height of the plant are the more suitable for scientific purposes and would be preferred as criteria of availability by those favoring the concept of a gradual decrease of availability of water as the soil dries. The yield of seed cotton is a suitable criterion for practical purposes and would be preferred as a criterion of availability by those advocating the concept of an abrupt transition from the available to the unavailable condition at the permanent wilting point.

Two differences in experimental conditions appear to have some bearing on the failure to reach agreement. One is that proponents of the view of an abrupt decrease of water availability at the permanent wilting point prefer to base judgment on results of field experiments. This procedure is justified from the practical standpoint, but from the scientific standpoint it may lead to ambiguity, since measurements of water content apply to the location of the sample, whereas the plant response is an integration of the total supply. During periods without rain or irrigation the soil dries from the surface downward. Because of uncertainty about root distribution, it is possible that in some instances plants are withdrawing water from soil at depths below those found to be at the permanent wilting point, thus fostering the illusion that plants have depleted the soil water to the permanent wilting point with a minimum of detrimental effects.

The other difference in experimental conditions has to do with the behavior of water in soils differing in texture. Table 3 shows the content of available water at the field capacity in soils of different textures and the proportion of the water removed from the soil at

Table 3:   Content of Available Water at Field Capacity in Soils of Different
Textures, and Proportions of Available Water Removed at Free-Energy
Levels above and below −1 Atmosphere

(Lehane and Staple, 1953)

Soil Texture	Available Water per Foot of Soil at Field Capacity, in.*	Proportion of Available Water Removed at Indicated Free-Energy Level, %	
		Above −1 atm.	Below −1 atm.
Coarse sand	0.44	95	5
Very fine sand	1.30	78	22
Very fine sandy loam	1.88	64	36
Silt loam	2.12	43	57
Silty clay	2.56	18	82
Clay	2.80	22	78

* Field capacity minus permanent wilting point.

specific free-energy levels above and below −1 atmosphere. The pressure membrane apparatus was used to make the separation at −1 atmosphere. Evidently most of the available water was extracted above this energy level from the coarse-textured soils and below this level from the fine-textured soils. Accordingly, if plants were to extract water at the same rate from the various soils, the free-energy level of the water would drop much more abruptly on approaching the permanent wilting point in the coarse-textured soils than in the fine-textured soils. In other words, the length of time during which plants would be subjected to conditions of low specific free energy of soil water short of permanent wilting would be less on coarse-textured than on fine-textured soils. The original experiments (Hendrickson and Veihmeyer, 1929) that served as the basis for the concept of an abrupt transition between available and unavailable water at the permanent wilting point were conducted in the field on soils of sand, sandy loam, and loam texture exclusively. These are the kinds of soils with which the transition should be most abrupt.

Clearly the availability of soil water to plants decreases gradually as the water content of the soil decreases from the field capacity toward the permanent wilting point. The existence of a gradual decrease simply is more evident with some criteria than others and with some soils than others.

Root extension

In the process of transportation of water from its original location in the soil to the aerial parts of plants, movement of water takes place partly through the soil and partly through the roots. In soil having a water content at or below the field capacity, movement of water to roots is a relatively short-range process. Root extension, on the other hand, is a relatively long-range process that acts mainly to bring the absorbing surfaces into position for the movement of soil water to be effective.

Environmental factors have a marked effect on root extension. When the water supply is ample throughout the soil, root extension is controlled by factors such as photosynthesis, nutrients, and temperature. As the water supply is depleted from the portion of the soil occupied by roots, however, the decreased availability of water in the soil causes a deficiency of water in the roots in that area. Root extension then occurs more readily in other areas where the availability of soil water is higher since cell elongation (which requires water absorption) is limited less in these areas.

Roots may continue to live in soil layers maintained at the permanent wilting point, provided water is available in some other part of the soil. Growth of new roots into such dry soil, however, is limited (Hendrickson and Veihmeyer, 1931; Hunter and Kelley, 1946). The maximum volume of soil that can be exploited by plant roots is not much greater than the original volume of contiguous moist soil. A dry layer lying between moist soil occupied by roots and a deeper layer of moist soil acts as a barrier to the use of water from the deeper layer. Observations made by Cole and Mathews (1939) (Fig. 11) at North Platte, Nebraska, may be cited as an example. These investigators found that in an area planted each year to wheat, the soil contained water in excess of the permanent wilting point at depths less than 2 feet and at depths greater than 5 feet in the spring of 1911. The water percentage in soil at the 2- to 5-foot depth was below the permanent wilting point as a result of growth of the previous crop.

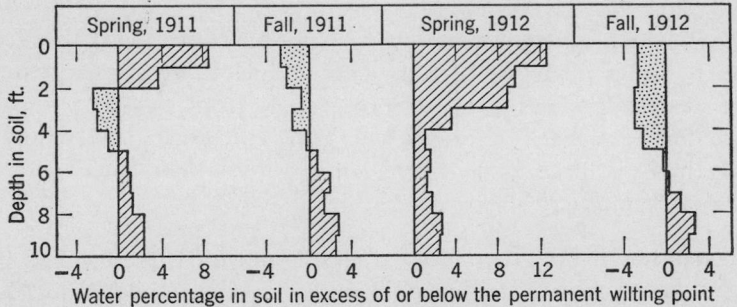

Fig. 11. Water percentage in soil in excess of or below the permanent wilting point at different depths in the spring and at harvest in two consecutive years at North Platte, Nebraska, on a plot planted each year to spring wheat. (Cole and Mathews, 1939.)

The 1911 crop removed all the available water in the upper part of the profile but did not use the water available below the 5-foot depth. By the spring of 1912 the water percentage in the profile was above the permanent wilting point throughout. In that year the soil was depleted of water to the permanent wilting point, or below, throughout the entire profile to a depth of 7 feet, and apparently a little water was removed from greater depths.

Pronounced differences exist among plants in regard to the maximum distance through which root extension takes place into moist soil. Such differences may have important practical consequences. For example, Burton et al. (1954) found that drought resistance of different grasses on a sandy soil in Georgia was associated with root extension. During a 2-month drought, foliage of carpet grass turned brown and died, whereas foliage of coastal bermuda grass showed little evidence of injury. Excavation of the roots showed that the proportion of the root system by weight in the soil below a depth of 2 feet was 6 per cent with the carpet grass and 35 per cent with coastal bermuda grass.

A second instance involving differences in root extension among plants was reported by Kiesselbach, Anderson, and Russel (1934), who investigated the utilization of subsoil water by crops in eastern Nebraska. They found that with a soil initially well supplied with subsoil water (as a result of accumulation over many years), 5 years of cropping to sweet clover and red clover failed to deplete the soil of water below a depth of 7 feet. With alfalfa, however, the subsoil water had been reduced nearly to the permanent wilting point to a depth of at least 15 feet (the maximum depth of sampling) by the end of 4 years. The response of these crops to a supply of subsoil water was rather different, as indicated in Table 4 by the comparative yields

Table 4. Yields of Crops in Eastern Nebraska with and without Previous
Cropping to Alfalfa

(Kiesselbach, Anderson, and Russel, 1934)

| | Yield of Hay per Acre Annually | | |
	Alfalfa, ton	Sweet Clover, ton	Red Clover, ton
Land previously in alfalfa	2.7	2.6	3.0
Land not previously in alfalfa	3.9	2.7	3.4

obtained on land not previously in alfalfa and on land that had been cropped previously to alfalfa. All crops produced higher yields on the land that had not been in alfalfa previously, but the increase was greatest with alfalfa, presumably because much more subsoil water was utilized by the alfalfa than by the red clover or sweet clover.

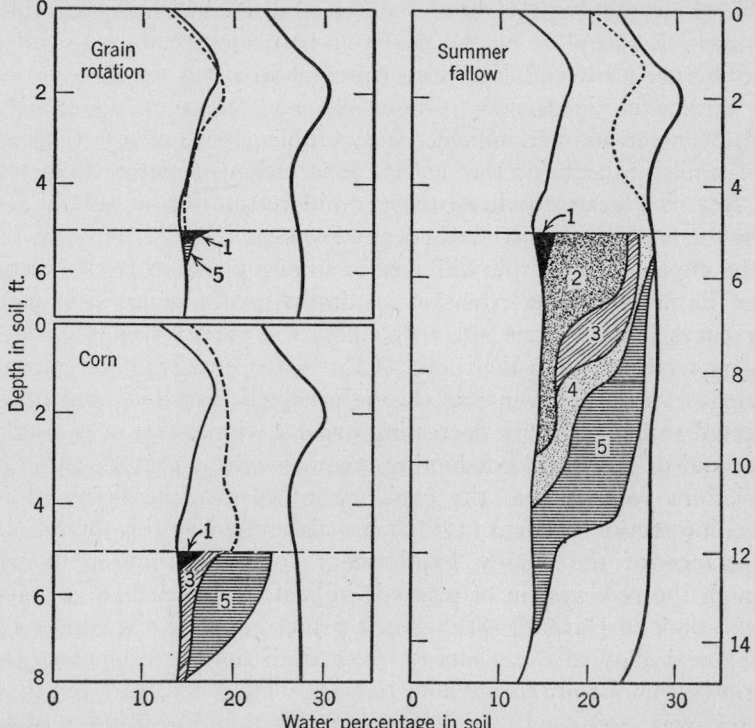

Fig. 12. Restoration of subsoil water during five years (1928–1932) of grain rotation (corn, oats, wheat), continuous corn, and continuous summer fallow in soil cropped formerly to alfalfa (1922–1927). (The solid line on the left in each diagram indicates the initial water content in the fall of 1927. The heavy solid line on the right indicates the calculated field capacity. The broken line above the 5-ft. level shows the average water content during the last 3 years. The shaded areas indicate the amounts of storage below the 5-ft. level during each of the five successive yearly intervals [Nos. 1–5] between sampling. The precipitation during the five years was as follows: 1928—30 in.; 1929—21 in.; 1930—15 in.; 1931—27 in.; 1932—35 in.) (Kiesselbach, Anderson, and Russel, 1934.)

Figure 12 shows that once the subsoil water had been depleted by growing alfalfa, considerable time would be required for its restoration under the prevailing conditions, even when the soil was kept fallow. The 2-year average yields of alfalfa grown on old alfalfa land were 2.8 tons per acre with no fallow, 3.5 tons after 1 year of fallow, and 3.8 tons after 2 years of fallow. The yield was 4.3 tons on land in alfalfa for the first time. Because of the slowness with which the subsoil water was restored, Kiesselbach, Anderson, and Russel concluded that under upland soil conditions in eastern Nebraska,

the most profitable procedure, once the subsoil had become depleted
of water, was to plow up the alfalfa and to reseed it on land that had
never before grown alfalfa.   Experimental work on this same problem
was conducted in Kansas (Grandfield and Metzger, 1936; Myers,
1936; Metzger and Grandfield, 1938; Hobbs, 1953) where the results
were similar except for the deeper penetration of sweet clover roots
(13 feet in 2 years) and the more rapid restoration of subsoil water
when the land was fallowed or cropped to cereals.

The explanation for the differences among plants in regard to maximum distance of root extension no doubt can be referred in part to
differences in plant structure that affect the energy requirements for
moving water through the roots.   Clearly the energy requirement for
moving water at a given rate through a fixed length of root may be
expected to increase with decreasing cross sectional area of conducting
tissue and of individual conducting channels within that tissue.   These
predictions follow from the capillary tube principle discussed in a
preceding section.   Wind (1955b) has elaborated on this theme.   The
importance of the energy requirement for transportation of water
through the root system of plants is indicated in a qualitative way by
observations of Davis (1940).   Davis planted corn in one end of a box
of soil and allowed the plants to grow until the roots appeared to be
distributed uniformly throughout the soil.   He noted that even though
the soil was moistened uniformly after this time the plants withdrew
the water near at hand more rapidly than that some distance away.
The water supply in soil near the plants was exhausted nearly to the
permanent wilting point while the water content of soil 3 feet away
remained near the field capacity.   The lesser absorption of water by
the more remote portion of the root system is consistent with a positive energy requirement for moving water from these parts to the
base of the stem.   If the energy requirement for transportation of
water through the root system had been zero, water should have been
withdrawn from the soil at approximately the same rate throughout
the box.

Water level

The level of free water sometimes is near enough to the surface of
the soil to make it appear that much of the water requirement of
plants is satisfied by water rising by capillarity.   Wind (1955a) investigated the upward movement of water by capillarity in a relatively impermeable clay soil under field conditions in Holland.   The
water level in this soil was about 45 cm. below the surface, and the
roots of the grass growing on the soil were confined almost entirely

to the surface 10 cm. Upward movement of water was demonstrated qualitatively by the fact that the surface 30 cm. of soil became drier when this layer was separated from the underlying soil by a sheet of waterproof material than when contact with the underlying soil was maintained. Quantitative measurements made in periods without drainage from May through September indicated that capillary rise of water totaled 153 mm. in 96 days. During this time the loss of water from the soil by evaporation and transpiration amounted to 322 mm. The rise by capillarity thus was equivalent to 48 per cent of the water lost by evaporation and transpiration.

Although further evidence is needed, the available data suggest that in a humid region with a free-water level at a depth of about 2 or 3 feet, water that is moved upward from the water level may be equivalent to a significant but not a major part of the water lost from the soil by evapotranspiration. At water levels of perhaps 6 feet or greater, the upward movement is small, and perhaps negligible, in relation to loss by evapotranspiration.

Under conditions of relatively low rainfall, on the other hand, a free-water surface in the soil may provide the major part of the water lost to the atmosphere. An instance in which this appears to be true was reported by Fox and Lipps (1955) from western Nebraska where the natural rainfall is inadequate to produce good yields of alfalfa. In the Platte River Valley of that area, a large acreage of relatively high-yielding alfalfa is produced by "subirrigation" from the free-water surface that exists within the depth of root penetration. Once the roots reach the moist soil that is fed by water from the free-water surface beneath, the plants have an additional source of water and their dependence on current rainfall greatly decreases. Figure 13 indicates that upward movement of water from the free-water surface in soils of this area may be effective over distances as great as 5 or 6 feet. Much of the water used by the alfalfa apparently is absorbed near the free-water surface, however, as indicated by the proliferation of roots within the foot of soil immediately overlying the free-water surface.

Two reasons may be advanced for attaching less importance to upward movement of water under conditions of high rainfall than under the conditions described by Fox and Lipps (1955). The first is that the water that falls as rain is used preferentially. Water that falls as rain is held primarily in the upper part of the soil, which is the zone from which plants withdraw water most rapidly if the water is available. Moreover, water that falls as rain brings about a decrease in the free-energy gradient from the free-water surface upward and thus

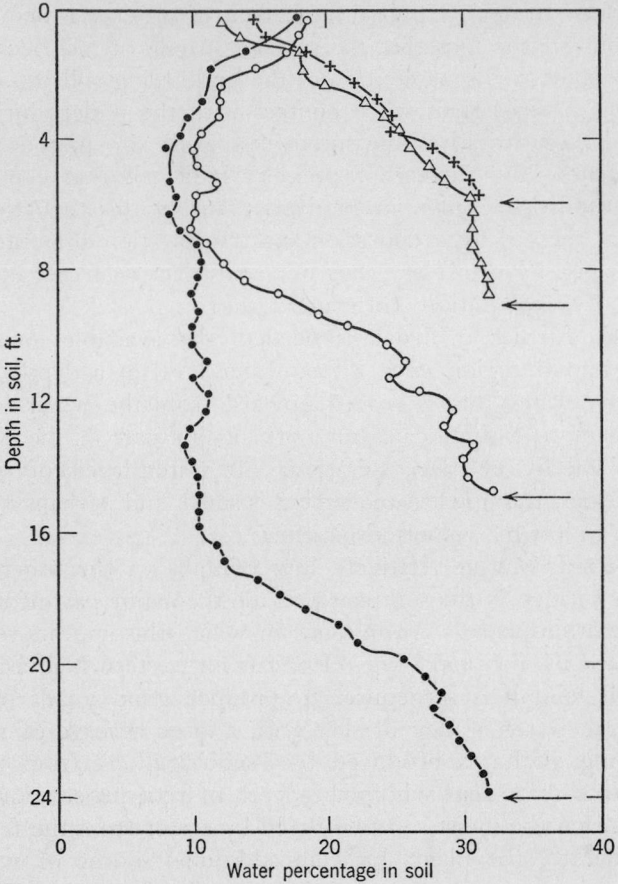

Fig. 13. Average water percentage during the period from April through October in four soils bearing alfalfa and having a free-water surface at the depth indicated by the horizontal arrows. (Lipps and Fox, 1956.)

decreases the tendency for upward movement. The second reason is that a temporary rise of the free-water level from heavy rainfall may cause plant roots below the water level to die because of poor aeration. Hence, as the water level falls, maintenance of the close proximity of active roots to the free-water level, near which upward movement is more effective, requires reinvasion of the subsoil by a new set of roots growing downward from above. (The water level remained at a fairly constant depth under the conditions described by Fox and Lipps, so that, once established, the root system of the alfalfa could operate continuously in the same soil zone.)

Different kinds of plants do not respond uniformly to variations in depth of free-water level. Such was found to be the case, for example, by Ellis and Morris (1946) in Indiana. These investigators compared the performance of several crops on muck soil with the water level maintained 16, 27, or 38 inches below the surface. As shown in Table 5, all the crops except mint benefited appreciably

Table 5. Yield of Crops on Muck Soil with Water Level Controlled at Different Depths
(Ellis and Morris, 1946)

Average Depth of Water Level, in.	Yield of Indicated Crop (maximum = 100)					
	Mint		Sweet Corn	Carrots	Red Beets	Onions
	Hay	Oil				
16	99	55	48	9	26	12
27	100	94	77	100	97	76
38	98	100	100	99	100	100

when the water level was lowered from 16 to 27 inches, but not all crops gave an additional response when the water level was lowered to 38 inches. Mint behaved singularly in that the yield of hay was unaffected by the water level, but only a 55 per cent yield of oil was produced with the shallow water level. Apparently a certain degree of water stress was necessary to raise the oil content.

The optimum depth of free water for accumulation of dry matter may change also between seasons and within seasons. Frankena and Goedewaagen (1942) found in experiments with grass that almost invariably the highest yield of grass was obtained with the water level held at the 20-cm. depth, but the degree to which the yield was decreased with the 50- and 80-cm. depths varied with the season, the yield from the latter treatments being lowest when the water requirement was greatest. The effect of seasonal conditions on the relationship between water level and crop yield can be explained on the basis that the plants exhaust the water from the upper part of the soil to a greater extent and draw more of their water supply from soil near the free-water level at times when rainfall is low and evapotranspiration is high than at times when rainfall is ample and evapotranspiration is low. The crop yield decreases primarily because of water deficiency, which follows from the greater energy requirement for moving water through the greater distance and through a smaller cross section of conducting tissue. The smaller cross section of conducting tissue is associated with the decrease in number of roots with increasing depth.

The significance to plants of the depth of the free-water surface is not limited entirely to the water supply. As the water level is raised toward the surface of the soil, the quantity of water at the disposal of the plant is increased but the quantity of oxygen is decreased. In consequence of the complementary relationship between water level and oxygen content of the soil, the most suitable water level will depend on the oxygen supply, and hence may be expected to be at a greater depth in fine-textured than in coarse-textured soils.

The most suitable water level depends also on the nutrient supply, but in a less simple manner. Indications from the work of Burgevin and Hénin (1943) are that the optimum depth of the water level in the soil tends to approach the surface as the supply of nutrients in the surface soil increases relative to that in the subsoil. Where the rainfall is sufficient to prevent the surface soil from becoming dry, raising the water level will reduce the nutrient availability. An example of this for nitrogen was reported by Eden et al. (1951) in England. They observed that nitrogen deficiency symptoms in the crop became more pronounced as the water level was raised toward the surface of the soil. The field observations were corroborated by data on the yield and nitrogen content of the crop shown in Table 6. On

Table 6.   Yield and Protein Content of Grass on Peat Soil with Water Level Maintained at Different Depths

(Eden et al., 1951)

Depth of Water Level, in.	Yield of Dry Grass per Acre, lb.	Crude Protein in Dry Matter	
		Per Cent	Per Acre, lb.
15	3350	14.8	497
24	6260	21.1	1318
38	6140	24.6	1513

the other hand, under conditions dry enough to prevent appreciable root activity in the surface soil, raising the free-water level will moisten the surface soil. The resulting increase in nutrient availability will tend to offset the decrease in availability associated with loss of root space in the subsoil. One may expect, therefore, that from the standpoint of nutrient availability the optimum level of free water in the soil will be closer to the surface under conditions of low rainfall than of high rainfall.

Evidently the depth at which the water level should be maintained for maximum yields is by no means constant. It varies with the characteristics of the crop, the season, and the soil.

WATER SUPPLY AND PLANT BEHAVIOR

Seed germination

During germination many seeds absorb enough water to double their weight. Under favorable conditions of water supply and temperature, the requisite water generally is absorbed in a short time. The rapidity of absorption can be accounted for on the basis of the large specific free-energy gradient that exists between the water in moist soil and dry seeds, and the short distances that are involved in movement of water to the seed.

The existence of a large difference in specific free energy of water in dry seeds and moist soil is indicated by the results of an experiment of Whitney and Cameron (1904) in which 50 g. of cowpeas were mixed with 50 g. of soil containing 7.5 g. of water. In 12 hours the cowpeas had absorbed all but 0.65 g. of the soil water, leaving the soil in essentially air-dry condition.

The significance of the distance of movement of water through the soil is indicated by further work of Whitney and Cameron. When they placed seeds in a relatively large mass of moist soil they found that the soil within about one-eighth inch of the seed became relatively dry and sometimes appeared to be nearly in air-dry condition. The bulk of the soil, however, appeared to have suffered no loss of water to the seed. In other work they observed that small seeds such as those of clover and wheat would germinate if placed on the surface of a moist soil. The large, flat seeds of lima beans, on the other hand, would not absorb the 100 to 120 per cent of their dry weight of water requisite for germination if they were present on the surface of moist soil and failed to germinate even if left on the soil indefinitely. Apparently, therefore, rewetting of the soil by rain may be needed before germination will take place if the demand of the germinating seed for water exceeds the quantity that can be absorbed from a thin layer of soil around the seed.

Differentiation products

Formation by plants of differentiation products, such as rubber, essential oils, and alkaloids, is favored by conditions under which the precursors accumulate in the plant and are not used for other purposes. Since water deficiency limits growth relatively more than photosynthesis, relatively more carbohydrate is available for purposes other than growth under conditions of water deficiency than of water sufficiency.

The work of Wadleigh, Gauch, and Magistad (1946) may be cited as an example of water-supply–growth–differentiation relationships in guayule, with rubber being the differentiation product. Figure 14 shows that as the specific free energy of the soil water decreased, the yield of millable bush (the air-dry stems and main roots of the plant) decreased likewise. The rubber content of the millable bush increased

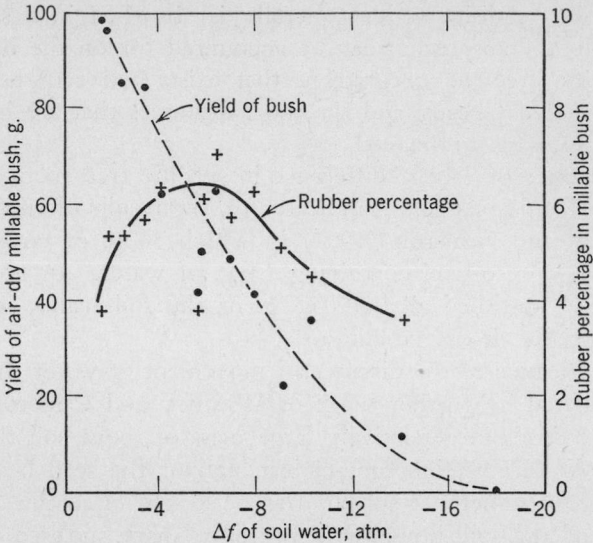

Fig. 14. Yield and rubber content of guayule bush versus specific free energy of soil water. (Wadleigh, Gauch, and Magistad, 1946.)

from about 4 per cent, where Δf of the soil water was —1.5 atmospheres, to a maximum of about 6 per cent, where Δf of the soil water was —4 to —8 atmospheres, and then decreased with further diminution in Δf of the soil water.   (The authors accounted for the decrease in rubber percentage on the basis that abscission of many of the leaves at the lower free-energy levels reduced the leaf surface and hence the rate of photosynthesis.)   The absolute yield of rubber, that is, the product of yield of millable bush and rubber percentage, remained approximately the same as Δf of the soil water was reduced from —1.5 to —4 atmospheres, and decreased with further reduction of the free energy.

Root and top growth

If the supply of water is deficient, addition of water usually increases the yield of both the roots and tops of plants.   The ratio of the weight of above-ground parts to below-ground parts increases with increasing water supply, as illustrated in Table 7 by the data of Davis (1942) on nutgrass.   Similar results were obtained in experiments of Harris (1914) and Miller and Duley (1925), where yields of tops and roots of corn grown with different amounts of water were determined.   The relatively low ratio of tops to roots under conditions

Table 7. Yield of Tops and Tubers of Nutgrass in Soil with Different
Minimum Water Percentages

(Davis, 1942)

Minimum Water Content of Soil before Irrigation,* %	Fresh weight of plants		Ratio of Tops to Tubers
	Tops, g.	Tubers, g.	
6	4	26	0.15
9	9	50	0.18
12	16	80	0.20
15	25	116	0.22
18	34	130	0.26

* The moisture equivalent of the soil was 16.9 per cent, and the permanent wilting point was 8.2 per cent.

of water deficiency probably is responsible for the common belief that water deficiency stimulates root growth.

The change in proportion of roots and tops of plants in response to changes in water supply may be explained on the basis of the direct effects of water on cell elongation and the indirect effects of water on the disposition of carbohydrates within the plant. The free energy of water in the roots exceeds that in the tops, as indicated by the fact that water moves from the roots to the tops. Hence the availability of water for cell elongation is greater in the roots than in the tops. This condition prevails whether the supply of water is ample or deficient. But with the accumulation of carbohydrate unused for growth in the aerial part of the plant because of water deficiency, a greater proportion of the total carbohydrate is transported to the roots, where it can be used in root growth. In confirmation of this view, Eaton and Ergle (1948) found that drought produced a large increase in percentage content of starch and sugars in the roots of cotton plants but not in the leaves. Thus the picture seems to be that the water relations of the plant favor root extension over top extension. This tendency is expressed to a greater extent under dry than moist condition because of a relatively greater supply of carbohydrate to the roots and a relatively lesser supply of water to the tops.

Grain and straw growth

As shown in Table 8, Hellriegel (1883) found that when barley was grown in sand cultures supplied with different amounts of water, the entire crop consisted of straw with the smallest amount of water. With increasing amounts of water the yields of both straw and grain passed through a maximum and then decreased, but the maximum grain yield occurred with a smaller amount of water than did the maximum straw yield. The maximum ratio of grain to straw oc-

Table 8.   Yield of Barley Grain and Straw in Sand Culture
with Different Amounts of Water
(Hellriegel, 1883)

Percentage of Water-holding Capacity	Yield of Dry Matter per Culture		Ratio of Grain to Straw
	Grain, g.	Straw, g.	
5	0	0.1	0
10	0.7	2.3	0.3
20	7.7	6.9	1.1
30	9.7	10.0	1.0
40	10.5	11.3	0.9
60	10.0	12.8	0.8
80	8.8	10.9	0.8

curred with a still smaller amount of water.   The causes of the difference in behavior between grain and straw are not known.

Interpretation of the results of Hellriegel's experiment is confused
by the fact that instead of adding at each application a quantity of
water sufficient to moisten the entire culture, only enough water was
added to bring the water content up to the desired level.   As was
pointed out previously, addition of a limited quantity of water to a
dry soil results only in wetting the upper part of the soil to field
capacity.   Volume of soil thus is confounded with water supply in
Hellriegel's experiment.   The same problem in general exists with
field experiments, and results reported from field experiments agree
with those of Hellriegel.   Figure 15 shows that the ratio of grain to
straw increased with the quantity of water used by the spring wheat
crop in North Dakota.   The range in yield of grain per acre was
from 240 lb. with the smallest water use to 2100 lb. with the greatest

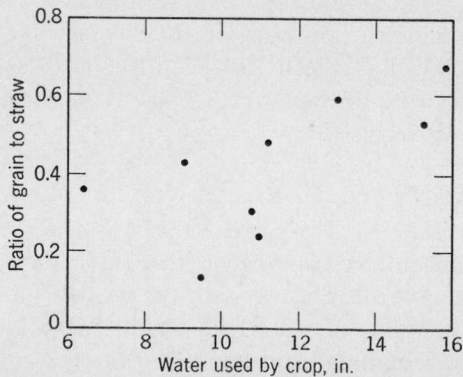

Fig. 15.   Ratio of grain to straw versus water use by spring wheat at Edgeley, North
Dakota, during the years 1907 to 1917.   (Cole and Mathews, 1923.)

water use, indicating the great importance of water as a limiting factor. The maximum in the ratio of grain to straw found in Hellriegel's experiment was not observed here, apparently because the range in water supply did not extend high enough.   In an experiment in Utah (Table

Table 9.   Ratio of Grain to Straw of Spring Wheat with Different Amounts
of Water Available from Precipitation and Irrigation
(Widtsoe, 1912)

Water available, inches	19	21	24	29	39	49	64
Ratio of grain to straw	0.80	0.76	0.75	0.69	0.63	0.60	0.49

9), where water was less important as a limiting factor, a decrease in ratio of grain to straw was associated with increasing water supply.

Time of maturity

In seed-producing crops, maturation is in part a matter of translocation of organic and mineral substances to the seed and in part a matter of desiccation. The time of maturity thus is influenced by the rate of these processes. The supply of water in the soil during the latter part of the season is of particular importance in connection with desiccation. The rate of desiccation increases and the rate of translocation decreases as the supply of water to the plant diminishes. The supply of water in the soil during the early part of the season also is of significance because of its influence on the rate at which the initial phases of the life cycle are traversed.

Table 10 gives the results of an experiment that shows the effect

Table 10.   Length of Growing Period of Wheat with Water Supply
Varied in Different Ways During Growth
(Harris, 1914b)

Water Content of Soil During Indicated Growth Stage			
Planting to Five Well-developed Leaves, %	Five Well-developed Leaves to Boot Stage, %	Boot Stage to Maturity, %	Number of Days from Planting to Maturity
30	30	30	208
30	30	15	205
30	15	15	204
15	15	15	212
15	15	30	215
15	30	15	208

of supply of water at different stages of growth on the length of the growing period of wheat. The growing period was shortest when the soil water supply was high in the first stage or in the first two stages and low in the last stage or in the last two stages. It was longest when the soil water supply was low in the first two growth stages and high in the third. The growing period was shorter when the water supply was high throughout than when it was low throughout.

The usual situation in the field is that the soil water supply is greater at the beginning of the season than at the end of the season; hence, additions of water to the soil when needed will have relatively less effect on the early growth of the plant than on the mid-season and late-season growth. As would be expected from the findings of Harris (1914b), such water applications often are observed to delay the maturity. Thus Harris (1914a) found that in Utah, corn receiving 40 inches of irrigation water matured a week later than did corn receiving no supplemental irrigation. Shutt and Hamilton (1934) reported that in British Columbia the average length of the growing period of wheat was 116 days under irrigation and 104 days without irrigation.

Field experiments of Schwalen and Wharton (1940) with lettuce in Arizona, where normally the early-season supply of soil water is low, showed that early maturity was achieved when ample irrigation water was supplied throughout the season. Still earlier maturity was obtained if the soil water content was lowered during harvest. On the other hand, if the lettuce was supplied with ample water after an early-season deficiency of water, the growth period was prolonged, and the lettuce matured relatively late. The effect of late irrigation in lengthening the growing period of barley was noted by Harlan and Anthony (1921) in Idaho. These investigators found that the water content of the grain on August 6 was 36 per cent where the barley had not been irrigated since June 23. On plots that had been irrigated June 23 and at later dates, the water percentages in the grain were 43, 50, and 47 where the barley was irrigated July 14, July 20, and July 29, respectively.

Plants supplied with an excess of water in the early part of the season usually mature relatively late. This behavior often is observed in areas where water has stood for some time during the early part of the season.

Critical period

The effect on final yield produced by a temporary water deficiency in the soil depends on the time in the growth cycle of the plant at which the deficiency occurs. Figure 16 shows the results of an experiment of Van der Paauw (1949) in which oats were grown in cul-

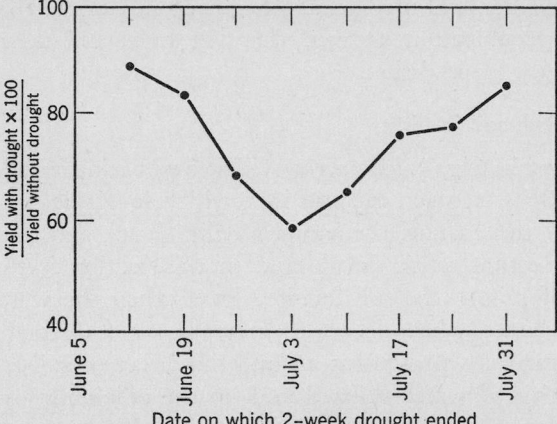

Fig. 16. Yield of oats subjected to a 2-week drought at different dates expressed as a percentage of the yield obtained from oats supplied continuously with ample water. (Van der Paauw, 1949.)

tures on a sandy soil. In one series of cultures the soil was maintained moist continuously. In other series the water content of the soil was maintained at the same level as that in the continuously moist cultures except for a period of 2 weeks, when the water content was allowed to drop to a low level and was maintained at that level by daily or twice daily additions of water. Evidently the yield of oats that received the 2-week drought treatment depended on the time at which the drought was experienced, being lowest with the drought ending July 3. This drought included the stage of heading (June 27 to 30). Drought during the heading stage caused greater shortening of the stem and greater barrenness of ears than did drought during other stages. Drought at this time thus was relatively critical. The concept of the "critical period" of water requirement was developed in Russia. In reviewing the earlier work, which was done mainly with cereals, Maximov (1929, pp. 396 to 399) concluded that temporary drought reduces the final grain yield to the greatest extent when it occurs during the period of rapid increase in length of internodes preceding heading. He accounted for the special sensitivity of the plant to drought at this time on the basis that the greatest requirement for water for tissue expansion occurs during the time of maximum rate of growth in length. A deficiency of water during this time decreases the size of the cells. In work with lima beans, Lambeth[5] found that much of the poor setting of pods associated with

[5] Lambeth, Victor Neal. (1950) Some factors influencing pod set and yield of the lima bean. Ph.D. Thesis, University of Missouri, Columbia, Missouri.

drought could be attributed to abscission of flowers in the bud stage. Microscopic examination showed that the buds and flowers became desiccated prior to abscission.

Interactions with soil fertility

As indicated in Fig. 17, the crop yield may be increased, decreased, or unaffected by a given change in fertility level, depending on the magnitude of the change, the initial fertility level, and the water supply. The question to be considered in this section is the effect on crop yield of raising the soil-fertility level when the water supply is limited, and hence when decreases in yield are a distinct possibility. The considerations will revolve around the effect of soil-fertility level on the quantity of water utilized and on the efficiency of utilization.

Measurements of water utilization in soil culture experiments with an ample supply of water have shown that when the crop yield is increased by raising the soil-fertility level, the evapotranspiration usually increases, but the ratio of evapotranspiration to yield decreases. That is to say, the water is used more efficiently at high than at low fertility levels. The behavior observed in these experiments would be expected from the findings of Penman (1948), noted

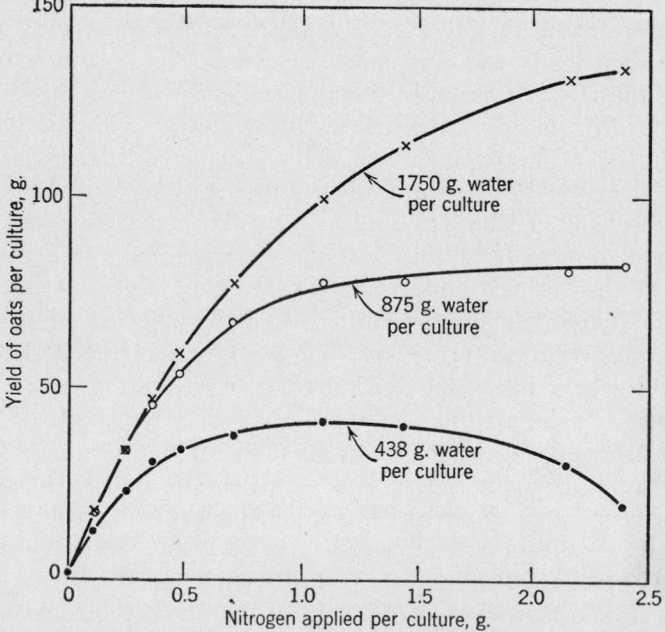

Fig. 17. Yield of oats in sand cultures with different levels of water and nitrogen as ammonium nitrate. (Lange, 1938.)

before, to the effect that for moist soils with a complete canopy of active vegetation the water loss from unit area within a similar larger area is independent of the yield. Under Penman's limiting conditions the supply of soil water would be depleted to almost the same extent by a large crop as by a small crop. The yield would not be limited by the water supply in either case.

Two clearly different situations may be distinguished in practice. In the first of these the available water supply is utilized fully by the crop growing at the existing fertility level. Any increase in yield from raising the fertility level thus requires an increase in efficiency of utilization of the same amount of water. In the second situation, the available water supply is not utilized completely by the crop growing at the existing fertility level. In this case increases in yield from raising the existing fertility level may be associated with an increase in the amount of water utilized as well as an increase in efficiency of utilization.

Complete utilization of available water. The condition of complete utilization of available water is found commonly in arid and semiarid regions where the subsoil is dry. The total available water in the soil may be represented as the amount of water in excess of the permanent wilting point to the depth of wetting. By the time the crop is mature the available water has been exhausted to the full depth of wetting.

When crops are grown with the natural rainfall, the greatest supply of water usually is at hand early in the growth of the crop. Water deficiency does not develop until later. Zubriski and Norum (1955) conducted experiments under these conditions. They found that at nine locations in North Dakota, the wheat yields averaged 17 and 24 bushels per acre on the control and fertilized plots, respectively. At harvest the average total content of water in the soils to a depth of 5 feet was 9.6 inches with both treatments. Evidently the efficiency of water utilization for the production of grain was considerably greater on the fertilized plots than on the unfertilized plots. No data on total dry matter were reported. Another example is given in Table 11. This table records the results of an experiment on wheat grown without fallow and without irrigation at North Platte, Nebraska. The effect of soil fertility on efficiency of water utilization is indicated by the yields. Raising the fertility level increased the total yield but decreased the yield of grain. Similar observations were made by Finnell (1929), who noted that under semiarid conditions in Oklahoma, application of manure caused an increase in yield of forage crops but not in yield of wheat grain.

Table 11. Average Yield of Winter Wheat with and without a Fall Topdressing
of Manure on Continuously Cropped Land at North Platte, Nebraska
(Zook and Weakly, 1950)

| | Yield of Wheat per Acre | |
	No manure, lb.	Manure, lb.
Grain	1014	912
Straw	1885	2390
Grain + straw	2899	3302

The exhaustion pattern of the water supply under semiarid, nonirrigated conditions is especially conducive to a depression of the yield of grain crops when the fertility level is raised. The reason for this is that the relatively good supply of water early in the season permits a luxuriant growth, if the fertility level is high, thereby causing the water supply to be depleted more rapidly than with moderate or low fertility. The grain is produced during the latter part of the season when the water supply is dwindling. Early exhaustion of the water supply as a result of raising the fertility level may halt grain development before full maturity has been reached, and thus may cause a decrease in yield of grain. (The date of final exhaustion is not of much importance for forage crops, where total dry matter is the criterion of yield, except as the crop on soil of low fertility may benefit from rains that fall after the crop on soil of high fertility has stopped growing). Whether the grain yield is increased or decreased probably turns on a small difference in water supply or environmental conditions.

Where the natural supply of water can be supplemented by irrigation, the probability can be much reduced that a decrease in yield will be obtained when the fertility level is increased. Under the circumstances described above, where the natural water supply is fairly adequate during the early part of the season, the use of a small amount of irrigation water late in the season to prevent the premature exhaustion of water at the high fertility level presumably would eliminate the possible yield depression.

Where the natural supply of water is low throughout the season, still more regulation can be provided by irrigation. The greatest efficiency of use and the lowest probability of obtaining a decrease in yield of grain-producing crops at high fertility levels probably can be obtained by applying the water in small increments and at intervals such that plants at the high fertility level are subjected to water stress before each irrigation. Crowther (1934) reported an instance in Egypt in which the yield of cotton was increased by nitrogen fertilization under conditions of substantial water deficiency when the cotton was irrigated at biweekly intervals.

Incomplete utilization of available water.   The condition of incomplete utilization of available water is found commonly in humid regions and irrigated regions, and occasionally in nonirrigated semiarid and arid regions.   In semiarid and arid regions certain soils may be found in which the supply of one or more nutrients is so low that plants do not make enough growth to utilize all the limited supply of water provided by the natural precipitation.   Under these circumstances, increasing the level of the limiting nutrient or nutrients will cause an increase in both the efficiency of water utilization and in the amount utilized.   The semiarid wheat-producing areas of Australia, perhaps, contain some examples.   Despite the limited supply of water, the use of phosphate fertilizer is a common practice because of the low availability of phosphorus in many of the soils.

In humid regions and in irrigated regions the subsoil usually is moist.   Raising the soil-fertility level is less likely to produce a decrease in yield under these circumstances than under the exhaustion pattern discussed in the preceding section, because the available water is never exhausted completely.   The limit to the supply of available water increases with the depth of root penetration.   Raising the fertility level may increase the growth of roots and the depth to which the water is exhausted.   The data of Gliemeroth (1951) in Fig. 18 indicate that where the subsoil is moist, a crop may extract water at a greater rate and to a greater depth from fertile than from infertile soil. Whether or not the differential utilization actually occurs appears

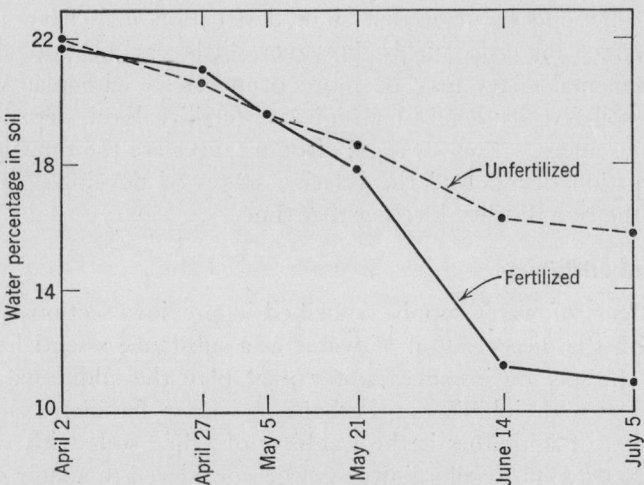

Fig. 18.   Water percentage at the 55-cm. depth at different dates in fertilized and unfertilized soil planted to rye.   (Gliemeroth, 1951.)

to depend on the density of vegetative cover. Once the canopy is complete, differences in growth associated with changes in fertility level have little or no effect on the total utilization of water. The results of experiments by Weaver and Pearson (1956) appear to support this view.

One of the important factors in the utilization of subsoil water appears to be the fertility of the subsoil itself. Gliemeroth (1955) found that placement of fertilizer in the subsoil increased the utilization of subsoil water. The effect of subsoil fertilization apparently is to produce in the subsoil a greater density of roots, or volume of water-absorbing and water-conducting tissue. Table 12 illustrates

Table 12.   Distribution of Barley Roots in a Loam Soil with NPK Fertilizer
Placed at Different Depths
(Gliemeroth, 1955)

	Percentage of Total Weight of Roots		
Depth of Soil Layer, cm.	Fertilizer in 0- to 18-cm. Layer	Fertilizer in 18- to 36-cm. Layer	Fertilizer in 36- to 54-cm. Layer
0–18	50	35	27
18–36	30	45	33
36–54	19	20	40

Gliemeroth's findings with respect to the effect of subsoil fertility on root distribution.

Mention should be made also of the possible effects of temporary desiccation of the crops during periods of excessive heat and wind velocity.   Beyond the fact that such desiccation may have an unfavorable effect on crop yields, however, little can be said about it. The detrimental effect may be more pronounced with plants grown at a low soil-fertility level or a high soil-fertility level, depending on the circumstances.   Two of these circumstances are the time at which the desiccation occurs and the relative stages of development of the plants at the two fertility levels at that time.

Removal of inhibitors

The effects of water supply described in previous sections are associated with the direct action of water as a substance essential to plant growth.   In specific instances water may play the additional role of removing growth inhibitors.   Perhaps the most familiar example of the removal of inhibitors is the leaching of saline soils with water to remove excess salts.   Soil salinity will be considered in a later chapter. The purpose here is to note two less familiar types of effects.

According to Went (1953), the seeds of certain desert annuals germinate after a heavy rainfall but not after a light rainfall even if the soil is kept moist continuously by artificial means. Germination occurs with less water in the presence of charcoal than in its absence. Went explained these observations on the basis that the seeds contain diffusible germination inhibitors that are removed by rain if movement of water past the seed continues over a long enough period of time. The action of charcoal indicates that inhibitors of an organic nature are involved. Inorganic inhibitors may be involved also, however, since Went stated that low concentrations of salts prevent germination. Germination of these seeds thus requires not only the presence of an ample supply of water around the seed, but also the previous movement of fresh water past the seed.

Removal of growth inhibitors by water may be important also in the survival of seedlings in specific instances. Bonner and Galston (1944) found that roots of the desert shrub, guayule, excrete substances that are toxic to seedlings of the same species. Cinnamic acid is one of these toxins. Went (1953) used this evidence as the explanation for the fact that the density of the shrubs increases as the rainfall increases, the inference being that the seedlings can become established if the toxins are washed down by the rain. As additional evidence he cited observations on another desert shrub, *Larrea divaricata*, which shows the same habit of wide, regular spacing of density that increases with the rainfall. After heavy summer rains *Larrea* seedlings were observed to develop under and between shrubs of that species. A few weeks later the seedlings under the old plants died. Competition for water apparently was not the deciding factor, since seedlings of other plants were not affected. With time, the radius of death of *Larrea* seedlings progressed outward from the old plants until only the seedlings farthest removed from the existing shrubs were left.

LITERATURE CITED

Adams, Frank, F. J. Veihmeyer, and Lloyd N. Brown. (1942) Cotton irrigation investigations in San Joaquin Valley, California, 1926 to 1935. **California Agr. Exp. Sta. Bul. 668.**

Bonner, James, and Arthur W. Galston. (1944) Toxic substances from the culture media of guayule which may inhibit growth. **Bot. Gaz. 106:185–198.**

Burgevin, H., and Hénin. (1943 Influence de la profondeur du plan d'eau sur le développement des plantes. **Ann. agron.** (N.S.) 13:288–294.

Burov, D. I. (1951) (The zone of evaporation of water in the conditions of the chernozem soils of Trans-Volga.) **Pochvovedenie** 1951:43–51. (Soils and Fertilizers 14:1002 [1951]).

Burton, Glenn W., E. H. DeVane, and R. L. Carter. (1954) Root penetration, distribution and activity in southern grasses measured by yields, drought symptoms and P^{32} uptake. **Agron. Jour.** 46:229–233.

Butler, P. F., and J. A. Prescott. (1955) Evapotranspiration from wheat and pasture in relation to available moisture. **Australian Jour. Agr. Res.** 6:52–61.

Cole, John S., and O. R. Mathews. (1923) Use of water by spring wheat on the Great Plains. **U. S. Dept. Agr. Dept. Bul.** 1004.

Cole, John S., and O. R. Mathews. (1939) Subsoil moisture under semiarid conditions. **U. S. Dept. Agr. Tech. Bul.** 637.

Crowther, Frank. (1934) Studies in growth analysis of the cotton plant under irrigation in the Sudan. I. The effects of different combinations of nitrogen application and of water supply. **Ann. Bot.** 48:877–913.

Davis, Charles Homer. (1940) Absorption of soil moisture by maize roots. **Bot. Gaz.** 101:791–805.

Davis, Charles Homer. (1942) Response of **Cyperus rotundus L.** to five moisture levels. **Plant Physiol.** 17:311–316.

Eaton, Frank M., and D. R. Ergle. (1948) Carbohydrate accumulation in the cotton plant at low moisture levels. **Plant Physiol.** 23:169–187.

Eden, A., G. Alderman, C. J. L. Baker, H. H. Nicholson, and D. H. Firth. (1951) The effect of ground water-level upon productivity and composition of fenland grass. **Jour. Agr. Sci.** 41:191–202.

Edlefsen, N. E., and Alfred B. C. Anderson. (1943) Thermodynamics of soil moisture. **Hilgardia** 15:31–298.

Ellis, N. K., and Richard Morris. (1946) Preliminary observations on the relation of yield of crops grown on organic soil with controlled water table and the area of aeration in the soil and subsidence of the soil. **Soil Sci. Soc. America Proc. (1945)** 10:282–283.

Finnell, H. H. (1929) The use of barnyard manure under semiarid conditions. **Panhandle (Oklahoma) Agr. Exp. Sta. Bul.** 10.

Fox, R. L., and R. C. Lipps. (1955) Subirrigation and plant nutrition. I. Alfalfa root distribution and soil properties. **Soil Sci. Soc. America Proc.** 19:468–473.

Frankena, H. J., and M. A. J. Goedewaagen. (1942) Een vakkenproef over den invloed van verschillende water-standen op den grasgroei bij drie grondsoorten. **Versl. Landbouwk. Onderzoekingen** 48A:407–461.

Furr, J. R., and J. O. Reeve. (1945) Range of soil-moisture percentages through which plants undergo permanent wilting in some soils from semiarid irrigated areas. **Jour. Agr. Res.** 71:149–170.

Gardner, Willard, O. W. Israelson, N. E. Edlefsen and Harry Clyde. (1922) The capillary potential function and its relation to irrigation practice. **Physical Rev.,** Ser. 2, 20:196.

Gliemeroth, G. (1951) Der Einfluss von Düngung auf den Wasserentzug der Pflanzen aus den Unterbodentiefen. **Zeitschr. Pflanzenernähr. Düng. Bodenk.** 52:21–41.

Gliemeroth, G. (1955) Möglichkeiten der Beeinflussung von Wurzelmasse und Wurzeldifferenzierung. **Landw. Forsch. Sonderheft** 6:69–85.

Grandfield, C. O., and W. H. Metzger. (1936) Relation of fallow to restoration of subsoil moisture in an old alfalfa field and subsequent depletion after reseeding. **Jour. Amer. Soc. Agron.** 28:115–123.

Harlan, Harry V., and Stephen Anthony. (1921) Effect of time of irrigation on kernel development of barley. **Jour. Agr. Res.** 21:29–45.

Harris, Frank S. (1914) The effect of soil moisture, plant food, and age on the ratio of tops to roots in plants. Jour. Amer. Soc. Agron. 6:65–75.

Harris, Frank S. (1914a) Irrigation and manuring studies: the effect of varying quantities of irrigation water and manure on the growth and yield of corn. Utah Agr. Exp. Sta. Bul. 133.

Harris, Franklin S. (1914b) Effects of variations in moisture content on certain properties of a soil and on the growth of wheat. New York (Cornell Univ.) Agr. Exp. Sta. Bul. 352.

Hayward, H. E., and Winifred B. Spurr. (1944) Effects of isosmotic concentrations of inorganic and organic substrates on entry of water into corn roots. Bot. Gaz. 106:131–139.

Hellriegel, Hermann. (1883) Beiträge zu den naturwissentschaftlichen Gundlagen des Ackerbaus mit besonderer Berücksichtigung der agricultur-chemischen Methode der Sandkultur. Friedrich Vieweg und Sohn, Braunschweig.

Hendrickson, A. H., and F. J. Veihmeyer. (1929) Irrigation experiments with peaches in California. California Agr. Exp. Sta. Bul. 479:3–56.

Hendrickson, A. H., and F. J. Veihmeyer. (1931) Influence of dry soil on root extension. Plant Physiol. 6:567–576.

Hobbs, J. A. (1953) Replenishment of soil moisture supply following the growth of alfalfa. Agron. Jour. 45:490–493.

Hopkins, J. W. (1940) Agricultural meteorology: a statistical study of conservation of precipitation by summer fallowed soil tanks at Swift Current, Saskatchewan. Canadian Jour. Res. 18C:388–400.

Hunter, Albert S., and Omer J. Kelley. (1946) The extension of plant roots into dry soil. Plant Physiol. 21:445–451.

Kelley, O. J. (1954) Requirement and availability of soil water. Adv. Agron. 6:67–94.

Kiesselbach, T. A., Arthur Anderson, and J. C. Russel. (1934) Subsoil moisture and crop sequence in relation to alfalfa production. Jour. Amer. Soc. Agron. 26:422–442.

Kramer, Paul J. (1944) Soil moisture in relation to plant growth. Bot. Rev. 10:525–559.

Krantz, B. A. (1949) Fertilize corn for higher yields. North Carolina Agr. Exp. Sta. Bul. 366.

Lange, Arthur. (1938) Untersuchungen über den Wachstumsfaktor Wasser. Landw. Jahrb. 85:465–499.

Lehane, J. J., and W. J. Staple. (1953) Water retention and availability in soils related to drought resistance. Canadian Jour. Agr. Sci. 33:265–273.

Lipps, R. C., and R. L. Fox. (1956) Subirrigation and plant nutrition: II. Utilization of phosphorus by alfalfa from the soil surface to the water table. Soil Sci. Soc. America Proc. 20:28–32.

Maximov, N. A. (1929) The Plant in Relation to Water. George Allen and Unwin, Ltd., London.

Metzger, W. H., and C. O. Grandfield. (1938) Extension of alfalfa roots into subsoil dried by a previous crop. Jour. Amer. Soc. Agron. 30:80.

Miller, M. F., and F. L. Duley. (1925) The effect of a varying moisture supply upon the development and composition of the maize plant at different periods of growth. Missouri Agr. Exp. Sta. Res. Bul. 76.

Myers, H. E. (1936). The differential influence of certain vegetative covers on deep subsoil moisture. Jour. Amer. Soc. Agron. 28:106–114.

Paauw, F. Van der. (1949) Water relations of oats with special attention to the influence of periods of drought. **Plant and Soil** 1:303–341.

Peele, T. C., and O. W. Beale. (1950) Relation of moisture equivalent to field capacity and moisture retained at 15 atmospheres pressure to the wilting percentage. **Agron. Jour.** 42:604–607.

Penman, H. L. (1941) Laboratory experiments on evaporation from fallow soil. **Jour. Agr. Sci.** 31:454–465.

Penman, H. L. (1948) Physics in agriculture. **Jour. Sci. Instruments** 25:425–432.

Penman, H. L. (1949) The dependence of transpiration on weather and soil conditions. **Jour. Soil. Sci.** 1:74–89.

Richards, L. A. (1936) Capillary conductivity data for three soils. **Jour. Amer. Soc. Agron.** 28:297–300.

Richards, L. A. (1941) Uptake and retention of water by soil as determined by distance to a water table. **Jour. Amer. Soc. Agron.** 33:778–786.

Richards, L. A. (1947) Pressure-membrane apparatus—construction and use. **Agr. Eng.** 28:451–454, 460.

Richards, L. A. (1949) Methods of measuring soil moisture tension. **Soil Sci.** 68:95–112.

Richards, L. A., and C. H. Wadleigh. (1952) Soil water and plant growth. **Agronomy** 2:73–251.

Russel, J. C. (1940) The effect of surface cover on soil moisture losses by evaporation. **Soil Sci. Soc. America Proc.** (1939) 4:65–70.

Russell, M. B. (1940) Soil moisture sorption curves for four Iowa soils. **Soil Sci. Soc. America Proc.** (1939) 4:51–54.

Schneider, G. William, and N. F. Childers. (1941) Influence of soil moisture on photosynthesis, respiration, and transpiration of apple leaves. **Plant Physiol.** 16:565–583.

Schofield, R. K. (1952) Control of grassland irrigation based on weather data. **Proc. Sixth Int. Grassland Congr.** 1:757–762.

Schwalen, H. C., and M. F. Wharton. (1940) Lettuce irrigation studies. **Arizona Agr. Exp. Sta. Bul.** 133.

Shutt, Frank T., and S. N. Hamilton (1934) The quality of wheat as influenced by environment. **Empire Jour. Exptl. Agr.** 2:119–138.

Staple, W. J., and J. J. Lehane. (1954) Wheat yield and use of moisture on substations in southern Saskatchewan. **Canadian Jour. Agr. Sci.** 34:460–468.

Veihmeyer, Frank J. (1927) Some factors affecting the irrigation requirements of deciduous orchards. **Hilgardia** 2:125–291.

Veihmeyer, F. J., and A. H. Hendrickson. (1950). Soil moisture in relation to plant growth. **Ann. Rev. Plant Physiol.** 1:285–304.

Wadleigh, C. H. (1946) The integrated soil moisture stress upon a root system in a large container of saline soil. **Soil Sci.** 61:225–238.

Wadleigh, C. H., H. G. Gauch, and O. C. Magistad. (1946) Growth and rubber accumulation in guayule as conditioned by soil salinity and irrigation regime. **U. S. Dept. Agr. Tech. Bul.** 925.

Wadleigh, C. H., and L. A. Richards. (1951) Soil moisture and the mineral nutrition of plants. In Truog, Emil (Editor) **Mineral Nutrition of Plants.** Pp. 411–450. The University of Wisconsin Press, Madison, Wisconsin.

Weaver, H. A., and R. W. Pearson. (1956) Influence of nitrogen fertilization and plant population density on evapotranspiration by sudan grass. **Soil Sci.** 81:443–451.

Went, F. W. (1953) The effects of rain and temperature on plant distribution in the desert. Int. Symposium Desert Research Proc. **Research Council of Israel, Spec. Publ. 2:230—237.** Jerusalem.

Whitney, Milton, and F. K. Cameron. (1904) Investigations in soil fertility. **U. S. Dept. Agr. Bur. Soils Bul. 23.**

Widtsoe, John A. (1912) The production of dry matter with different quantities of irrigation water. **Utah Agr. Exp. Sta. Bul. 116.**

Wilson, B. D., and Sterling J. Richards. (1938) Capillary conductivity of peat soils at different capillary tensions. **Jour. Amer. Soc. Agron. 30:583—588.**

Wind, G. P. (1955a) A field experiment concerning capillary rise of moisture in a heavy clay soil. **Netherlands Jour. Agr. Sci. 3:60—69.**

Wind, G. P. (1955b) Flow of water through plant roots. **Netherlands Jour. Agr. Sci. 3:259—264.**

Zook, L. L., and H. E. Weakly. (1950) Crop rotation and tillage experiments at the North Platte (Nebr.) Substation 1907—34. **U. S. Dept. Agr. Tech. Bul. 1007.**

Zubriski, J. C., and E. B. Norum. (1955) What effect do fertilizers have on soil moisture utilization by wheat? **North Dakota Agr. Exp. Sta. Bimon. Bul. 17:126—127.**

3. SOIL AERATION[1]

The gaseous phase of soils serves simultaneously as a pathway for the intake of the oxygen that is absorbed by plant roots and soil microorganisms and as a pathway for the escape of the carbon dioxide they produce. This two-way process is termed soil aeration. Soil aeration may become critical when the water content of soils is high, since the water displaces the air.

COMPOSITION OF SOIL AIR AND ATMOSPHERIC AIR

Soil air has qualitatively the same composition as the atmosphere, that is, nitrogen, oxygen, the inert gases, and carbon dioxide. Such substances as methane and hydrogen, if present, occur in quantities too small to admit detection by ordinary methods. From the quantitative standpoint, the main difference in composition between soil air and atmospheric air lies in the content of carbon dioxide. Carbon dioxide occurs in the atmosphere to the extent of about 0.03 per cent. The content commonly is about 0.2 to 1 per cent in air extracted from surface layers of soil in which aeration is thought to be adequate. Much more carbon dioxide is found under some circumstances. The atmosphere contains about 21 per cent oxygen. Soil air contains less oxygen than atmospheric air, but the difference between the two is relatively small unless the soil air has been enriched with carbon dioxide to an extent much greater than the usual 0.2 to 1 per cent. Under aerobic conditions the volume of carbon dioxide produced in the soil is approximately equal to the volume of oxygen consumed; hence the sum of the carbon dioxide and oxygen percent-

[1] The literature on soil aeration has been reviewed by Clements (1921) and M. B. Russell (1952). These reviews should be consulted for a comprehensive coverage of the subject.

ages is approximately the same in the soil air as in the atmosphere. Under conditions of poor drainage the sum of the carbon dioxide and oxygen percentages may be lower in the soil air than in the atmosphere.

When soil is submerged, as in rice culture, circumstances are much different. Submerged soils contain no air in the usual sense of the word. Instead, gases from the atmosphere dissolve in the overlying water and are conducted through it by diffusion or mass movement to the soil. The oxygen is consumed, and methane, carbon dioxide, and small amounts of other gases, such as hydrogen and carbon monoxide, are produced in the soil. The amount of these gases produced is in excess of that of oxygen entering the soil. Bubbles of gas thus form and rise from the surface of the soil through the overlying water. Although these bubbles contain methane, carbon dioxide, and hydrogen, they often are composed mainly of nitrogen, which probably originates principally from the atmospheric nitrogen dissolved in the water.

FACTORS AFFECTING SOIL AIR COMPOSITION

The extent to which soil air differs in composition from atmospheric air is determined by the rate at which oxygen is consumed and other gases are produced, and by the rate of gaseous interchange between the soil and the atmosphere. Respiration by plant roots and microorganisms is the principal cause of oxygen absorption and carbon dioxide production by soils. The rate of respiration is controlled by such conditions as temperature, water supply, and the type and amount of respiring tissue. The relative importance of plants and microorganisms in producing carbon dioxide is suggested by the values of 0.31 and 0.42 per cent, which were found by Russell and Appleyard (1915) to be the average concentrations of carbon dioxide in air from fallow soil and soil cropped to wheat, respectively. The interpretation of these data, of course, is not entirely straightforward because the percentage content of carbon dioxide in soil air is not strictly proportional to the rate of carbon dioxide production; furthermore, the presence of the crop and the conditions associated with it probably caused the microbial production of carbon dioxide to be different in the cropped soil than in the fallow soil. Indications are, however, that in this instance the microorganisms produced more carbon dioxide than the crop.

Equilibration between soil and atmospheric air takes place for the most part slowly and continuously by the process of diffusion. In consequence, the similarity of composition of soil air to atmospheric air is greatest with samples from the surface layers of soil and decreases with increasing depth of sampling, as illustrated in Table 1.

Table 1. Carbon Dioxide and Oxygen in Air Extracted at Different Depths
from Soil Profiles within the Same Orchard in New York
(Boynton, 1941)

Depth of Sample, ft.	Composition of Soil Air, as per Cent by Volume of Air					
	Sandy Loam		Silty Clay Loam		Silty Clay	
	CO_2	O_2	CO_2	O_2	CO_2	O_2
1	0.8	19.9	1.0	19.8	1.7	18.2
2	1.3	19.4	3.2	17.9	2.8	16.7
3	1.5	19.1	4.6	16.8	3.7	15.6
4	2.1	18.3	6.2	16.0	7.9	12.3
5	2.7	17.9	7.1	15.3	10.6	8.8
6	3.0	17.5	7.9	14.8	10.3	4.6

The data in this table represent the averages of analyses made on three dates (July 12, September 22, and November 22) at which air could be withdrawn from all depths in all soils. The two finer-textured soils were saturated with water at the lower sampling depths on a number of occasions, and hence no air could be withdrawn for analysis.

For a given rate of oxygen consumption and carbon dioxide production in soil, the difference in composition between soil and atmospheric air decreases with increasing rate of diffusion. The rate of diffusion is proportional to the square of the absolute temperature. The rate of diffusion is approximately proportional also to the fraction of the total soil volume occupied by gas-filled pores, as noted by Penman (1940) and others. Penman found that up to porosities of 0.6, the apparent diffusion coefficient for movement of gas through columns of soil is about 0.66 times that for the gas in bulk. The lower rate of diffusion of gas through soil pores than through the same volume in bulk can be attributed primarily to the fact that in soil the gas molecules must follow the tortuous pathway provided by the pore spaces. The actual diffusion distance thus is greater than the measured distance. Pore size has little effect. The reason for this is that diffusion results from the random movement of gas molecules. The distance individual molecules move between collisions is small relative to the size of the gas-filled pores, so that the main impediment to diffusion is collisions with other gas molecules and not collisions with the pore walls. Total pore space commonly is greater in fine-textured than in coarse-textured soils. In consequence, the rate of diffusion through dry, fine-textured soils exceeds that through dry, coarse-textured soils. When the soils are moist, however, the reverse may obtain. At equal free-energy levels, fine-textured soils usually contain more water per unit volume than do coarse-textured soils; hence the fraction of the soil volume occupied by air may be less in fine-textured than in coarse-textured soils.

AERATION AND PLANT GROWTH

The plant responses associated with various soil treatments or conditions often suggest the importance of soil aeration as a causal factor. An outstanding example was given by Baver and Farnsworth (1940), who investigated the growth of sugar beets on fine-textured, poorly-drained soil in northwestern Ohio. Chemical fertilizers were relatively ineffective in increasing the yield, as compared with applications of green manure or animal manure. The effect of the latter treatments was correlated with the noncapillary porosity of the soil, as shown in Fig. 1. From the visual evaluation of soil conditions and the correlation shown in Fig. 1, the inference that differences in aeration were important is entirely reasonable. Admittedly, however, the evidence is indirect.

Perhaps the only way to be certain whether or not aeration is adequate is to find how plant growth is affected when aeration is improved by supplying additional air without appreciably altering the soil environment in other respects. If no improvement in plant growth results when air is forced through a soil, aeration may be presumed to be adequate. That is to say, the oxygen supply is sufficient and the carbon dioxide content is not excessive. The concentrations of oxygen and carbon dioxide in soil air that correspond to this condition of adequate aeration may be found by analysis. On the other hand, if forced aeration brings about an improvement in growth,

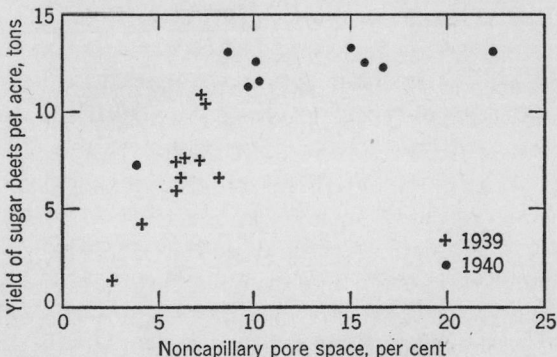

Fig. 1. Yield of sugar beets versus noncapillary pore space of soil in two years in Ohio. (Baver and Farnsworth, 1940.)

aeration may be presumed to be inadequate. Although analyses of the soil air may be made as before, the exact cause of the inadequacy is not clear, because the contents of oxygen and carbon dioxide are correlated. As oxygen decreases, carbon dioxide increases. Thus an increase in plant growth from forced aeration might conceivably result from an increase in oxygen, a decrease in carbon dioxide, or both, or from a change in some other condition associated with the forced aeration. An instance in which this approach was tried in the field was reported by Melsted, Kurtz, and Bray (1949). The experiment was conducted using large lysimeters filled with soil having good structure. In 1947 the yield of corn per acre was 94 bushels without aeration and 144 bushels with forced aeration. In 1949 the yield of soybeans per acre was 41 bushels without aeration and 44 bushels with forced aeration. The importance of aeration as a limiting factor under the control conditions with natural aeration thus appeared to be great with corn and small with soybeans.

Soil air composition and plant response

In an attempt to obtain a basis for interpreting results of measurements of soil air composition, investigators have carried out special experiments with nutrient solutions in which different mixtures of gases have been bubbled through the solution. Leonard and Pinckard (1946) conducted such experiments using cotton as a test plant. They found that when the oxygen concentration in the aerating gas was maintained at 21 per cent, growth was not affected by carbon dioxide concentrations as high as 15 per cent. Root growth was reduced with 30 per cent, and both root and top growth were reduced with 45 or 60 per cent carbon dioxide. When the carbon dioxide content of the aerating gas was maintained at 10 per cent, growth was better with oxygen at 15 per cent than at 10 per cent or less, or at 85 per cent.

According to standards derived from experiments with culture solutions, oxygen deficiency in soils is a cause of poor plant growth more frequently than is carbon dioxide toxicity. Oxygen concentrations in soil air sometimes fall below those found in solution culture experiments to produce unfavorable effects, but carbon dioxide concentrations rarely are as high as those required to produce unfavorable effects. Conditions in soils, however, are not entirely analogous to those in culture solutions. In consequence, the utility of the results obtained with culture solutions for explaining observations in soils is uncertain.

The difficulties in interpretation may be illustrated by the results of experiments by Seeley (1948) and Boicourt and Allen (1941) on roses. Seeley found that when solution cultures were aerated with various nitrogen-oxygen mixtures, essentially no increase in growth resulted from oxygen levels in excess of 10 per cent. Boicourt and Allen found that linear growth was doubled by placing tiles beneath the soil of rose beds and forcing air through the tiles for 1 hour daily. The plant response was thus of the type to be expected if the oxygen content were below 10 per cent. Measurements showed, however, that the oxygen content of soil air in both aerated and nonaerated beds was well above 10 per cent, and that aeration had produced only a small change in composition (Table 2).

Table 2.   Growth of Roses and Composition of Soil Air
with and without Forced Aeration
(Boicourt and Allen, 1941)

Treatment	Soil Air Composition at 8-inch Depth		Linear Growth per Plant, in.
	O_2, %	CO_2, %	
Control	18.8	1.5	37
Forced aeration	20.3	0.3	68

Several different hypotheses have been proposed to account for the failure of the measured composition of soil air to reflect the apparent aeration condition of the soil. First, there is the question of the validity of measurements made by the usual technique of removing a sample of soil air under reduced pressure. Taylor and Abrahams (1953) found that this technique may give erroneous results, apparently because some of the air sampled is sucked downward from the atmosphere or parts of the soil above the sampling chamber. They found a higher percentage of oxygen in air samples obtained by reduced pressure than in samples obtained by diffusion into the sampling chamber. In an extreme case, they obtained an oxygen content of 18 per cent by the reduced-pressure technique and 8 per cent by the diffusion technique at a sampling depth of 8 inches below the soil surface. Most differences were smaller.

Second, the concentration of oxygen might be much lower and the concentration of carbon dioxide much higher in air near the roots than in air at some distance removed, with the result that the composition of a bulk sample of soil air is different from the composition of air near the roots. Theoretical considerations indicate, however, that the existence of a marked concentration gradient in soil air near the roots is unlikely. The rates of diffusion of oxygen and carbon dioxide in air are such that, with roots well dispersed through the soil, a marked change in concentration near the roots would be reflected in a substantial change in concentration in a bulk sample.

Third, the concentration of oxygen at part of the root surface may be low and the concentration of carbon dioxide high because of slower diffusion of dissolved gases through the surrounding water films than through the air. That is to say, concentration changes between atmospheric air and the root do exist, but these occur principally in the water films that separate the root protoplasm from the soil air and not in the soil air itself. This hypothesis is plausible because of the high solubility of carbon dioxide, the low solubility of oxygen, and the slow diffusion of dissolved gases in water. At room temperature and sea-level pressure, 100 c.c. of water will dissolve 75 c.c. of carbon dioxide or 3 c.c. of oxygen from atmospheres of the respective gases, or 1.7 c.c. of air, including 0.6 c.c. of oxygen. The volume of oxygen in 100 c.c. of dry atmospheric air is 21 c.c. Water containing dissolved oxygen in equilibrium with the air thus holds only 3 per cent as much oxygen per unit volume as does air. The diffusion coefficient of oxygen is of the order of one ten-thousandth as great in water as it is in air. Because of these solubility and diffusion-rate effects, the gas composition may be much different in the aqueous phase from the composition in the gaseous phase. With constant oxygen concentration in the soil air, the supply of oxygen at root surfaces should decrease with increasing content of water in the soil because of the increase in distance of diffusion through water. Conversely, the concentration of carbon dioxide at root surfaces should increase with increasing content of water in the soil.

Finally, changes in composition of the gaseous phase may be associated with secondary, unfavorable effects in soils that are not duplicated in solution culture experiments carried out in the manner of those of Seeley (1948) referred to above. For example, Seeley's technique of supplying oxygen at the desired level by bubbling a mixture of nitrogen and oxygen through the solution would have the effect of sweeping carbon dioxide out of the solution. Thus, at a given concentration of oxygen, carbon dioxide toxicity might exist in soil and not in solution culture because of removal of carbon dioxide from the latter. Other possible effects from changes in nutrient availability may be surmised from a subsequent section on that topic.

Evidently there is need for a technique more suitable for characterizing soil aeration that the present method of measuring soil air composition. Several methods have been employed but none of them meet the need. One of these methods is the measurement of redox potentials, with which the difficulty is that they do not seem to be well related to plant response, and it is not certain what they mean. Redox potentials have been discussed by Russell (1952) and Scott and Evans (1955). Another method is the test of Hoffer (1945) for ferrous and ferric forms of iron in a hydrochloric acid extract of soil. This test is essentially qualitative in nature and is based on the principle that iron is reduced from ferric to ferrous form in soil in the absence of elemental oxygen. Still another approach is the measurement of the total content of elemental oxygen (Karsten, 1939). The original work on this technique was done under conditions of water saturation, where all the free oxygen present was in dissolved form. With unsaturated soils the fact that some of the free oxygen is in the dissolved form and some is in the gaseous form probably is of some concern. Since dissolved oxygen appears to be of more direct significance to plants than gaseous oxygen, some method to measure the dissolved form separately from the gaseous form is needed. A fourth technique is the one proposed by Raney (1950) for measuring the rate of diffusion of oxygen from soil into a chamber of nitrogen placed at the desired depth. Since the oxygen diffusion measured in this way takes place almost exclusively through the gas-filled pores, the numerical value obtained is essentially a characterization of the pores and the partial pressure of oxygen in the pores.

Development of a technique for measuring the significant quantity or quantities is only the starting point in acquiring some quantitative knowledge of soil aeration. Aeration is a fluctuating characteristic, which means that to evaluate the aeration of a soil during the growth of plants, a number of measurements must be made and then combined in some way that has not yet been worked out. Furthermore, present evidence suggests that the criteria on which the adequacy of aeration is judged may depend on the temperature. Work of Cannon (1925), for example, demonstrated that production of a given growth of cotton roots relative to that with good aeration requires a higher concentration of oxygen in the soil air at high than at low temperatures. This observation apparently can be attributed to the fact that as temperature increases, the solubility of oxygen in water decreases, whereas the rate of consumption of oxygen by microorganisms and plant roots increases. In addition to the direct effects, aeration may modify plant growth indirectly through its influence on the availability of plant nutrients and the incidence of plant diseases. These effects will be discussed in the last two sections in this chapter. Finally, there is the complicating matter of the adaptation of plants to conditions of poor aeration. The effect of a given period of poor aeration on plants will be less severe if the plants have become adapted to poor aeration than if they have been grown under conditions of good aeration. The nature of this adaptation is discussed in the following section.

Although an attempt has been made in this section to point out the unsatisfactory state of present knowledge of soil aeration, it may be worth re-emphasizing, in conclusion, that present ideas about the importance of soil aeration to plant growth under field conditions are not based, for the most part, on solid experimental evidence. Many observations about plant behavior are attributed to poor aeration, but without adequate verification. One such observation is the tendency of tree roots to flatten out and grow laterally when they reach the surface of the B horizon of certain soils. Trees with roots of this type are easily uprooted by wind. A second such observation is that on some soils the growth of crops is better if the soil has been loosened by plowing than if it has been loosened only slightly. The scarcity of knowledge of soil aeration probably results from the fact that the necessary experimental work is much more costly and difficult than that involved in finding, for example, whether the supply of soil nitrogen is deficient for the growth of plants. It is suggested here that when the evidence has been obtained, the importance of aeration as a limiting factor will be found to rank along with that of the individual major nutrients. The importance of aeration as a limiting factor undoubtedly will increase as irrigation becomes more prevalent in humid regions.

Plant adaptation

When aeration is poor, plants tend to develop large internal air spaces. Aerobic respiration in the roots is then supported in part by oxygen transmitted downward through these cavities from the aerial portion of the plant. Experimental work of Conway (1940) may be cited as evidence for this view. Conway found that the oxygen content of air from internal air spaces of roots of the aquatic plant, *Cladium Mariscus*, was 17 per cent when the tops were attached and projecting out of the water, and only 3 per cent when the tops were removed below the water level. Elimination of the possibility of internal conduction of oxygen from the tops to the roots thus caused a reduction of oxygen concentration in the roots. Further evidence for internal conduction is obtained from a comparison of the concentration of oxygen in air in the roots with that of air with which the oxygen content of the water surrounding the roots is in equilibrium. As would be expected if the oxygen were conducted downward internally, the internal oxygen concentration was above the equilibrium value when the tops were attached and below the equilibrium value when the tops were removed below the water level.

According to Alberda (1953), the supply of oxygen to roots of young plants of lowland rice is maintained by downward transmission through air spaces in the stems. Older plants develop a superficial mat of fine roots that grow either horizontally in the irrigation water or vertically upward into the air. These roots absorb oxygen.

Production of air spaces in roots is not limited to plants indigenous to poorly aerated environments, as evidenced by the fact that corn and other plants adapted to conditions of good aeration will produce air spaces in roots under conditions of poor aeration (McPherson, 1939). The effectiveness of the air spaces in supplying the roots with oxygen may be important in determining the adaptability of the plant to conditions of poor aeration, as suggested by experiments of Vlamis and Davis (1944) on rice and barley. Literature on air spaces in plants was reviewed by Sifton (1945).

Availability of nutrients and water

Effects of aeration on nutrient availability are of two types, namely, those produced in the soil and those produced indirectly through the plant. Perhaps the most important of the soil effects are those connected with nitrogen availability. The rate of mineralization of organic nitrogen in wet or water-logged soils is less than that in moist soils. Fixation of nitrogen by symbiotic and aerobic nonsymbiotic means is affected similarly. Nitrogen transformations will be discussed in more detail in the chapter on nitrogen.

Availability of manganese and iron is affected in quite a different manner. These elements occur in the soil in more than one valence state. The reduced forms produced under conditions of poor aeration are more soluble than the oxidized forms that predominate when aeration is good. The marked increase in manganese availability associated with reducing conditions is indicated in Table 3. In the experi-

Table 3. Yield and Manganese Content of Oats Grown on a Manganese-Deficient Soil with Various Treatments

(Piper, 1931)

Treatment	Yield of Dry Matter per Culture, g.	Mn in Dry Matter, p.p.m.
Control	1	5
MnSO$_4$, 1 cwt. per acre	87	17
MnSO$_4$, 5 cwt. per acre	77	46
Waterlogged before planting	75	42

ment recorded in this table, the water content of the soil was kept at 60 per cent of saturation in all treatments during growth of the plants, but prior to planting, one portion of soil was kept waterlogged for a week. The waterlogging had about the same effect on the yield and the manganese content of the plants as did application of manganese sulfate at a rate of 5 cwt. per acre. Observations on iron availability have been published by Gile and Carrero (1920) and Ponnamperuma et al. (1955). The latter investigators obtained evidence that flooding of soil for rice sometimes induces iron toxicity. Concentrations of ferrous iron as high as 525 p.p.m. occurred in percolates from soil cultures exhibiting leaf necrosis symptoms thought to be the result of iron toxicity.

If the aeration is poor enough to result in reduction of ferric iron, the concentration of phosphorus in solution may be increased because of dissolution of ferric phosphates in soils that contain such substances. In soils that contain calcium phosphates the phosphorus solubility may be increased as a result of the extra carbonic acid in solution.

Not all effects of aeration on nutrient availability result from changes in the chemical status of the nutrients in the soil. The low potassium availability that accompanies poor aeration in many instances is attributable to a decrease in the tendency of the plant to absorb potassium rather than a change in chemical status of potassium in the soil. Evidence for this view will be discussed in the chapter on potassium. The physiological effect of aeration on availability seems to be more pronounced with potassium than with any of the other nutrients. The fact that potassium availability is reduced by poor aeration suggests that the potassium deficiency, sometimes associated with minimal loosening of the soil in tillage operations (Bower, Browning, and Norton, 1945), likewise results from poor aeration despite the lack of confirmation from analyses of soil air composition.

Availability of water is decreased under conditions of poor aeration, as evidenced by the wilted condition of many plants after flooding. This behavior is caused by the physiological effect of aeration on the plant and not on the condition of water in the soil. According to Kramer (1940), the physiological effect appears to be twofold, namely, a reduction in the rate of metabolism in root cells and an increase in resistance of the root to the entry and transmission of water.

Disease incidence

Many observations have been made on the connection between soil water content and the incidence of plant diseases. Summaries of such information have been published by Garrett (1938) and Berkeley

(1944). Changes in aeration are undoubtedly responsible for some of the effects observed to be associated with soil water content. For most plant diseases no detailed work on the rôle of aeration has been done. It appears, however, that the effect of aeration is primarily on the organism in some instances and on the susceptibility of the plant in others.

The effect of aeration on the "take-all" disease of cereals, caused by the fungus, *Ophiobolus graminis*, appears to be primarily on the growth of the organism and not on the plant. In the absence of the host plant this organism gradually disappears from the soil, presumably because it is a poor competitor with other microorganisms under these conditions. In nonsterile soil it grows actively only along the surface of roots of the host, sending many short infection hyphae into the root. Experience with the disease under field conditions shows that the infection of plants is more frequent and severe in loose and sandy soils than in compacted and fine-textured soils, suggesting the importance of good aeration for rapid growth of the hyphae. This supposition was confirmed by Garrett who found that forced aeration increased the rate of advance of the hyphae along root surfaces (Garrett, 1937), and that the growth rate is decreased by the presence of as little as 5 per cent carbon dioxide in the atmosphere (Garrett, 1936). These observations, together with additional evidence of a more indirect nature, led Garrett to propose that the concentration of carbon dioxide in the vicinity of the plant roots is greater than that in the remainder of the soil, and that differences in concentration of carbon dioxide around the roots are primarily responsible for the apparent aeration effect on growth rate of the hyphae observed in practice.

McNew (1953) cited an instance in which the effect of aeration is on the susceptibility of the plant. According to McNew, anaerobic respiration in soils may result in accumulation of salicylic aldehyde in concentrations as great as 50 p.p.m. Such concentrations do not affect the growth of wheat, sugar cane plants, or the root-rot organism, *Pythium arrhenomanes*, but they increase the susceptibility of the plants to attack.

_____ **LITERATURE CITED**

Alberda, Th. (1953) Growth and root development of lowland rice and its relation to oxygen supply. Plant and Soil 5:1—28.
Baver, L. D., and R. B. Farnsworth. (1940) Soil structure effects in the growth of sugar beets. Soil Sci. Soc. America Proc. 5:45—48.

Berkeley, G. H.   (1944)   Root-rots of certain non-cereal crops.   **Bot. Rev.** 10:67—123.

Boicourt, A. W., and R. C. Allen.   (1941)   Effect of aeration on growth of hybrid tea roses.   **Proc. Amer. Soc. Hort. Sci.** 39:423—425.

Bower, C. A., G. M. Browning, and R. A. Norton.   (1945)   Comparative effects of plowing and other methods of seed-bed preparation on nutrient element deficiencies in corn.   **Soil Sci. Soc. America Proc.** (1944) 9:142—146.

Boynton, Damon.   (1941)   Soils in relation to fruit-growing in New York.   Part XV. Seasonal and soil influences on oxygen and carbon-dioxide levels of New York soils.   **Cornell Univ. Agr. Exp. Sta. Bul.** 763.

Cannon, William Austin.   (1925)   Physiological features of roots, with especial reference to the relation of roots to the aeration of the soil.   **Carnegie Inst. Washington Publ.** 368.

Clements, Frederick E.   (1921)   Aeration and air-content.   The role of oxygen in root activity.   **Carnegie Inst. Washington Publ.** 315.

Conway, Verona M.   (1940)   Aeration and plant growth in wet soils.   **Bot. Rev.** 6:149—163.

Garrett, S. D.   (1936)   Soil conditions and the take-all disease of wheat.   **Ann. Appl. Biol.** 23:667—699.

Garrett, S. D.   (1937)   Soil conditions and the take-all disease of wheat.   II. The relation between soil reaction and soil aeration.   **Ann. Appl. Biol.** 24:747—751.

Garrett, S. D.   (1938)   Soil conditions and the root-infecting fungi.   **Biol. Rev.** 13:159—185.

Gile, P. L., and J. O. Carrero.   (1920)   Cause of lime-induced chlorosis and availability of iron in the soil.   **Jour. Agr. Res.** 20:33—62.

Hoffer, G. N.   (1945)   Fertilized corn plants require well-ventilated soils.   **Better Crops with Plant Food** 29, No. 1:6—9, 45.

Karsten, Kenneth S.   (1939)   Root activity and the oxygen requirement in relation to soil fertility.   **Amer. Jour. Bot.** 26:855—860.

Kramer, Paul J.   (1940)   Causes of decreased absorption of water by plants in poorly aerated media.   **Amer. Jour. Bot.** 27:216—220.

Leonard, O. A., and J. A. Pinckard.   (1946)   Effect of various oxygen and carbon dioxide concentrations on cotton root development.   **Plant Physiol.** 21:18—36.

McNew, George L.   (1953)   The effects of soil fertility.   In **Plant Diseases, The Yearbook of Agriculture**, 1953, pp. 100—114.   United States Department of Agriculture, Washington, D. C.

McPherson, D. C.   (1939)   Cortical air spaces in the roots of **Zea Mays** L.   **New Phytol.** 38:190—202.

Melsted, S. W., Touby Kurtz, and Roger Bray.   (1949)   Hydrogen peroxide as an oxygen fertilizer.   **Agron. Jour.** 41:97.

Penman, H. L.   (1940)   Gas and vapour movements in the soil.   I. The diffusion of vapours through porous solids.   **Jour. Agr. Sci.** 30:437—462.

Piper, C. S.   (1931)   The availability of manganese in the soil.   **Jour. Agr. Sci.** 21:762—779.

Ponnamperuma, F. N., R. Bradfield, and M. Peech.   (1955)   Physiological disease of rice attributable to iron toxicity.   **Nature** 175:265.

Raney, W. A.   (1950)   Field measurement of oxygen diffusion through soil.   **Soil Sci. Soc. America Proc.** (1949) 14:61—65.

Russell, Edward John, and Alfred Appleyard.   (1915)   The atmosphere of the soil: its composition and the causes of variation.   **Jour. Agr. Sci.** 7:1—48.

Russell, M. B.   (1952)   Soil aeration and plant growth.   **Agronomy** 2:253—301.

Scott, A. D., and D. D. Evans.   (1955)   Dissolved oxygen in saturated soil.   **Soil Sci. Soc. America Proc.** 19:7—12.

Seeley, J. G.   (1948)   **Some responses of greenhouse roses to various oxygen concentrations in the substratum.**   Ph.D. Thesis, Cornell University, Ithaca, New York. (Quoted by Russell, 1952.)

Sifton, H. B.   (1945)   Air-space tissue in plants.   **Bot. Rev.** 11:108—143.

Taylor, George S., and J. H. Abrahams.   (1953)   A diffusion-equilibrium method for obtaining soil gases under field conditions.   **Soil Sci. Soc. America Proc.** 17:201—206.

Vlamis, J., and A. R. Davis.   (1944)   Effects of oxygen tension on certain physiological responses of rice, barley, and tomato.   **Plant Physiol.** 19:33—51.

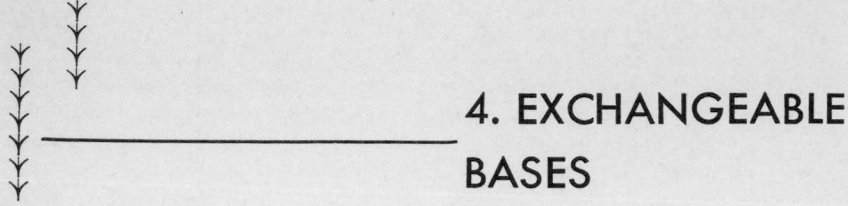

4. EXCHANGEABLE BASES

The exchangeable cations of soils represent the portions of the respective cations associated with the solid phase that are subject to interchange with cations in solution under conditions of little or no decomposition of the remainder of the solid phase. The process of interchange between cations in exchangeable form and in solution is known as cation exchange.

The principal exchangeable cations in soils from the standpoint of quantity are calcium, magnesium, potassium, sodium, aluminum, and hydrogen. This chapter will deal primarily with the first four of these cations, which commonly are termed bases, with particular reference to their utilization by plants. Succeeding chapters will deal more specifically with soil acidity, which is associated with exchangeable aluminum and hydrogen, and with soil salinity and alkalinity, where exchangeable and soluble sodium are of importance.

EXCHANGEABLE AND NONEXCHANGEABLE BASES

The definition of exchangeable cations implies that a portion of the cations is not in exchangeable form and hence may be termed "nonexchangeable." If this is true, the process of exchange may be written

$$C^*_{solution} + C_{exch.} + C_{nonexch.} = C_{solution} + C^*_{exch.} + C_{nonexch.}$$

where C refers to cations and the asterisk is used to denote the cations present initially in solution form. According to this equation, the cations in solution exchange only with cations in exchangeable form in the soil. None of the cations marked with an asterisk change places with the nonexchangeable cations. $C_{nonexch.}$ thus may be subtracted from both sides of the equation. In actuality the boundary line between exchangeable and nonexchangeable is somewhat arbitrary.

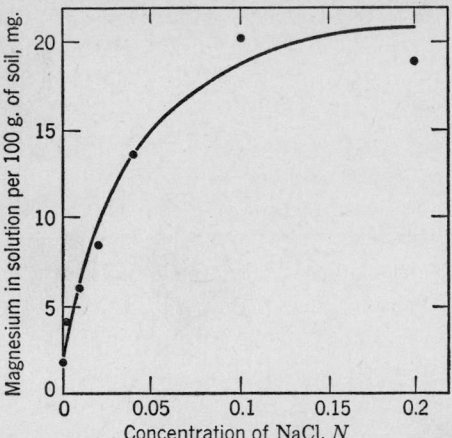

Fig. 1.   Removal of magnesium from soil by exchange with sodium chloride solutions differing in concentration.   (Kelley and Cummins, 1921.)

Nevertheless, both chemical and biological evidence shows that there is a significant distinction in behavior between the two classes.

Application of the law of mass action to the foregoing equation leads to the conclusion that as $C^*_{solution}$ is increased, the concentration of $C_{solution}$ will increase and approach a limiting value, which represents $C_{exch.}$. Figure 1 shows the results of an experiment on exchange of sodium in solution for magnesium in soil that bears out the prediction about the maximum value of $C_{solution}$. No analyses for total magnesium were made on this sample of soil, but it may be inferred from other information, to be given later, that the maximum quantity of magnesium released was considerably less than the total present in the soil. That is to say, a portion of the total magnesium was not subject to appreciable exchange.

Similar evidence is provided by experiments in which samples of soil are leached with successive portions of a salt solution. Hissink (1922) leached a 25-g. sample of soil with four 250-ml. portions of normal ammonium chloride solution and determined the content of calcium in each leachate. He found 120 mg. in the first leachate, 9 mg. in the second, 3 mg. in the third, and a trace in the fourth. Further leaching with the same solution evidently would have removed little additional calcium from the soil. Nonexchangeable calcium was still present in the soil, however, as shown by the fact that a single treatment of the soil with strong hydrochloric acid removed 57 mg. more calcium than did the four treatments with ammonium chloride.

Another type of evidence is provided by the use of isotopes. If an isotopic form of a soil cation is added in solution, the isotope will start immediately to exchange with the common form of the cation present initially in the soil. Subsequent analysis of the solution thus will show that some of the isotope has disappeared and at equilibrium will permit one to calculate how much of the common form of the cation in the soil has become involved in the exchange. Blume and Smith (1954) conducted such an experiment using the radioactive isotope Ca^{45}. Figure 2 shows that with most of the soils tested, the quantities of soil calcium that equilibrated with Ca^{45} were virtually the same as those extracted with N ammonium acetate, thus verifying the reality of the distinction between exchangeable and nonexchangeable calcium. In a few cases, substantially more soil calcium equilibrated with Ca^{45} than was extracted with ammonium acetate, which demonstrates that the apportionment of a cation between "exchangeable" and "nonexchangeable" forms may change somewhat from one method to another.

Two types of biological evidence for the distinction between exchangeable and nonexchangeable forms of cations will be noted. First, the type of evidence provided by radioisotopes will be described. Consider the case when the quantity a of calcium labeled with the radioisotope Ca^{45} is added to soil containing the ordinary isotope Ca^{40}.

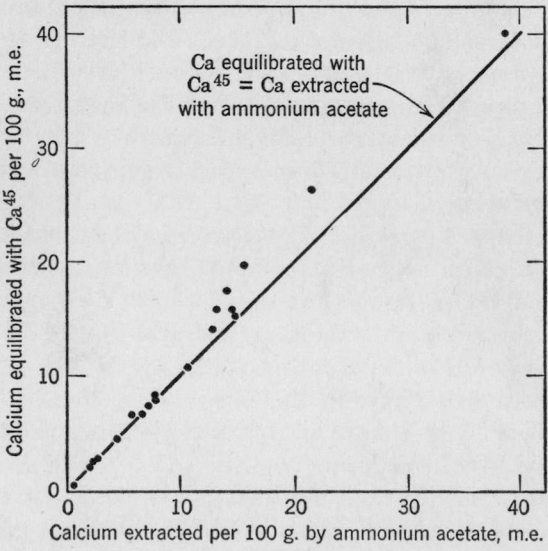

Fig. 2. Calcium in different noncalcareous soils equilibrated with Ca^{45} and extracted with normal ammonium acetate. (Blume and Smith, 1954.)

Analysis of plants grown on the soil will show that the ratio of Ca^{45} to total calcium in the plant is lower than that in the added calcium, because the plants have absorbed calcium ions from the supply present initially in the soil as well as from the tagged source added. This difference in ratios makes possible a calculation of the proportion of the calcium in the plants that came from the soil. If the plants have absorbed soil calcium from the quantity b of Ca^{40}, which has come to isotopic equilibrium with a, this proportion may be represented by $b/(a+b)$. Since a is known, the ratio $b/(a+b)$ can be estimated independently by analysis of the soil for b. If the correct value of b can be found in this way, both estimates of $b/(a+b)$ will have the same numerical value, within experimental error.

Davis et al. (1953) conducted an experiment with labeled calcium that may be used as an example. They applied 1.77 g. of Ca^{45}-labeled calcium to a quantity of Hartsells soil containing 1.92 g. of exchangeable calcium, and also to a quantity of Claiborne soil containing 7.18 g. of exchangeable calcium. If the exchangeable calcium is b, the ratio $b/(a+b)$ evidently is $1.92/(1.77+1.92) = 0.52$ with the Hartsells soil and $7.18/(1.77+7.18) = 0.80$ with the Claiborne soil. When crops of rye grass, red clover, crimson clover, and oats were grown on these soils, the proportions of the plant calcium derived from the soil were found to be 0.55 and 0.78 in the Hartsells and Claiborne soils, respectively. The close similarity of the values obtained in the two different ways indicates that the added calcium had equilibrated with the exchangeable calcium in the soil, and that the calcium absorbed by the plants came essentially from the mixture of added calcium and exchangeable calcium, and not from the nonexchangeable calcium.

A second type of biological evidence is supplied by the work of Pratt (1951), who grew alfalfa on samples of different soils and used statistical methods to relate the potassium content of the plants to the quantities of different potassium fractions in the soils. His results indicated that about four times as much potassium was absorbed from unit quantity of exchangeable potassium as from the same quantity of nonexchangeable potassium released on incubation with an acid cation exchange resin. About 300 times as much potassium was absorbed from unit quantity of exchangeable potassium as from the same quantity of nonexchangeable potassium that was not released on incubation with the acid cation exchange resin.

The chemical evidence thus indicates that the dividing line between exchangeable and nonexchangeable forms of a soil cation may be somewhat arbitrary and diffuse, but that nevertheless there is a real difference in behavior between the two forms. The biological evidence indicates that the distinction made by chemical methods is significant as far as plant behavior is concerned.

Analyses of different soils indicate that exchangeable cations seldom constitute the bulk of the total supply and often represent only a small fraction of the total. The data of Bear, Prince, and Malcolm (1945) for twenty soils of New Jersey may be cited as an example. A summary of their results is given in Table 1. Another example

Table 1. Average Content of Exchangeable, Nonexchangeable, and Total Bases in Twenty Soils of New Jersey
(Bear, Prince, and Malcolm, 1945)

	Content of Indicated Base per 100 g. of Soil		
	Calcium, m.e.	Magnesium, m.e.	Potassium, m.e.
Exchangeable	4.0	1.6	0.2
Nonexchangeable	13.3	40.7	46.3
Total	17.3	42.3	46.5
Percentage of total in exchangeable form	23.1	3.8	0.4

may be taken from the work of Anderson, Keyes, and Cromer (1942). These investigators found that as an average of three soils, one each from South Dakota, Iowa, and Indiana, the exchangeable bases calculated as a percentage of the total amounted to 47 per cent with calcium, 16 per cent with magnesium, 2 per cent with potassium, and 2 per cent with sodium.

DETERMINATION AND REPRESENTATION OF CATION-EXCHANGE PROPERTIES OF SOILS

In practice, the bases calcium, magnesium, potassium, and sodium usually are extracted from soils by continuous leaching with a normal solution of ammonium acetate. Recently, however, there has been increasing interest in sodium as a replacing ion because of certain technical difficulties (to be discussed later) in the use of ammonium with certain clays. Barium acetate or calcium acetate commonly are used for extracting titratable hydrogen. The total number of exchange positions may be found by summing the numbers occupied by individual cations or by displacement and determination of a cation, such as ammonium or sodium, retained by the soil after the soil has been leached with a neutral, normal solution of the acetate and washed to remove the excess. More details on methodology are given in papers by Schollenberger and Simon (1945), Peech et al. (1947), Shaw and MacIntire (1951), and Bower, Reitemeier, and Fireman (1952).

The results of measurements of cation-exchange properties of soils usually are expressed in terms of milligram equivalents (m.e) per 100 g. of soil. This convention has the advantage that the effective quantities of different cations are additive when expressed on this basis; also, the numbers involved are neither exceedingly large nor exceedingly small, usually lying in the range from 0.1 to 40.

The term "exchangeable bases" or "total exchangeable bases" refers to the sum of the bases (calcium, magnesium, potassium, and sodium) in exchangeable form expressed as milligram equivalents per 100 g. The "cation-exchange capacity" (also called the "total exchange capacity" and sometimes the "base exchange capacity") represents the total number of exchange positions or exchangeable cations expressed as milligram equivalents per 100 g. The percentage base saturation is the percentage of the cation-exchange capacity occupied by exchangeable bases.

SOURCE OF CATION-EXCHANGE PROPERTIES

Organic matter

Soil organic matter has pronounced properties of cation exchange, as can be shown by determining the cation-exchange capacity of soil before and after treatment with a strong solution of hydrogen peroxide to remove most of the organic matter. Calculations made from the data in Table 2 indicate that the cation-exchange capacity of the

Table 2. Cation-Exchange Capacity of the Mineral and Organic Fractions in Soils (Baver, 1930)

Soil Type	Organic Matter Content, %	Cation-Exchange Capacity per 100 g. of Soil			Percentage of Cation-Exchange Capacity Due to Organic Matter, %
		Entire Soil, m.e.	Organic Matter, m.e.	Mineral Matter, m.e.	
Huntington fine sandy loam	2.6	9.9	2.9	7.0	29.8
Blanchester silt loam	2.2	14.9	5.5	9.4	36.7
Chippewa silty clay loam	6.0	28.3	15.1	13.2	53.5
Toledo silty clay	12.1	46.9	28.2	18.7	60.3

organic matter was 112, 250, 252, and 233 m.e. per 100 g. of organic matter in the Huntington, Blanchester, Chippewa, and Toledo soils, respectively. In a study of fourteen soil samples, Mitchell (1932) found that the calculated cation-exchange capacity of the organic matter ranged between 70 and 200 m.e. per 100 g. of organic matter, with thirteen of the values between 113 and 200 m.e.

The relative contribution of the organic and mineral fractions to the cation-exchange capacity of four soils is shown in Table 2. From 30 to 60 per cent of the cation-exchange capacity of these soils was attributable to organic matter. McGeorge (1930) found that in certain low-organic-matter soils of Arizona and California, the cation-exchange properties reside almost entirely in the mineral fraction. At the other extreme, nearly all the cation-exchange properties of peat and muck soils from the north central states are attributable to organic matter. Peech (1939) made a similar finding for some of the sandy soils of Florida.

Broadbent and Bradford (1952) investigated the extent to which the cation-exchange capacity of soil organic matter was reduced by treating the organic matter with various organic reagents that react with specific functional groups in organic compounds. On the basis of the results they obtained with samples of several soils, they estimated that 54 per cent of the organic exchange positions were attributable to carboxyl groups, 36 per cent to phenolic and enolic hydroxyl groups, and 10 per cent to imide nitrogen groups.

Mineral matter

Particle-size effects. The cation-exchange capacity of the mineral fraction of soils is dependent upon both the amount of surface exposed by the particles and the nature of the surface. Table 3 shows the

Table 3.   Cation-Exchange Capacity and Specific Surface of Mineral Soil
Particles Separated from the Putnam Clay Soil
(Whitt and Baver, 1930)

Soil Separate	Equivalent Diameter of Particles, mm.	Calculated Surface Area per g.,* cm.^{2}	Cation-Exchange Capacity per 100 g., m.e.
Silt	0.02–0.005	1,800	3
	0.005–0.002	6,200	7
Coarse clay	0.002–0.001	16,000	22
	0.001–0.0005	30,000	35
	0.0005–0.0001	74,000	52
Fine clay	0.0001–0.00005	320,000	56
	<0.00005	920,000	63

* Calculated on the basis of the average size of particles for each group.

relationship between the size of the particles separated from a soil, the calculated amount of surface exposed, and the cation-exchange capacity. The smaller particles, with their greater surface exposure per unit weight, possessed a much greater cation-exchange capacity than did the coarser particles.

Most of the cation-exchange properties of the inorganic portion of soils are concentrated in the clay fraction. The percentage of clay therefore is a major factor in determining the cation-exchange capacity of the soil. If the soils in Table 2 are arranged according to their increasing content of fine materials, that is, fine sandy loam, silt loam, silty clay loam, silty clay, a corresponding increase in the cation-exchange capacity of the mineral matter will be noted. There is also a corresponding increase in the cation-exchange capacity of the entire soil, but the rate of increase with fineness of texture is exaggerated because of the presence of more organic matter in the finer-textured soils.

Nature of clay minerals. The clay fractions of soils contain a number of different minerals, the cation-exchange properties of which may differ considerably. According to Grim (1953, p. 129), the cation-exchange capacity per 100 g. of different clays is approximately 3 to 15 m.e. for kaolinite, 10 to 40 m.e. for illite, 100 to 150 m.e. for vermiculite, and 80 to 150 m.e. for montmorillonite. Thus a mechanical analysis to determine the clay content will not permit a precise estimate of the cation-exchange capacity of the mineral portion of soils in general unless something is known of the minerals present in the clay fraction.

The silicate clay minerals are said to have a layer-lattice structure. That is to say, one molecule is not distinct from another, but the mineral has a repeating pattern that occurs in what is essentially a two-dimensional layer. The crystals are built up from the superposition of these layers in much the same way as are crystals of mica.

The schematic structure for kaolinite in Fig. 3 shows that each layer in the kaolinite crystal consists of one alumina sheet and one silica sheet. The kaolinite particles are built up of layers stacked on each other. The layers show little tendency to separate from each other, probably because of the attraction between the oxygen and hydroxyl layers that are adjacent in the superposed layers. The cation-exchange properties of kaolinite are thought to originate from ionization of hydrogen from hydroxyl groups on the basal-plane surfaces and from hydroxyl groups formed at the edges of the layers where the mineral structure is discontinued. Individual crystals of kaolinite tend to be large compared with those of the other silicate clay minerals, and so the cation-exchange capacity is limited.

The montmorillonite lattice, shown in Fig. 3, consists of an alumina sheet enclosed above and below with silica sheets. Montmorillonite crystals are composed of layers of the three sheets stacked on each other. As the structure is shown, the only place for exchangeable

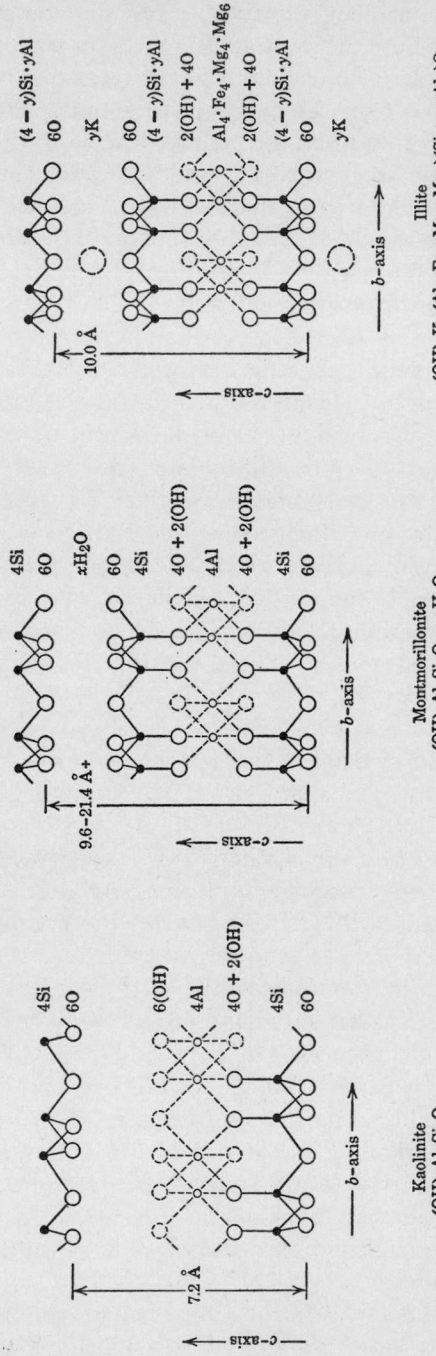

Fig. 3. Schematic representation of the structure of three types of clay minerals occurring in soils. (Grim, 1939.)

cations to be held is in edge positions. The opinion is held rather generally, however, that the high exchange capacity of montmorillonite results from certain isomorphous lattice substitutions in addition to the edge positions. Chemical analyses of montmorillonite usually show the presence of magnesium not called for in the "ideal" structure. This magnesium probably exists as a lattice constituent in positions occupied by aluminum in the ideal structure. Each substitution of a divalent cation in a position occupied ordinarily by a trivalent cation would leave one excess negative charge on the lattice, that is, one valence for holding an exchangeable cation. The replacement of approximately 20 per cent of the aluminum positions by magnesium would account for a cation-exchange capacity of 100 m.e. per 100 g.

The cations needed to balance the charge on the montmorillonite structure presumably are held between the layers on the outside of the lattice. The layers of montmorillonite are forced apart readily by water molecules, in consequence of which the balancing cations are exchangeable. Montmorillonite thus has a large amount of "internal surface" available for cation exchange in addition to the "external surface." Hendricks, Nelson, and Alexander (1940) concluded that approximately 20 per cent of the cation exchange positions of montmorillonite are at the edge of the flakes, and the remaining 80 per cent are on the basal-plane surfaces.

The structure of illite, shown in Fig. 3, is similar to that of montmorillonite. Illite also consists of units of one alumina sheet between two silica sheets. In the illite structure, however, considerable aluminum replaces silicon in the outside sheets, and the excess charge is balanced chiefly by potassium ions. The replacement provides an excess charge originating near the surface of the layer instead of at the center, as in montmorillonite. Moreover, the number of charges requiring balancing cations per unit area of interlayer surface may be greater in illite than in montmorillonite. In consequence of these differences, the charge is stronger at the surface of illite than of montmorillonite layers, and holds the layers together more firmly so that water molecules do not enter. The potassium ions may be considered to act as a bridge holding the layers together. The potassium ions are exchangeable where they occur on the surface, but those lying between the layers are not exchangeable, except perhaps for a few near the edges. Because of the limited "internal surface" for cation exchange, the cation-exchange capacity of illite is much lower than that of montmorillonite.

The various clay minerals described must be considered to represent types found within a large number of individual minerals, much as

Tama silt loam represents one soil type in the large group of prairie soils, and Miami silt loam represents one soil type in the large group of gray-brown podzolic soils. Many different clay minerals have been given a distinctive name, such as halloysite, vermiculite, non-tronite, or saponite, because their properties differ sufficiently to justify a separation. The evidence indicates also that certain clay minerals may occur in mixed crystals containing more than one mineral species.

In addition to the crystalline clay minerals, noncrystalline inorganic materials with exchange properties probably exist in soils. Kelley and Page (1943), for example, reported that the clay fraction of certain soils of Hawaii is largely amorphous in nature, as judged by the absence of a well-defined X-ray diffraction pattern; nevertheless, the clays have a high cation-exchange capacity. Fieldes, Swindale, and Richardson (1952) obtained evidence suggesting that the cation-exchange properties of the clay fraction of certain strongly weathered soils of the Cook Islands near New Zealand could be attributed largely to hydrous aluminum oxide.

Evidently the cation-exchange positions in soils are heterogeneous in nature. The make-up of the cation-exchange capacity may differ from one soil to the next. Such differences lead not only to some ambiguity in laboratory measurements, but also to significant effects on plant nutrition.

CHARACTERISTICS OF CATION-EXCHANGE REACTIONS

Equivalence

If the exchange positions in a sample of soil were saturated successively with different cations, one would expect the quantities of the different ions held by the soil to be chemically equivalent. In some instances the quantities are equivalent, but in others they are not. Two different explanations have been advanced to account for the apparent lack of equivalence in such reactions: (a) the actual valency of the cations is different from that which is assumed in making the calculations, and (b) the number of exchange positions depends in part on the nature of the cation.

Bower and Truog (1941) used the first explanation to account for differences in cation-exchange capacity of clays found with different cations. They obtained average exchange capacities of 58, 62, and 71 m.e. per 100 g. with ammonium, calcium, and magnesium, respectively, as the exchangeable cations. With a sample of montmorillonite, the values obtained for the cation-exchange capacity were higher with various polyvalent cations than with monovalent cations, when the exchange was carried out in water in the usual manner. When the exchange was carried out in alcohol, however, the values with all cations were approximately the same as that obtained with the monovalent cations in water. Bower and Truog attributed these observations to the attachment of some of the polyvalent cations in the form of basic ions (for example, $MgOH^+$) in the aqueous medium. The cause of the apparent lack of equivalence in the aqueous medium thus was inferred to be the incorrectness of the usual assumption that polyvalent cations are attached entirely in polyvalent form.

The second explanation has been used in connection with soil organic matter. Broadbent (1955) reported that the cation-exchange capacity per 100 g. of preparations of organic matter from various soils averaged 67 m.e. with potassium, 134 m.e. with barium, and 287 m.e. with divalent copper. These differences are too great to be attributed to attachment of some of the polyvalent cations in the basic form, but may be accounted for by differences in the tendency of various cations to form covalent bonds with the organic matter. Many compounds are known in which such metal-organic links are present. Various names such as complexes, inner complexes, and chelates have been applied to them. The chemistry of these compounds has been reviewed by Martell and Calvin (1952). Although the existence of such compounds in soils has not been demonstrated unequivocally, there is considerable indirect evidence for their presence. If a cation forms a covalent bond, its ionic tendency and ease of replacement are reduced. The difference among cations in their tendency to form covalent linkages is so great that certain cations may be retained in positions where others are not.

Reversibility

Most cation exchange reactions in soils are easily reversible; others are not, however, because of the relatively strong attachment of certain cations in certain exchange positions. There are several types of strong attachments.

Ensminger and Gieseking (1941) found that the addition of gelatin to clays reduced the cation-exchange capacity. With a sample of montmorillonite the reduction was from 90 to 20 m.e. per 100 g. when 150 g. of gelatin were added. This is an example of strong attachment of a large organic cation to an inorganic exchange material.

Potassium and ammonium ions become attached strongly in interlayer positions of illite and vermiculite, apparently in large part because these ions fit closely in certain openings in the surfaces. Sodium calcium, magnesium, and lithium ions in the same positions exchange readily. The strong attachment of potassium in these interlayer positions is of considerable practical importance and is discussed at some length in the chapter on potassium. This is an example of strong attachment of an inorganic cation to an inorganic exchange material.

Bremner et al. (1946) found that when they treated samples of soil with substances such as malate, citrate, and pyrophosphate that form soluble, slightly ionized compounds with copper, iron, and manganese, considerable amounts of these metals were extracted. Considerable amounts of organic matter were extracted at the same time. When such extracts were dialyzed to remove the extractant, the metals also were removed. But when the metals were added again to the dialyzed extract in the absence of the extractant, the organic matter was precipitated immediately in a form insoluble in water, and soluble in pyrophosphate. These results indicate that the organic matter peptized on addition of the extractants was present originally in the soil in combination with the polyvalent metals and was maintained in insoluble form by this combination. The polyvalent metals removed by extractants such as pyrophosphate are not exchanged appreciably on addition of ammonium acetate, but they may be exchanged upon addition of another ion that forms strong covalent linkages. For example, Heintze and Mann (1949) found that normal ammonium acetate containing 0.02-normal copper sulfate extracted as much as 40 times more manganese from soil than did normal ammonium acetate alone. These observations constitute evidence for the strong attachment of certain inorganic cations to organic exchange material.

Rapidity

According to the kinetic theory of matter, exchangeable cations are in continual motion around the point of their attachment. If an invading cation from the solution happens to penetrate within this hemispherical area of motion at an instant when the exchangeable cation is far away, the attractive force emanating from the solid surface may be transferred to the invading cation, which then will become the exchangeable cation. The process of transference of the attractive force from one cation to another, which may be said to represent the actual exchange, undoubtedly is instantaneous.

Measurements of rates of cation exchange do not show the process to be instantaneous, because measurements involve not only the time required for the actual exchange but also the time involved in getting the exchanging ions up to and the exchanged ions away from the exchange site. Hissink (1925) found that measured exchange in soil was rapid when he added a salt solution. He shook a 25-g. sample of soil with 250 ml. of normal sodium chloride solution and found that the resulting quantities of calcium exchanged per 100 g. of soil were 27 m.e. after 5 seconds, and 28 m.e. after 3 minutes, 1 day, or 7 days. Measured exchanges are not always this fast. Cernescu (1931), for example, found that exchange equilibrium was established in 5 minutes with a clay, 10 days with permutite, and 92 days with chabazite. With the latter two materials, the slowness of the overall process probably resulted from the slowness of diffusion of ions between the solution at the surface of the particles and the points of exchange in the interior of the particles. The reaction of limestone with acid soil under field conditions is another example of a slow reaction. Here the limiting factor is the slow solution of limestone granules, once they are surrounded by neutralized soil. Granules of unreacted limestone may be detected in soils many years after application if the original material was ground coarsely.

EXCHANGEABLE BASES IN SOILS

Relative proportions

As a general rule the relative quantities as milligram equivalents of the major exchangeable bases in soils follow the order, calcium > magnesium > potassium. The content of exchangeable sodium may be either larger or smaller than that of potassium. Table 4 shows a summary of results of different investigators.

Table 4. Proportions of Exchangeable Bases in Soils

		Milligram Equivalents of Indicated Base per 100 m.e. of Total Exchangeable Bases			
Soils Analyzed	Author	Ca	Mg	K	Na
Nine acid soils	C. A. Bower (unpublished) and Baver (1928)	69.4	25.1	2.7	2.9
Six neutral or slightly alkaline soils	Kelley and Brown (1924)	62.1	25.6	3.9	8.4
Two strongly alkaline soils	Richards (1954)	25.5*		20.0	54.5

* Sum of calcium and magnesium.

Soils of humid regions commonly contain substantial quantities of exchangeable hydrogen and aluminum, so that the degree of base saturation is less than 100 per cent. Although these soils contain bases in the form of soluble salts, in addition to those in exchangeable form, the amount usually is relatively small (see Table 8), and is included with the exchangeable bases in most instances. Soils of humid regions seldom contain much exchangeable sodium except near the seacoast. The B and C horizons, however, may contain relatively more magnesium than is indicated in Table 4, which lists analyses of surface samples. This tendency is particularly pronounced in highly weathered soils, in which the content of exchangeable magnesium in the B and C horizons may exceed that of exchangeable calcium.

Soils of arid regions usually are base-saturated; in fact, special procedures often are needed to distinguish between exchangeable bases and the substantial amounts of bases present as soluble salts or calcium carbonate. Strongly alkaline soils are characterized by a relatively high ratio of monovalent bases (particularly sodium) to divalent bases.

Renewal

If the exchangeable calcium, magnesium, and potassium in soils represented the total supply of the respective bases, deficiencies of these bases for plant growth in many soils would appear within a period of only a few years. This is particularly true of potassium, which is found in the exchangeable form in relatively small amounts and is used by plants in relatively large amounts. As was pointed out earlier, however, the content of calcium, magnesium, and potassium in nonexchangeable form usually exceeds that in exchangeable form. Bases in nonexchangeable form probably are not of appreciable value per se as sources of nutrients for plants, but their gradual release serves to replenish the supply of exchangeable bases.

Primary minerals, such as the feldspars, ferromagnesians, and micas, form one source of nonexchangeable bases. Experiments of Graham (1940), McClelland (1951), and others have demonstrated that if such minerals are ground to particle sizes in which they occur in soil, appreciable release of bases to acid clays will occur. The nature of the cations released and the rapidity of release differ among minerals.

The silicate clays form a second source of nonexchangeable bases in soils. Illite and montmorillonite contain nonexchangeable magnesium, and illite contains nonexchangeable potassium. Weathering causes the release of magnesium and potassium from these forms. Calcium apparently is not found as a lattice constituent of the clay minerals, and hence must be liberated from other minerals. Since kaolinite does not hold calcium, magnesium, or potassium in nonexchangeable form, this clay is of no value as a source of these constituents.

The rate of release of bases from nonexchangeable forms increases with the intensity of weathering if the soil materials are uniform.

Long-continued, intense weathering, however, will deplete the supply of nonexchangeable bases so that the rate of release is much lower than it is from initially comparable soil material that has been maintained under conditions of moderate or weak weathering. If a soil becomes acid, the liberation of bases from nonexchangeable forms evidently is not proceeding fast enough to keep the exchange positions saturated with bases. The percentage base saturation of a natural soil thus is some indication of the balance between loss of exchangeable bases from the soil and their accumulation from nonexchangeable forms. The data of Craig and Halais (1934) in Table 5 may be noted in this connection.

Table 5. Annual Rainfall and Cation-Exchange Properties of Lateritic Soils at Different Locations in Mauritius

(Craig and Halais, 1934)

Annual Rainfall, in.	Cation-Exchange Capacity per 100 g., m.e.	Exchangeable Bases per 100 g., m.e.	Base Saturation, %
25–50	29.5	24.0	81
50–75	26.2	15.9	61
75–100	22.9	8.2	36
100–125	22.3	5.4	24
125–150	20.6	4.0	19

Investigation of the rate of release of specific bases from nonexchangeable forms under field conditions has been confined mainly to potassium. Fluctuations in content of exchangeable potassium are more marked than those of exchangeable calcium and magnesium. Volk (1941) reported that the content of exchangeable potassium averaged 187 lb. per acre in the soil of sixty-four cotton fields in Alabama on October 29, the day following a killing frost. The fields lay fallow during the winter. On March 12 of the following spring, the exchangeable potassium content of the fields averaged 235 lb. per acre, an increase of 48 lb. DeTurk, Wood, and Bray (1943) reported that at a particular location in Illinois, the content of exchangeable potassium in the plowed layer of soil decreased 40 per cent from May to October during the growth of a corn crop. The original level was regained by the following May. Unpublished data of Kirk Lawton showed relatively small decreases in the content of exchangeable potassium during the growth of corn on certain soils in Iowa. The rate of potassium release from nonexchangeable forms apparently was higher in the soils Lawton analyzed than in the soil analyzed by DeTurk, Wood, and Bray.

Removal of ions from solutions by roots

Plant roots remove ions from the surrounding solution by several different processes. The first may be termed "active transport." Active transport is thought to take place as a result of carrier molecules in a protoplasmic membrane that combine with the ions at the outer membrane surface, transport them to the inner surface, and release them there as a result of some chemical change. Active transport is associated with metabolism, is highly selective among ions, and changes ions to a form that is relatively nonexchangeable with external ions of the same or other species.

The second mechanism by which ions are removed from the surrounding solution may be termed "passive permeation." Passive permeation is the free diffusion of the ions of the solution into the portion of the root external to the membrane across which active transport occurs. Indications are that this "outer space" constitutes a substantial part of the root volume. Epstein (1955) found that with young barley roots it was about one-fourth the total root volume. Ions present in this outer space will diffuse back into the surrounding medium if the original solution is replaced with water. The outer space of the root may be considered to be an extension of the external solution into the root as far as the mineral ions are concerned.

The third mechanism by which plant roots remove ions from the surrounding medium is "exchange adsorption." Roots, as well as soils, have cation-exchange properties. Cations held by exchange adsorption do not diffuse out of the root when the original solution is replaced by water, but they are released when other cations are added. Judging from the work of Epstein (1955) with barley roots, anion-exchange properties of roots are of relatively minor importance compared with the cation-exchange properties.

Cations held in the root in both the exchangeable form and the freely diffusible form can be absorbed by active transport. They are then no longer removable by exchange with other cations or by free diffusion into water. Experimental work bearing on these concepts was reviewed by Epstein (1956).

Transport of bases from soil to root

The bases present in the soil solution accompanied by small anions are freely diffusible and will enter by diffusion into the outer space of the root, from which they may be absorbed by active transport.

Along the way they will equilibrate with the cations held in exchangeable form by the root.

Cations held in exchangeable form by the soil are not freely diffusible and must be replaced by other cations before uptake by the plant. There are two principal sources of replacing ions, namely, various species of cations from the soil solution and hydrogen ions from the root. The hydrogen ions from the root may reach the soil particles by diffusing through the outer space of the root and through the soil solution accompanied by an anion like bicarbonate. On the other hand, if the hydrogen ions become attached to the exchange positions of the root, they may reach the soil particles either by exchanging first with cations of the soil solution or by exchanging directly with the soil exchangeable cations if these cations are sufficiently close.

At one time the cation-exchange properties of roots were thought to be of fundamental significance in the nutrition of plants. Current evidence indicates that the exchange positions are distinct from the sites involved in active transport of the ions into roots and that the ions from the soil can reach the sites of active transport by free diffusion through solution without necessarily becoming attached in exchangeable from. Hence the cation-exchange properties of roots appear to play no essential role in the transportation of ions from the soil solid phase into the interior of plant roots.

Release of bases from exchangeable form

When a complete exchange occurs, the exchangeable cations are released in the proportions in which they occurred in exchangeable form. With incomplete exchanges, however, the proportionate quantities of the various cations released may be rather different from those of the exchangeable cations present in the soil. The behavior of individual cations in this respect is described by the complementary-ion principle, which may be stated as follows: The proportionate release of a given cation from the exchangeable form to the solution in an incomplete exchange reaction increases with the increasing strength of bonding of the complementary exchangeable cations.

The effect of complementary ions on the release of a given ion is illustrated in Table 6 by the results of an experiment of Jarusov (1937). In this experiment 5 m.e. of ammonium chloride in 200 ml. of solution were added to 1.91-g. samples of soil. Each sample of soil contained 0.5 m.e. of exchangeable calcium and 0.5 m.e. of a complementary ion. The displacement of the exchangeable calcium was greatest with hydrogen, intermediate with magnesium, and least with

Table 6.   Release of Exchangeable Calcium by Exchange with Ammonium
Ions in the Presence of Exchangeable Hydrogen, Magnesium,
and Sodium as Complementary Cations

(Jarusov, 1937)

| | Quantity of Exchangeable Calcium Displaced by Ammonium Chloride | |
Exchangeable Cations in Soil Sample	Milligram Equivalents	Per Cent of Total
0.5 m.e. Ca + 0.5 m.e. H	0.30	60
0.5 m.e. Ca + 0.5 m.e. Mg	0.18	36
0.5 m.e. Ca + 0.5 m.e. Na	0.09	19

sodium as the complementary cation. Among the complementary cations, by inference, hydrogen was attached most strongly and sodium least strongly.

A reasonably clear conception of the action of the complementary-ion principle can be obtained from consideration of cation-exchange reactions with a substance like a synthetic cation-exchange resin in which all the exchange positions are of the same type, because all ions of a kind will behave in accordance with the same relatively simple pattern. This statement is not true for soils, as may be inferred from

Table 7.   Retention of Calcium and Ammonium in Exchangeable Form by Different
Materials after Leaching with a Solution Containing a Mixture of 0.05 N
Calcium Acetate and 0.05 N Ammonium Acetate

(Schachtschabel, 1940)

| | Proportion of Exchange Positions Occupied by | |
Material	Calcium, %	Ammonium, %
"Humic acid"	92	8
Montmorillonite	63	37
Kaolinite	54	46
Muscovite	6	94

Table 7, which shows the retention of calcium and ammonium in exchangeable form when different exchange substances were leached with an equinormal solution of calcium and ammonium acetates. Since each material was in equilibrium with a solution in which the equivalent ratio of calcium to ammonium was unity, a substantial difference evidently existed in the bonding of calcium and ammonium to the different materials. The release of cations from soils upon the addition of an exchanging cation may be visualized in terms of the behavior of a mixture of materials like those in Table 7, in which the proportions of cations released would represent the net consequence of unequal removal from the different types of exchange positions as well as equilibration of the cations removed with those remaining in exchangeable form.

The overall complementary-ion effects in natural soils containing a variety of cations usually may be summarized by the series Na > K > Mg > Ca, where sodium is released most readily and calcium least readily in an incomplete exchange. Thus sodium is released more readily if it is accompanied by a high proportion of calcium than by a high proportion of potassium; magnesium is released more readily if it is accompanied by a high proportion of calcium than of potassium; and so on. The magnitude of the spread between members of the series is indicated in Table 8, which shows the quanti-

Table 8. Bases in Exchangeable Form and in Solution in a Sample
of Barnes Loam Soil from South Dakota

(Anderson, Keyes, and Cromer, 1942)

Base	Content of Bases in Indicated Form per 100 g. of Soil		Bases in Solution as Percentage of Total in Exchangeable and Solution Forms
	Exchangeable, m.e.	Solution,* m.e.	
Calcium	34.4	0.175	0.5
Magnesium	7.8	0.074	0.9
Potassium	0.9	0.011	1.2
Sodium	0.5	0.016	3.1

* "Displaced soil solution" obtained with a soil to water ratio of 5 to 1.

ties of individual bases in solution expressed as a percentage of the sum of the exchangeable and soluble bases in a particular sample of soil.

Table 9 shows the uptake of calcium by plants from cultures of soil in which a fixed quantity of exchangeable calcium was accompanied by different complementary ions. The uptake of calcium was greater

Table 9. Yield and Calcium Content of Wheat Seedlings Grown on Soil Saturated
with Calcium or with Calcium and Different Complementary Cations

(Ratner, 1938)

Exchangeable Cations in Soil Sample	Air-dry Weight of Seedlings, g.	Calcium in Seedlings, mg.
100 % Ca	1.8	9.7
60 % Ca + 40 % H	1.7	8.6
60 % Ca + 40 % Mg	1.7	8.1
60 % Ca + 40 % Na	1.6	5.2
Control (sand without soil)	1.7	5.2

with hydrogen than with magnesium as the complementary cation, and greater with magnesium than sodium. The same relative effects were shown for release of calcium in an incomplete exchange in Table 6. Because of such similarities, it appears that the same principles are involved in removal of exchangeable cations from soils by plants as by an incomplete exchange.

Estimation of proportionate content of bases in plants

Plants grown in culture solutions rarely absorb the various ions in the proportions in which the ions are supplied; rather, they exert a selective action, absorbing greater proportions of some ions than others. The selectivity varies with the kind of plant. In consequence, there is no reason to expect that when plants are grown in soil they will absorb ions in the proportion in which the ions occur in the soil solution, in the exchangeable form, or in any other form. The proportionate quantities of the bases absorbed by plants can be predicted, nevertheless, on the basis of coefficients that are determined empirically, provided the appropriate measurements are made on the sources of the bases in the soil.

The most extensive experimental work on predicting the proportionate content of bases in plants from measurements on soils has been done by Mehlich and co-workers in North Carolina. (Much of this work was reviewed by Mehlich and Coleman [1952].) Profiting by the earlier work of Bray (1942), these investigators have found that the quantities of the various bases in solution after an incomplete exchange, brought about by a small addition of hydrochloric acid, are useful in predicting the proportionate content of the bases in plants. An acid has been used as the exchanging electrolyte because the release of ions from exchangeable form during plant growth involves hydrogen ions supplied by the plants.

The work of Milam and Mehlich (1954) may be cited as a specific example. These investigators grew *Crotolaria* in greenhouse cultures of five different soils. Each soil had received various treatments in order to provide four or more different proportions of exchangeable calcium, magnesium, and potassium. The proportionate content of the various bases in the *Crotolaria* was estimated from the soil measurements by means of an equation, which may be simplified to the following form for calcium:

$$\frac{Ca_{plant}}{Ca_{plant} + Mg_{plant} + K_{plant}} = \frac{Ca_{HCl}}{Ca_{HCl} + \alpha Mg_{HCl} + \beta K_{HCl}}$$

where Ca_{plant}, Mg_{plant}, and K_{plant} represent the milligram equivalents of the respective bases per 100 g. of plant material, where Ca_{HCl}, Mg_{HCl}, and K_{HCl} represent the milligram equivalents of the respective bases in the extract obtained by shaking 100 g. of soil for 15 minutes with 500 ml. of water containing 1 mg. equivalent of hydrochloric acid, and where α and β are constants. An analogous equation was used to estimate the proportionate content of the other bases in plants. To estimate the proportionate content of magnesium, for example, Mg_{plant} and Mg_{HCl} are substituted for Ca_{plant} and Ca_{HCl} in the numerator of the left- and right-hand sides of the equality, respectively.

The comparative precision with which the proportionate content of calcium in the *Crotolaria* was predicted by several different methods is indicated in Table 10 by the correlation coefficients calculated by

Table 10. Correlation of Proportionate Content of Calcium in *Crotolaria* with Different Measures of Soil Calcium, Based on Data of Milam and Mehlich (1954)

Variate Correlated with $Ca_{plant}/(Ca_{plant} + Mg_{plant} + K_{plant})$	Correlation Coefficient (r)
Exchangeable calcium ($Ca_{exch.}$)	0.49
Calcium released by incomplete exchange with hydrochloric acid (Ca_{HCl})	0.89
$Ca_{exch.}/(Ca_{exch.} + 2.31\ Mg_{exch.} + 3.21\ K_{exch.})$*	0.94
$Ca_{HCl}/(Ca_{HCl} + 0.97\ Mg_{HCl} + 3.41\ K_{HCl})$*	0.95

* Constants fitted by the method of least squares.

Ethel Tyler, of Cornell University. Evidently the correlations were higher if all ions were considered than if only calcium was considered. The correlations were higher with ions released in an incomplete exchange than with the total exchangeable ions.

This general approach has been given a more physicochemical background by Schofield and Taylor (1955) and Woodruff (1955a, 1955b). The essence of the proposal of these investigators is that under certain conditions, a constant ratio of the activities of any two cations, each raised to the $1/v_i$ power (where v_i is the valence of the respective cations), exists in solutions in equilibrium with the solid phase of a given soil. Constancy of this activity ratio is postulated only if the exchanges involved take place in dilute solutions, if the exchanges are small in relation to the cation-exchange capacity, and if the soil has a predominantly negative charge. Thus, for example, the same numerical value of the ratio $a_{K^+}/(a_{Ca^{++}})^{1/2}$ in the solution phase of a particular soil is expected with different ratios of solution phase to solid phase, with different additions of electrolytes, or with different removals of salts from the solution phase by plants, if these processes meet the indicated restrictions.

Schofield and Taylor (1955) have obtained experimental verification of the constancy of the ion activity ratio, making the corrections needed to obtain ion activities from ion concentrations. Woodruff[1]

[1] Woodruff, C. M. (1954) The energies of replacement of cations in soils. Unpublished manuscript, University of Missouri, Columbia, Missouri.

also has obtained experimental verification, but without making activity corrections. Table 11 summarizes (in a form somewhat dif-

Table 11.   Potassium and Calcium Concentrations and Ratios under Different
Conditions in the Solution Phase of Two Soils and the
Tracheal Sap of a Pear Tree

Water Content	Concentration per Liter of Solution Phase			
of Soil, %	HCl Added, mole*	K+, mole*	Ca++, mole*	$c_K{}^+/(c_{Ca}{}^{++})^{1/2}$
Solution phase displaced from soil, data of Burd and Martin (1923)				
9.9	0	3.20	21.1	22.0
22.0	0	2.17	10.2	21.5
Solution phase displaced from soil, data of Woodruff[1]				
51.5	0	0.067	1.50	1.73
51.5	5	0.104	3.09	1.87
51.5	20	0.139	7.24	1.63
Tracheal sap from pear tree, data of Anderssen (1929)				
Sample taken on Nov. 10		0.604	0.414	29.7
Sample taken on May 10		1.525	2.114	33.1

* Values in these columns have been multiplied by 1000.

ferent from the original) some of the data Woodruff has marshaled as evidence. The ion concentration ratio in the last column is approximately constant for both the first soil, despite a change in water percentage, and the second soil, despite different additions of hydrochloric acid. The ion concentration ratio in the tracheal sap of a pear tree likewise was approximately constant, despite a considerable difference in the absolute concentration between dates of sampling. Apparently, therefore, the ion concentration ratio in the sap in the tree was related by an approximately constant factor to the corresponding ratio in a solution in equilibrium with the soil:

$$[c_K{}^+/(c_{Ca}{}^{++})^{1/2}]_{\text{tracheal sap}} = k[c_K{}^+/(c_{Ca}{}^{++})^{1/2}]_{\text{soil solution}}$$

where k is a proportionality factor. If the value of k is independent of the nature of the soil and the proportions of exchangeable cations within individual soils, the proportionate content of various cations in the tracheal sap could be predicted from measurements on the soil. Whether such a simple relationship exists is doubtful. In any event, it should be noted that the potassium and calcium in the tracheal sap were actually in solution and not in part in insoluble form (calcium pectate, calcium oxalate) as would have been the case if the total content of these elements in the tree had been determined. The removal of an element from the tracheal sap to form insoluble substances will be followed by uptake of more of that element even though the ionic ratio remains the same in the soil. Thus, as a result of the change in condition of the element in the plant, the value of k will not be the same for the plant as a whole as for the tracheal sap.

Ion ratios versus ion quantities

In the preceding section the discussion focused on the proportionate release of various bases in an incomplete exchange and the relation thereof to the proportionate content of these bases in plants. Now one may ask to what extent the ratio of bases offered the plant suffices to define the nutritional status of the plant regarding these nutrients. If the total supply of bases is present in solution at the beginning of the growth cycle, as with plants grown in a nonrenewed nutrient solution, the growth of plants will be increased up to a limit by increasing the concentration of the solution. Under these conditions, the ratios may be sufficient to predict the proportionate content of the bases and other nutrients in the plant, but they do not account for differences in total uptake and yield. The situation in strongly weathered soils that have only a small amount of bases in exchangeable form may be expected to correspond to the situation in the nonrenewed nutrient solution, that is, plant growth would be increased by adding the bases in the ratio in which they are released in an incomplete exchange. In many soils, however, the total amount of bases subject to absorption far exceeeds the actual absorption. In such soils an improvement in crop growth presumably might result from changing the ratio by adding one or more constituents in relative deficit, but not by adding more of all the bases in the ratio in which they are released in an incomplete exchange. This is a problem for future investigation.

LITERATURE CITED

Anderrsen, F. G. (1929) Some seasonal changes in the tracheal sap of pear and apricot trees. **Plant Physiol.** 4:459–476.

Anderson, M. S., Mary G. Keyes, and George W. Cromer. (1942) Soluble material of soils in relation to their classification and general fertility. **U. S. Dept. Agr. Tech. Bul.** 813.

Baver, L. D. (1928) The relation of exchangeable cations to the physical properties of soils. **Jour. Amer. Soc. Agron.** 20:921–941.

Baver, L. D. (1930) The effect of organic matter upon several physical properties of soils. **Jour. Amer. Soc. Agron.** 22:703–708.

Bear, Firman E., Arthur L. Prince, and John L. Malcolm. (1945) Potassium needs of New Jersey soils. **New Jersey Agr. Exp. Sta. Bul.** 721.

Blume, James M., and Donald Smith. (1954) Determination of exchangeable calcium and cation-exchange capacity by equilibration with Ca^{45}. **Soil Sci.** 77:9–17.

Bower, C. A., R. F. Reitemeier, and M. Fireman. (1952) Exchangeable cation analysis of saline and alkali soils. **Soil Sci.** 73:251–261.

Bower, C. A., and E. Truog. (1941) Base exchange capacity determination as influenced by nature of cation employed and formation of basic exchange salts. **Soil Sci. Soc. America Proc.** (1940) 5:86—89.

Bray, R. H. (1942) Ionic competition in base-exchange reactions. **Jour. Amer. Chem. Soc.** 64:954—963.

Bremner, J. M., P. J. G. Mann, S. G. Heintze, and H. Lees. (1946) Metallo-organic complexes in soil. **Nature** 158:790—791.

Broadbent, F. E. (1955) Basic problems in organic matter transformations. **Soil Sci.** 79:107—114.

Broadbent, F. E., and G. R. Bradford. (1952) Cation-exchange groupings in the soil organic fraction. **Soil Sci.** 74:447—457.

Burd, John S., and J. C. Martin. (1923) Water displacement of soils and the soil solution. **Jour. Agr. Sci.** 13:265—295.

Cernescu, Niculae C. (1931) Cation exchange and structure. Comparative studies with clay, permutite and chabazite. **Annuar. inst. geol. Romaniei** 16:777—859. (**Chem. Abstr.** 29:3897 [1935]).

Craig, N., and P. Halais. (1934) The influence of maturity and rainfall on the properties of lateritic soils in Mauritius. **Empire Jour. Exptl. Agr.** 2:349—358.

Davis, Donald E., W. H. MacIntire, C. L. Comar, W. M. Shaw, S. H. Winterberg, and H. C. Harris. (1953) Use of Ca^{45} labeled quenched calcium silicate slag in determination of proportions of native and additive calcium in lysimeter leachings and in plant uptake. **Soil Sci.** 76:153—163.

DeTurk, E. E., L. K. Wood, and R. H. Bray. (1943) Potash fixation in corn belt soils. **Soil Sci.** 55:1—12.

Ensminger, L. E., and J. E. Gieseking. (1941) The absorption of proteins by montmorillonitic clays and its effect on base-exchange capacity. **Soil Sci.** 51:125—132.

Epstein, Emanuel. (1955) Passive permeation and active transport of ions in plant roots. **Plant Physiol.** 30:529—535.

Epstein, Emanuel. (1956) Mineral nutrition of plants: mechanisms of uptake and transport. **Ann. Rev. Plant Physiol.** 7:1—24.

Fieldes, M., L. D. Swindale, and J. P. Richardson. (1952) Relation of colloidal hydrous oxides to the high cation-exchange capacity of some tropical soils of the Cook Islands. **Soil Sci.** 74:197—205.

Graham, E. R. (1940) Primary minerals of the silt fractions as contributors to the exchangeable-base level of acid soils. **Soil Sci.** 49:277—281.

Grim, Ralph E. (1939) Relation of the composition to the properties of clays. **Jour. Amer. Ceram. Soc.** 22:141—151.

Grim, Ralph E. (1953) **Clay Mineralogy.** McGraw-Hill Book Co., New York.

Heintze, S. G., and P. J. G. Mann. (1949) Studies on soil manganese. **Jour. Agr. Sci.** 39:80—95.

Hendricks, S. B., R. A. Nelson, and L. T. Alexander. (1940) Hydration mechanism of the clay mineral montmorillonite saturated with various cations. **Jour. Amer. Chem. Soc.** 62:1457—1464.

Hissink, D. J. (1922) Beitrag zur Kenntnis der Adsorptionsvorgänge im Boden. Methode zur Bestimmung der austauschfähigen oder absorptiv gebundenen basen im Boden und die Bedeutung dieser basen für die Prozesse, die sich im Boden abspielen. **Intl. Mitt. für Bodenkunde** 12:81—172.

Hissink, D. J. (1925) Base exchange in soils. **Faraday Soc. Trans.** 20:551—566.

Jarusov, S. S. (1937) On the mobility of exchangeable cations in the soil. **Soil Sci.** 43:285—303.

Kelley, Walter P., and S. Melvin Brown. (1924) Replaceable bases in soils. **California Agr. Exp. Sta. Tech. Paper 15.**

Kelley, W. P., and A. B. Cummins. (1921) Chemical effect of salts on soils. **Soil Sci. 11:139—159.**

Kelley, W. P., and J. B. Page. (1943) Criteria for the identification of the constituents of soil colloids. **Soil Sci. Soc. America Proc.** (1942) 7:175—181.

Martell, Arthur, E., and Melvin Calvin. (1952) **Chemistry of the Metal Chelate Compounds.** Prentice-Hall, New York.

McClelland, J. E. (1951) The effect of time, temperature, and particle size on the release of bases from some common soil-forming minerals of different crystal structure. **Soil Sci. Soc. America Proc.** (1950) 15:301—307.

McGeorge, W. T. (1930) The base exchange property of organic matter in soils. **Arizona Agr. Exp. Sta. Tech. Bul. 30.**

Mehlich, A., and N. T. Coleman. (1952) Type of soil colloid and the mineral nutrition of plants. **Adv. Agron. 4:67—99.**

Milam, F. M., and A. Mehlich. (1954) Effect of soil-root ionic environment on growth and mineral content of **Crotolaria striata. Soil Sci. 77:227—236.**

Mitchell, John. (1932) The origin, nature, and importance of soil organic constituents having base exchange properties. **Jour. Amer. Soc. Agron. 24:256—275.**

Peech, Michael. (1939) Chemical studies on soils from Florida citrus groves. **Florida Agr. Exp. Sta. Bul. 340.**

Peech, Michael, L. T. Alexander, L. A. Dean, and J. Fielding Reed. (1947) Methods of soil analysis for soil-fertility investigations. **U. S. Dept. Agr. Cir. 757.**

Pratt, P. F. (1951) Potassium removal from Iowa soils by greenhouse and laboratory procedures. **Soil Sci. 72:107—117.**

Ratner, E. I. (1938) The availability for plants of exchangeable cations in connection with chemical amelioriation of soils. **Bul. acad. sci. U.R.S.S., classe sci. math. nat.,** Sér. Biol. 1938:1153—1183.

Richards, L. A. (editor) (1954) Diagnosis and improvement of saline and alkali soils. **U. S. Dept. Agr., Agr. Handbook 60.**

Schachtshabel, Paul. (1940) Untersuchungen über die Sorption der Tonmineralien und organischen Bodenkolloide, und die Bestimmung des Anteils dieser Kolloide an der Sorption im Boden. **Kolloid-Beihefte 51:199—276.**

Schofield, R. K., and A. Wormald Taylor. (1955) Measurements of the activities of bases in soils. **Jour. Soil Sci. 6:137—146.**

Schollenberger, C. J., and R. H. Simon. (1945) Determination of exchange capacity and exchangeable bases in soil—ammonium acetate method. **Soil Sci. 59:13—24.**

Shaw, W. M., and W. H. MacIntire. (1951) Exchangeable hydrogen as determined by various procedures in relation to the soil's capacity for calcite decomposition. **Jour. Assoc. Off. Agr. Chem. 34:471—492.**

Volk, N. J. (1941) Available potassium in Alabama soils. **Better Crops with Plant Food 25, No. 4:6—8, 38—42.**

Whitt, D. M., and L. D. Baver. (1930) Particle size in relation to base exchange capacity and hydration properties of Putnam clay. **Jour. Amer. Soc. Agron. 29:703—708.**

Woodruff, C. M. (1955a) Ionic equilibria between clay and dilute salt solutions. **Soil Sci. Soc. America Proc. 19:36—40.**

Woodruff, C. M. (1955b) The energies of replacement of calcium by potassium in soils. **Soil Sci. Soc. America Proc. 19:167—171.**

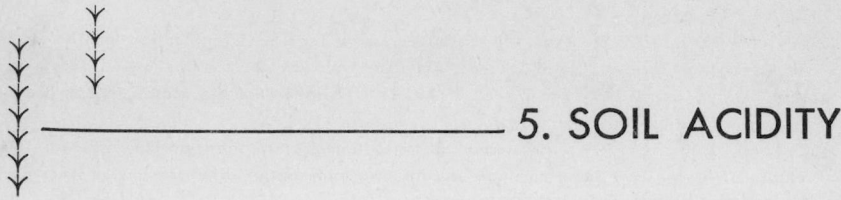

5. SOIL ACIDITY

Acidity of soils is associated with the presence of hydrogen and probably of aluminum in exchangeable form. For this reason the subjects of acidity and exchangeable bases might be treated simultaneously under the general heading of exchangeable cations. The importance of the many indirect effects of soil acidity on plant behavior, however, is such as to merit the consideration of soil acidity separately.

The concept of acidity was developed in connection with the behavior of aqueous solutions, which are said to be acid when the activity of hydrogen ions exceeds that of hydroxyl ions. The same criterion may be applied to soil. There is no agreement, however, as to the conditions under which the measurement should be made. Since the results obtained vary somewhat with the conditions of measurement, there is, in effect, no agreement as to what constitutes an acid soil. Moreover, because of the indirect effects of soil acidity on plants, the term "soil acidity" has come to have a broad connotation that goes beyond the meaning of acidity in the chemical sense. The subject of soil acidity and its various implications will therefore be considered without an exact definition of acid soil.

TITRATABLE HYDROGEN

Exchangeable hydrogen and aluminum

The addition of increments of a base to base-unsaturated soils causes the pH value to rise in a gradual manner without sharp inflections, as indicated in Fig. 1. Since this behavior is characteristic of weak polybasic acids, the exchangeable hydrogen of soils has been thought to represent a similar type of acid. When base-unsaturated soil is leached with a solution of a neutral salt, the solution becomes acid, as would be expected if the cation of the salt had exchanged for hy-

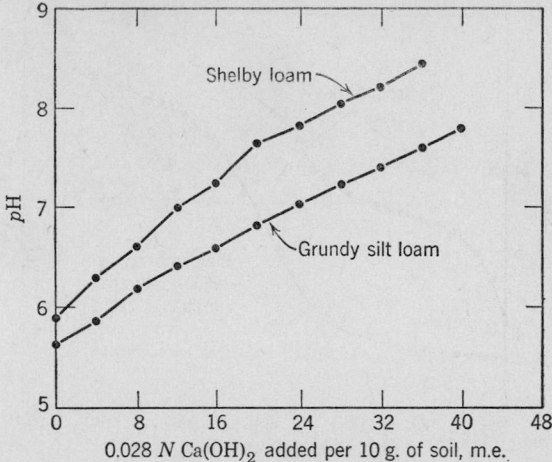

Fig. 1. Potentiometric titration curves for two soils. (Walker, Brown, and Young, 1932.)

drogen ions in the soil. The quantity of titratable hydrogen in the extract exceeds the hydrogen-ion concentration inferred from a pH measurement to be present originally in the soil. These observations likewise support the idea that base-unsaturated soils contain hydrogen in exchangeable form.

Further examination of the acid, neutral-salt extract obtained from base-unsaturated soils shows the presence of aluminum, perhaps together with a little iron. The quantity of aluminum extracted depends on the nature of the neutral salt solution. On a chemically-equivalent basis the aluminum may be more, but usually is less, than the titratable acidity. These observations on aluminum have been the cause of a disagreement about the nature of soil acidity that has existed for many years and still is not settled. One group of investigators has held that base-unsaturated soils contain exchangeable aluminum and that the acidity in a neutral-salt extract is caused chiefly by the hydrolysis of aluminum that was replaced from the exchangeable form in the soil by the salt. Another group of investigators has held the view that the neutral salt replaces hydrogen ions from the soil, and that these are the chief source of acidity. The aluminum in the extract is supposed to come from decomposition of the aluminosilicate minerals of the soil by the acid solution. Earlier work on this subject was reviewed by Mukherjee, Chatterjee, and Banerjee (1947).

Experiments on clays leave little doubt of the presence of exchangeable aluminum. Harward and Coleman (1954), Low (1955), and

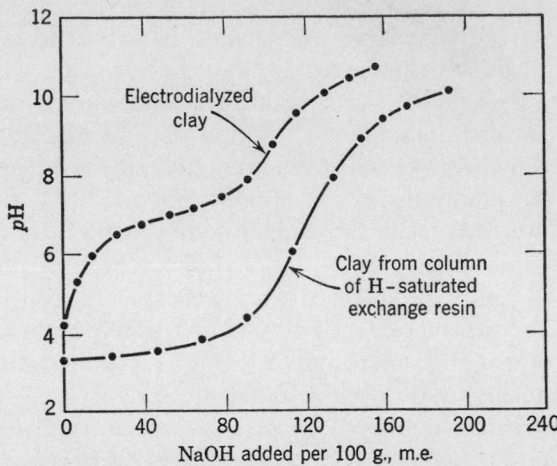

Fig. 2. Potentiometric titration curves for electrodialyzed bentonite and for bentonite that had been passed through a column of hydrogen-saturated exchange resin. (Harward and Coleman, 1954.)

others have found that the potentiometric and conductometric titration curves of clays are not the same when special precautions have been taken to insure that the clay is saturated with hydrogen, and not with aluminum, as when no such precautions have been taken. An example is given in Fig. 2. Evidently the sample that was prepared specially to contain exchangeable hydrogen by passage through a column of hydrogen-saturated exchange resin had a much more strong-acid character than did a corresponding sample prepared by electrodialysis. Other work has shown that with increasing time of standing after passage through a column of hydrogen-saturated exchange resin, the titration curve of bentonite changes gradually from the "strong-acid" titration curve indicated in Fig. 2 toward the "weak-acid" curve. This behavior suggests that the hydrogen-saturated clay is unstable and that it decomposes spontaneously to produce a hydrogen-aluminum clay. Various other types of experiments confirm the existence of exchangeable aluminum in clays that are prepared for experimentation by treatments in the laboratory. This work provides presumptive evidence for the existence of exchangeable aluminum in base-unsaturated soils, but further research is needed to establish the relative proportions of exchangeable aluminum and hydrogen.

Measurement

The hydrogen in strong acids such as hydrochloric and nitric acid can be measured readily by titration with an alkali such as sodium hydroxide. The endpoint is sharp. That is to say, at the point of equivalence, a relatively large pH change is associated with a small addition of alkali. As indicated in Fig. 1, however, when a base-unsaturated soil is titrated with alkali, the endpoint is not sharp; in fact there is no definite endpoint. Moreover, the equilibrium condition is approached slowly, and the results obtained with one base may differ somewhat from those obtained with another.

The indefinite nature of the endpoint of the titration of soils can be accounted for largely on the basis of the source of the hydrogen being titrated. Some of this hydrogen appears to be in electrovalent combination in exchangeable form, and is titrated at low pH values (see the portion of the lower curve in Fig. 2 corresponding to additions of sodium hydroxide below about 80 m.e. per 100 g.). Another part of the titratable hydrogen appears to exist in exchangeable form in combinations intermediate between electrovalency and covalency (see the portion of the lower curve in Fig. 2 corresponding to additions of sodium hydroxide in excess of about 100 m.e. per 100 g.). How much of this electrovalent-covalent type of hydrogen is titrated depends on the pH value of the solution and the strength of attachment of the replacing cation in the particular position in question. A third part of the titratable hydrogen is produced during the titration by hydrolysis of salts of aluminum or iron that results when these metal ions are displaced from exchange positions, as described in the preceding section. (A fourth part of the titratable hydrogen comes from soluble acids; this part is negligible compared with the others.) Probably the electrovalent-covalent and hydrolytic types of hydrogen are principally responsible for the absence of a distinct boundary between titratable and nontitratable hydrogen in soils.

The distinction between titratable and nontitratable hydrogen is considerably more arbitrary than the distinction between exchangeable and nonexchangeable bases, in consequence of which more rigid standardization of methods is needed in determining titratable hydrogen than is needed in determining exchangeable bases. The widespread adoption of neutral, normal, ammonium acetate for the purpose of determining the cation exchange capacity of soils represents, in effect, a conventional means of distinguishing between titratable and nontitratable hydrogen. Thus, the difference between the cation-exchange capacity and the total exchangeable bases may be taken arbitrarily as the titratable hydrogen. (Although exchangeable aluminum is an exchangeable base in the strict sense of the word, it is not considered to be such in soils for reasons of tradition and the fact that the common titration procedure of Bray and Willhite [1929] for determinating total exchangeable bases excludes aluminum automatically.) Other methods have been developed to obtain a direct estimate. Literature on this subject was reviewed by Peech and Bradfield (1948) and Shaw (1953). Shaw and MacIntire (1951) and Shaw (1952) recommended that titratable hydrogen be determined by extracting soil with neutral, 0.5 N calcium acetate, and titrating the extract to pH 8.8 with barium hydroxide. This procedure gives results that are concordant with the ammonium acetate method, and it is simpler and more precise.

Arable mineral soils seldom contain more than 15 m.e. of titratable hydrogen per 100 g., when titratable hydrogen is defined as the difference between the cation-exchange capacity that is found using neutral, normal, ammonium acetate and the total exchangeable bases. The titratable hydrogen content of organic soils may be considerably greater. On a percentage-saturation basis, the titratable hydrogen of cultivated soils is usually less than 50 per cent and seldom as great as 80 per cent of the cation-exchange capacity.

From the practical standpoint, data on the titratable hydrogen of soils are of value mainly as an aid in judging the relative effect of different applications of calcium carbonate or limestone. A titration curve obtained with different applications of calcium carbonate provides more and better information, but is less convenient to prepare, because of the slow rate of reaction between calcium carbonate and soil, and the necessity of treating several samples of each soil.

pH VALUES

Practice

The negative logarithm of the activity of hydrogen ions in solution is known as the pH. In practice, the pH value of soils usually is measured potentiometrically using a glass electrode. A quantity of dry soil is shaken with water, and the mixture is allowed to stand for perhaps 30 minutes. Then the mixture is stirred, the electrodes are inserted, and the measurement is made on the soil suspension. According to this technique, the pH values of most soils lie in the range between pH 4 and pH 8.5; however, values have been recorded as low as pH 2.2 (Jensen, 1927) and as high as pH 10.7 (Fireman and Wadleigh, 1951). Bailey (1944, 1945) has tabulated pH values of a number of soils of the United States.

The pH value of soils is not a constant and characteristic value. The result varies with the ratio of soil to water employed. Crowther (1925) found that when the ratio of soil to water was decreased from

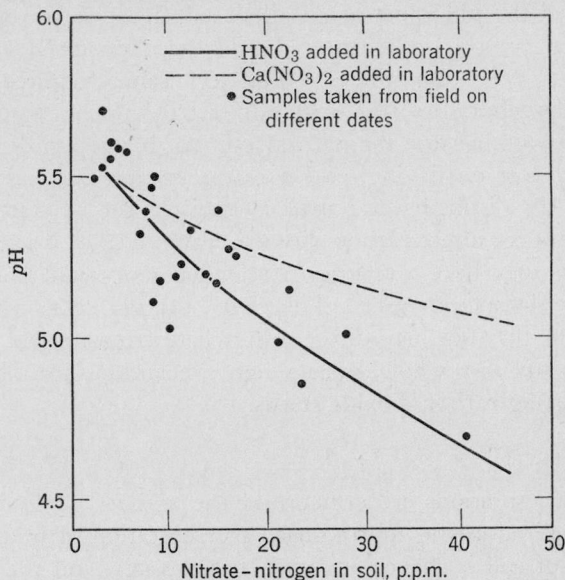

Fig. 3.   Nitrate content and pH of a sandy soil.   (Lehr, 1950.)

½ to ¹⁄₁₆, the pH value of one soil increased from 6.9 to 7.4 and that of another increased from 4.8 to 5.1.   Because of these effects of soil to water ratio the International Society of Soil Science (Anonymous, 1927) adopted a ratio of 1 part of soil to 2.5 parts of water by weight as standard.   More recently some investigators have used a 1 to 1 ratio.   Some have used only enough water to bring the soil to a paste-like consistency, and a few have used even less water.

Natural variations in electrolyte content of a soil from time to time may cause measurable changes in pH values.   The data of Lehr (1950) in Fig. 3 may be cited as an example.   Lehr found that the pH value of a sandy soil sampled at different times during the season decreased as the nitrate content of the soil increased.   Upon adding different quantities of nitric acid to samples of the soil in the laboratory, he obtained a curve showing the same trend as the samples taken from the field.   A different trend was obtained from additions of calcium nitrate.   Apparently, therefore, the pH value of the soil was affected by the nitric acid produced by nitrification.

Carbon dioxide may lower considerably the pH value of alkaline and slightly acid soils because of the carbonic acid it produces in solution.   Whitney and Gardner (1943) found that the soil pH decreased linearly with the increase in the logarithm of the partial pressure of carbon dioxide in the atmosphere.   In the most extreme case they reported the pH value of an alkali soil decreased from 9.2 to 6.4 as the partial pressure of carbon dioxide was increased from 0.0003 atmosphere to 0.77 atmosphere. The pH value found in the usual manner in the laboratory thus may differ from that in the field at the time of sampling, because the natural content of carbon dioxide in the soil has been lost on drying, and a different quantity has been reintroduced in the distilled water used to moisten the laboratory sample. Since plant roots excrete carbon dioxide, a thin film of water surrounding the roots may have a reaction somewhat more acid than water in the soil some distance removed. Therefore, the pH value at the absorbing surface of the root may differ somewhate from the pH value measured in the soil as a whole, even when precautions are taken to preserve the existing carbon dioxide status.

Validity

Where true solutions are concerned the activity of hydrogen ions may be visualized as the approximate concentration of hydrogen ions. If a sample of soil is shaken up with some water, and the pH of the supernatant liquid is measured after the soil has settled, the result clearly is the pH value of a solution, and it can be interpreted as the approximate concentration of hydrogen ions in a solution in equilibrium with the soil solid phase.

If the electrodes are moved from the supernatant solution down into the soil suspension or sediment beneath, the pH value sometimes increases but usually decreases. Table 1 gives the results obtained with

Table 1.   pH Values of a Soil Measured under Different Conditions
(Coleman et al., 1951)

	Supernatant Liquid, pH	Suspension, pH	Sediment, pH
Natural soil	6.2	5.8	4.7
Soil leached to remove soluble salts	6.5	5.9	5.2
Soil in 1 N KCl	5.1	5.1	5.1

a sample of one soil. Differences such as this would not be expected if the measurement in the suspension or soil sediment represented the pH of the solution phase between the soil particles, since in this event the value should be the same as the one obtained in the supernatant solution.

Differences in measured pH between the solution and sediment phases have been known to exist for many years. But since the sediment phase might conceivably have a pH different from the supernatant liquid because of the presence of exchangeable hydrogen, little thought was given to the cause of the observations. In 1950, however, Jenny et al. questioned the validity of electrometric measurements of pH values of soil suspensions on the basis of the possible existence of a "junction potential" of unknown and variable magnitude.

The paper of Jenny et al. brought into focus a question that had not received sufficient attention, namely, that the procedure for calculating pH values from potentiometric measurements involves the assumption that no electrical potential arises at the junction between the medium being tested and the potassium chloride bridge leading to the calomel half cell. The validity of this assumption had been verified for solutions but not for soils. Jenny and co-workers thought that in soil suspensions, which contain charged particles, a junction potential might exist.

The possibility of a junction potential immediately raised the question of the cause of the difference in pH between the supernatant liquid and the soil suspension or soil sediment illustrated in Table 1. Perhaps the results obtained for the soil suspension and the soil sediment are not pH values but some undefined combination of pH value and junction potential. Further work will be required to clear up the question of junction potentials and the validity of pH measurements made by placing the electrodes in a suspension of soil in water.

Modification of methods

Since the variations in soil pH values caused by differences in solute content are mostly temporary fluctuations and not permanent changes, a few investigators prefer to leach the soil sample with water before measuring the pH. This modification of procedure yields pH values that are more nearly constant than those obtained without the preliminary leaching. Others measure the pH value of the soil after adding a normal solution of potassium chloride, which is a practice common in Europe. Measurements obtained upon addition of a normal solution of potassium chloride are essentially free of seasonal fluctuations, because the concentration of potassium chloride added is much greater than that of salts present normally in soils.

Addition of potassium chloride causes the soil pH to decrease (Table 1), presumably because the potassium ions exchange with the exchangeable hydrogen, thereby lowering the pH of the solution. According to one view, the pH value registered upon addition of a normal potassium chloride solution approaches that supposed to be present at the surface of soil particles. Although the pH value measured after the addition of a normal potassium chloride solution is rather different from the pH value measured in its absence, the use of potassium chloride has the advantage that the results obtained are independent of the location of the electrodes (Table 1). The error from the junction potential (if such be present) thus is eliminated or, at least, reduced to the level of the error in the equilibrium solution. The action of the potassium chloride in this respect is thought to be that it essentially eliminates the charge on the soil particles.

Following the lead of Teräsvuori (1930) in Finland, Schofield and Taylor (1955) proposed that where C represents a cation having the valence v, the ratio $a_H/(a_C)^{1/v}$ is constant in dilute solutions in equilibrium with a given soil. The idea involved and the limitations are the same as those described in the preceding chapter for exchangeable bases. Table 2 contains data that verify the proposal. The ratio $a_H/\sqrt{a_{(Ca+Mg)}}$ was substantially constant despite differences in weight

Table 2. Experimental Test of Constancy of $a_H/\sqrt{a_{(Ca+Mg)}}$
Employing Rothamsted Soil
(Schofield and Taylor, 1955)

Weight of Soil in 50 ml. of CaCl$_2$ Solution, g.	pH	a_H	Concentration of Ca + Mg per Liter, mole	$a_{(Ca+Mg)}$	$\dfrac{a_H}{\sqrt{a_{(Ca+Mg)}}}$	pH − $\frac{1}{2}p$(Ca + Mg)
30	4.04	0.0000913	0.029	0.0112	0.00086	3.06
15	4.06	0.0000871	0.029	0.0112	0.00082	3.09
30	4.52	0.0000302	0.0018	0.00134	0.00082	3.09
15	4.52	0.0000302	0.0015	0.00115	0.00089	3.05

of soil and concentration of calcium chloride solution added. Schofield and Taylor prefer to express the result in terms of the negative logarithm of the ion activity ratio, as shown in the last column of the table. They call this value the "lime potential." The lime potential is a more characteristic soil property than is the pH value and is essentially constant under conditions that cause the pH to change.

For routine measurement the procedure is simplified by shaking 25 g. of soil in 50 ml. of M/100 calcium chloride solution and determining the pH of the suspension. Since the amount of salt contributed by most soils is small compared with the amount added in the calcium chloride solution, the pH value is measured at what is essentially a constant salt concentration. If desired, the result can be expressed in terms of the lime potential by subtracting 1.14 [which is the value of $\frac{1}{2}p$(Ca + Mg)] from the observed pH value.

Schofield and Taylor found that the pH values of the soil suspension and the supernatant solution were the same when measurements were made in the presence of a calcium chloride solution. Under these conditions, therefore, it may be concluded that if a junction potential exists, it is no different in the suspension than in the equilibrium solution. The pH value obtained in the dilute calcium chloride solution is not the pH value of the soil, but a pH value can be calculated for any desired concentration of calcium and magnesium below the concentration at which the pH is measured. The Schofield and Taylor approach provides a satisfactory means of describing the changes in pH value discussed above in connection with the effects of ratio of soil to water, content of electrolytes, and content of carbon dioxide.

Interpretation

From the discussion in the preceding sections it is clear that the pH value is not a fixed characteristic of a given soil, that different procedures for measuring the pH do not give the same result, and that some question still exists regarding the physical significance of the measurements in certain instances. In work with nutrient solutions, where the procedure and validity are not questioned, knowledge of the hydrogen-ion activity per se is not of particular value in predicting plant response except in extreme situations. A greater amount of direct information thus cannot be expected from pH measurements on soils. The principal value of soil pH measurements is the knowledge they give about associated characteristics, like phosphorus availability, that are found empirically to be associated with pH measurements made in a certain way. The most suitable procedure must be determined by trial and will undoubtedly depend on the particular purpose for which the measurements are made.

DEVELOPMENT OF SOIL ACIDITY

Under natural conditions the leaching action of water percolating through the soil is the most important single factor in removing bases to produce an acid soil. In soils of dry regions a large supply of bases usually is present because little water passes through the soil. With an increase in rainfall the content of soluble salts is reduced to a low level, and any gypsum and calcium carbonate are removed, in the order named. With further increase in rainfall a point is reached at which the rate of removal of bases exceeds the rate of liberation from nonexchangeable forms. The main features of this sequence are illustrated in a paper by Jenny and Leonard (1934). The paper is based on observations of soils lying along the 11° C. annual isotherm in the central United States, where the rainfall increases from west to east. Some of the results are reproduced in Fig. 4. The soil reaction

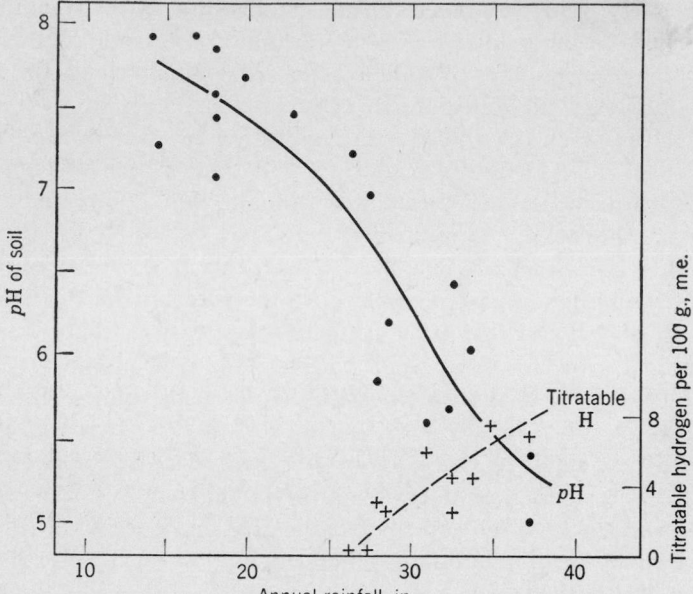

Fig. 4. The pH and titratable hydrogen of soils versus the annual rainfall along the 11°C. annual isotherm in the central United States.   (Jenny and Leonard, 1934.)

changed from about pH 8 at a rainfall of 13 inches in eastern Colorado to about pH 6.7 to 6.8 at a rainfall of 26 to 27 inches in east central Kansas, where titratable hydrogen first appeared. Going eastward into Missouri, the titratable hydrogen increased rapidly.

The titratable hydrogen of soils comes from several sources. One of these is water, which reacts directly with the soil in hydrolysis reactions, and a second source is the contact exchange that may occur between exchangeable hydrogen of plant roots and exchangeable bases of soils. The other principal source of titratable hydrogen in soils is the exchange that occurs with soluble acids. These acids arise in soils in several different ways. Large quantities of carbonic acid are produced in soils by microorganisms and higher plants. The effect is relatively small, however, since most of the carbonic acid decomposes and is lost to the atmosphere as carbon dioxide. Microbial production of more stable acids, like nitric and sulfuric, probably is of more importance, particularly when leaching is limited. Desai and Subbiah (1951), for example, found that when they allowed various organic and inorganic fertilizers to incubate in moist soil, the quantities of water-soluble calcium, magnesium, and potassium present at the end of incubation were correlated with the quantities of nitrate nitrogen (that is, nitric acid) produced during incubation. No correlation was found between the oxidized carbon and the cations made soluble.

The foregoing sources of soluble acids are common to all soils; however, others may be important in certain instances. One such source is the sulfuric acid produced from oxidation of iron pyrite (FeS_2). Jensen (1927) in Denmark found an acid soil of pH 2.2 containing significant quantities of sulfate and soluble iron compounds. The source of the acidity presumably was iron pyrite. Iron pyrite is a common constituent in marshes (Harmsen, et al., 1954) and sedimentary deposits associated with coal measures. The acidity produced during its oxidation is primarily responsible for the failure of plants to grow on many spoil banks from coal mining operations. A second source is the soluble acid from acid-forming fertilizers. Fertilizers usually are not particularly acid per se, but nitrogenous fertilizers may undergo reactions in soils that result in the production of acid. Nitrification of the ammonium in ammonium sulfate, for example, produces two molecules of nitric acid and one of sulfuric acid for each molecule of ammonium sulfate added.

Table 3 shows the soil pH values obtained in an experiment with

Table 3.   pH Value of Norfolk Sand from Control Plot and Corresponding Plot
Treated with 750 Pounds of Ammonium Sulfate per Acre
(Pierre, 1927)

Depth of Sampling, in.	Soil Reaction	
	Control Plot, pH	Ammonium Sulfate Plot, pH
0–6	5.5	4.9
6–12	5.5	5.0
12–18	5.4	5.0
18–24	5.5	5.4

ammonium sulfate. The fertilized plot received ammonium sulfate at the rate of 750 lb. per acre in 1925. Soil samples were taken for analysis in the fall of 1926. Within this short period of time the pH of the soil from the ammonium sulfate-treated plot was lowered about 0.5 unit to a depth of 18 inches. The marked effect in this particular case can be attributed in part to the low buffer capacity of the sandy soil employed. At one time, the soil acidification resulting from application of acid-forming fertilizers was of major importance in areas of heavy and sustained use. At present, however, the acidifying action of certain fertilizers is well recognized, and steps usually are taken to minimize or eliminate unfavorable effects from undue acidification. Pierre (1928) worked out a theory to account for the effect of different fertilizers on soil acidity and eventually proposed a laboratory method that would permit a quantitative estimation of the acid-forming tendency of fertilizers (Pierre, 1933).

Finally, note may be taken of acids added in the precipitation. At Geneva, New York, Collison and Mensching (1932) found that an average of 9 lb. of nitrogen per acre was added annually. Calculated as nitric acid, the amount is 40 lb. Alway (1940) estimated that the annual addition of sulfur per acre amounts to perhaps 5 pounds annually, which is equivalent to 15 lb. of sulfuric acid. Additions of acids from atmospheric sources are of only minor importance in most localities.

SOIL ACIDITY AND PLANT GROWTH

Plant growth is controlled by the joint action of many factors. When neutral soils are acidified or when acid soils are neutralized, many factors of the soil environment are changed simultaneously. Some of these changes may have no significant effect on the plant, and others may be critical. Factors that are critical in one soil may have no significant effect in another because of differences between the soils concerned. The nature of the plant also is of importance, since plant tolerances and requirements are by no means the same. Thus, both the magnitude of the effect and the importance of the various components may vary from one case to another. For this reason, present considerations will be limited mainly to an enumeration of the components.

Toxic substances

Soil acids. The value of limestone as a soil amendment was known long before the discovery that some soils are acid and others are not. The knowledge that the beneficial effects of liming are associated with the application of limestone to acid soils naturally led to the hypothesis that the acids in soils are detrimental to plants and that limestone benefits plants by neutralizing these acids.

Experimental evidence cast doubt on the correctness of the acid toxicity hypothesis. Plants grown in nutrient solutions were found to make satisfactory growth at pH values lower than those tolerated in soils. For example, barley grown in the field failed at a pH value of 5 or below (Ohio Agricultural Experiment Station, 1938), but grew fairly well in nutrient solutions having a reaction of pH 4.5 (Ligon and Pierre, 1932) or even lower (Russell, 1932, p. 497). The acid toxicity hypothesis was discredited further by investigation of the pH value of tissue fluids of plants. As early as 1919 Truog and

Meacham (1919) expressed the sap from the roots of a number of plants and found reactions as acid as pH 4. Pierre and Pohlman (1933) found that the sap exuded from the stump of several different plants, after removal of the tops, was strongly acid by standards used for evaluating soils, and was unaffected by liming. According to Small (1946), the pH value of plant tissue fluids seldom is as high as the pH range of soils that do not benefit from an application of limestone. This evidence indicates, therefore, that plant tissues tolerate acidity of the same or greater degree than that commonly found in acid soils and leads to the reasonable inference that the acids in acid soils are not toxic to plants.

Although the possibility exists that exchangeable hydrogen ions on the surfaces of soil particles have a greater direct effect on plant roots than would be inferred from the pH value of the soil, this possibility seems remote in the light of the concept of ion absorption developed in the preceding chapter. The possibility exists also that certain acid anions in acid soils are toxic. Schreiner and Shorey (1909), for example, extracted dihydroxystearic acid from acid soils with a 2 per cent solution of sodium hydroxide and demonstrated the toxicity of this acid to plants. Whether or not dihydroxystearic acid occurs in soils in free and toxic form is not known. In any event such a toxicity is not a hydrogen effect.

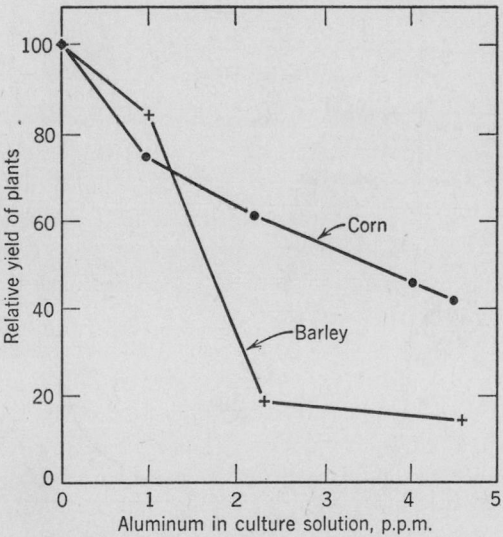

Fig. 5. Relative yields of corn and barley plants grown in culture solutions at pH 5 with different concentrations of aluminum. (Ligon and Pierre, 1932.)

Aluminum. Aluminum probably acts as a toxin in certain acid soils. As noted above it seems likely that much of the titratable hydrogen found analytically is in reality exchangeable aluminum that hydrolyzes to furnish hydrogen ions when the soil is treated with a neutral or alkaline solution.

The nature of the evidence for aluminum toxicity in acid soils is essentially as follows. First, addition of aluminum to culture solutions depresses the growth of plants. Figure 5 shows that as little as 1 p.p.m. of aluminum in culture solution may have a significant effect. Second, concentrations of aluminum in displaced soil solutions of certain strongly acid soils are equal to or greater than those required to produce detrimental effects. Figure 6 shows data of Magistad (1925) on the concentration of aluminum in solution at different pH values (when aluminum sulfate was treated with different concentrations of sodium hydroxide) and data of Magistad (1925) and Pierre, Pohlman, and McIlvaine (1932) on the concentration of aluminum in the soil solution displaced from different soils. The concentration of alumi-

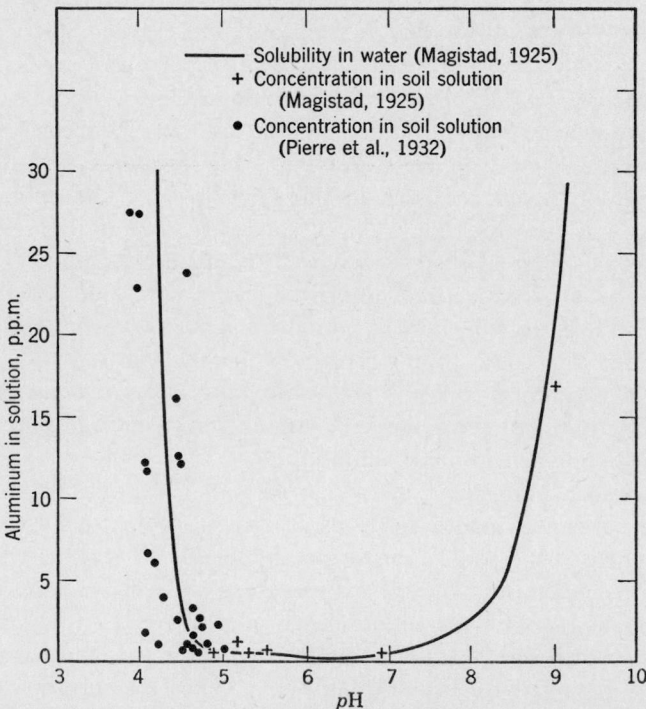

Fig. 6. Solubility of aluminum in water, and concentration of aluminum in displaced soil solutions at different pH values. (Magistad, 1925; Pierre et al., 1932.)

num was in excess of 1 p.p.m. in most of the soil solutions having pH values below 4.5.

Third, Vlamis (1953) has bridged the gap between the nutrient solution and soil solution data by experiments that combine the two approaches. He displaced the solution from an unlimed soil and from the corresponding limed soil and grew plants on each, with and without various additions. The results are summarized in Table 4, which

Table 4. Growth of Barley in Solutions Displaced from Corresponding Unlimed and Limed Samples of Soil

(Vlamis, 1953)

Substrate for Growth of Barley	Reaction of Solution, pH	Al in Solution, p.p.m.	Mn in Solution, p.p.m.	Yield of Barley, mg.
Solution displaced from unlimed soil				
Original solution	4.2	1.8	16.0	139
Treated with $Ca(OH)_2$	5.8	0.4	12.8	340
Treated with NaOH	5.8	0.4	12.0	286
Solution displaced from limed soil				
Original solution	5.8	0.3	7.6	353
Treated with H_2SO_4	4.2	0.35	7.4	315
Treated with $H_2SO_4 + Al_2(SO_4)_3$	4.2	1.8	7.7	176
Treated with $H_2SO_4 + MnSO_4$	4.2	0.3	16.0	341

shows that the major changes in growth of barley were associated with changes in aluminum content of the solutions, and not with pH, calcium content, or manganese content. The results leave little doubt that aluminum toxicity existed in the solution from the unlimed soil. Additional experiments employing a special technique to prevent depletion effects showed that the growth of plants was equally poor in acid soils or in solutions in equilibrium therewith, and equally good in limed soils or in solutions in equilibrium therewith. These results indicate that the cause of poor growth in the acid soil and of good growth in the limed soil was the same as that responsible for poor and good growth in the respective equilibrium solutions, namely, the difference in concentration of aluminum.

Manganese. Manganese occurs in soils in exchangeable form and also in the form of oxides, hydrous oxides, or both. All these forms are thought to have some bearing on the supply of soil manganese to plants. The chemistry of soil manganese is complicated by the fact that manganese may exist in different valence forms. As far as the relation between soil pH and solubility is concerned, the behavior of manganese is similar to that of aluminum. The concentration of both elements in the soil solution increases as the pH decreases.

Evidence for the toxicity of manganese in acid soils is similar in nature to that for aluminum. Experiments with culture solutions show that low concentrations of manganese may depress the yield of plants. As little as 1 to 4 p.p.m. of manganese in culture solution may depress the yields of lespedeza, soybeans, and barley (Morris and Pierre, 1949; Olsen, 1936), while corn may tolerate over 15 p.p.m. and *Deschampsia flexuosa* over 60 p.p.m. of manganese without yield depression (Olsen, 1936). Experiments with soils show that the manganese concentration in displaced solutions may be in the range in which toxicity occurs in nutrient solutions. Table 5 shows the data of Morris (1949) on the manganese content of displaced soil solutions.

Table 5. Manganese Content and pH of the Solution Displaced from 3 Soils
(Morris, 1949)

Soil Type	Location	Soil Treatment	Soil Reaction, pH	Manganese in Displaced Soil Solution, p.p.m.
Cecil sandy loam	Georgia	None	5.2	13
		$CaSO_4$	4.6	71
		$CaSO_4 + P$	4.5	57
Thurman sand	Iowa	None	4.8	50
		$CaSO_4$	4.5	78
Carrington silt loam	Iowa	None	4.9	3
		$CaSO_4$	4.6	16

Plants grown in soils usually do not contain more than 100 p.p.m of manganese, but the content may be much higher. Hale and Heintze (1946) reported an extreme case in which the dry leaves of field-grown potato plants contained 11,300 p.p.m. of manganese. Plants high in manganese often show characteristic leaf symptoms, particularly when they are young. The potato plants of Hale and Heintze showed marked symptoms. Several investigators, however, have noted the occurrence of leaf symptoms without any apparent decrease in growth.

Nutrient availability

Exchangeable bases. The results of experiments with plants in nutrient solutions (Jacobson et al., 1950) suggest that hydrogen ions decrease absorption of bases by a competitive process. That is to say, plants absorb hydrogen ions as well as bases. Individual cation-binding sites in plants may hold either bases or hydrogen, and the probability that a given site will contain hydrogen at a given moment increases with the external concentration of hydrogen ions. Maintenance of the base status of the cation-binding sites in the plant thus requires an increase in concentration of bases in the external medium as the acidity increases.

Although detailed work on this subject remains to be done, an experiment described by Jacobson et al. (1950) illustrates the strongly competitive nature of the hydrogen ion. Barley roots suspended for 2 hours in a solution containing 1 m.e. of hydrochloric acid per liter required the presence of about 15 m.e. of potassium chloride per liter to prevent loss of potassium from the roots to the solution. An experiment of Arnon and Johnson (1942) illustrates the same principle in a different way for calcium. These investigators found that in culture solutions the concentration of calcium required to attain the maximum yield of lettuce increased as the pH of the nutrient solution decreased. The results of this experiment are shown in Fig. 7.

If competitive absorption between hydrogen and bases occurs in solution cultures, there is reason to infer that the same is true in soil cultures. The effects of base unsaturation on the availability of exchangeable bases to plants then may be visualized by extending the concepts of the preceding chapter to include hydrogen and aluminum among the cations offered to the plant. With increasing degree of base unsaturation in a given soil, the ratio of bases released to total cations released in an incomplete exchange will decrease, hence decreasing the competitive position of the bases as compared with hydrogen and aluminum.

The degree of base unsaturation is not sufficient as a criterion for judging the competitive position of bases for absorption against hydrogen and aluminum, because the relative strength of bonding differs so widely between different exchange materials. As an illustration,

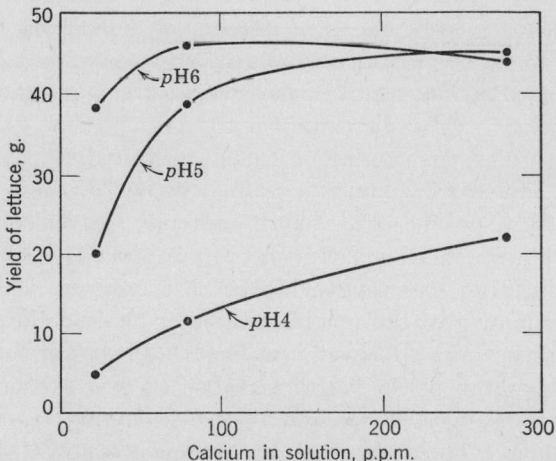

Fig. 7. Yield of lettuce in culture solutions maintained at different pH values and calcium concentrations. (Arnon and Johnson, 1942.)

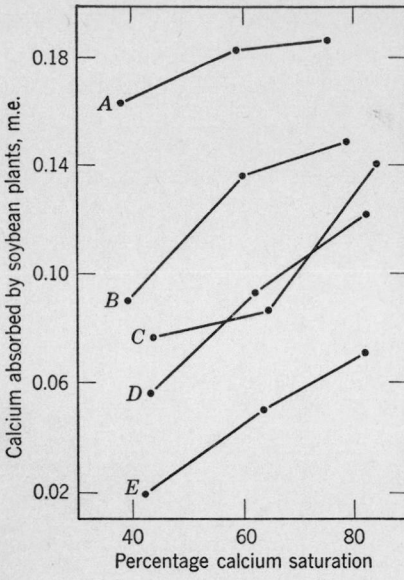

Fig. 8. Calcium absorbed by soybean plants from various exchange substances at different degrees of calcium saturation, all supplying 1 m.e. of exchangeable calcium (letters A through E refer to peat, kaolinite, illite, Wyoming bentonite, and Mississippi bentonite, respectively.) (Allaway, 1945.)

Figure 8 shows the quantity of calcium absorbed by soybeans grown in mixtures of sand and exchange materials, all of which supplied 1 m.e. of exchangeable calcium. That the differences in calcium absorption were related to the relative strength of bonding of calcium and hydrogen (or aluminum) is indicated by the fact that the quantity of calcium absorbed by the soybeans increased regularly with the calcium released in an incomplete exchange with hydrochloric acid (the correlation coefficient was $r = 0.97$).

Calcium. Calcium warrants special consideration. Since calcium is a plant nutrient and is added when soils are treated with limestone, it is not unreasonable to infer that the nutritive effect of the calcium is responsible for at least a part of the beneficial effect of liming. Calcium deficiency is now known to be only one of a number of conditions that may be ameliorated by liming. Considerable divergence of opinion remains, however, regarding the relative importance of calcium deficiency and other conditions. Albrecht and Smith (1952), for example, state that they consider the conditions called "soil acidity" to be nutrient deficiencies, and that calcium is a prominent one of these deficiencies. Åslander (1952), on the other hand, contends that calcium supply is seldom, if ever, the limiting factor in crop production on acid soils.

Perhaps the most extensive evidence that calcium deficiency may be a cause of poor growth on acid soils under field conditions has been obtained with peanuts. Colwell and Brady (1945) conducted a number of field experiments in North Carolina on low-exchange-capacity soils having exchangeable calcium contents ranging from 0.2 to 2.2 m.e. per 100 g. They obtained a correlation of 0.95 between exchangeable calcium and the ratio of the yield of the control plots to the yield of the limed plots for the group of experiments. Liming did not increase the yield when the soil contained in excess of 1.4 m.e. of exchangeable calcium per 100 g. Rogers (1948) obtained similar results on low-exchange-capacity soils of Alabama. Liming failed to increase the yield when the soil contained in excess of 0.7 to 0.8 m.e. of exchangeable calcium per 100 g. As evidence that the effect of liming on peanuts was a calcium effect and not a pH effect, Colwell and Brady (1945) found a low correlation between soil pH and the ratio of the yield of the control plots to the yield of the limed plots. Moreover, Brady and Colwell (1945) conducted an experiment in which they added calcium, potassium, and magnesium sulfates separately to the rooting and fruiting zones, and determined the yields. In this experiment the additions would not have the marked pH effect produced by calcium carbonate. When calcium sulfate was applied in the fruiting zone, the yield of peanuts was approximately doubled. All other treatments decreased the yield. The peanut plant is peculiar in that the calcium requirement is high for fruit production. Calcium does not seem to move freely into the gynophore from the remainder of the plant but must be absorbed from the soil into which the gynophore grows.

Melsted (1953) verified the existence of calcium deficiency in corn on certain fields in southern Illinois. Calcium deficiency symptoms were observed in the plants, and the plants with deficiency symptoms had a relatively low calcium percentage. At two locations the exchangeable calcium content of the soil was 2.0 and 1.8 m.e. per 100 g. and the calcium saturation was 14 and 17 per cent, respectively. Both locations had received a heavy application of fertilizer, including 100 lb. of potassium per acre, which would be expected to decrease calcium release in accordance with the complementary-ion principle. Calcium deficiency was observed at a third location where the soil contained 1.5 m.e. of exchangeable calcium per 100 g., and the degree of calcium saturation was 20 per cent.

The foregoing cases of calcium deficiency in acid soils are authenticated fairly well. The deficiency in peanuts apparently is attributable to a combination of low soil calcium with a high crop requirement. The deficiency in corn apparently is attributable to the low content of exchangeable calcium plus the relatively large number of other exchangeable cations. These authenticated cases appear to be of an extreme nature as far as soil or soil-plant combinations are concerned.

If poor crop growth on acid soils is generally attributable to calcium deficiency and not to acidity per se or some other condition associated with it, addition of calcium in a form that does not change the pH value should benefit the crop. Moreover, raising the pH by the use of a basic source of calcium should benefit the crop much more than an equivalent pH change made in other ways. The experiment of Brady and Colwell (1945) described above, in which the yield of peanuts was increased by application of calcium sulfate, thus is evidence that calcium deficiency was involved in that instance. Application of calcium sulfate usually decreases the soil pH somewhat.

Other experiments with calcium sulfate have not had the same effect. The results of an experiment by Kipps (1947) are shown in Table 6. The pH of the soil, the yield of the crop, and the calcium

Table 6. Yield and Chemical Composition of Alfalfa with Different Additions of Calcium and Magnesium Compounds to an Acid Soil
(Kipps, 1947)

Treatment per Culture	Soil Reaction, pH	Yield of Dry Matter per Culture, g.	Calcium Content of Dry Matter, %	Manganese Content of Dry Matter, p.p.m.
None	5.6	51	1.2	323
Ca(OH)$_2$				
139 m.e.	6.9	64	1.4	166
278 m.e.	7.3	69	1.5	130
CaSO$_4$				
139 m.e.	5.2	43	1.4	191
279 m.e.	5.2	42	1.4	277
MgO				
177 m.e.	6.8	66	1.1	167
353 m.e.	7.3	71	1.0	103

content of the crop all were increased by application of calcium hydroxide. Calcium sulfate increased the calcium content but decreased the soil pH and the yield. Since the manganese content of the crop was reduced by the calcium sulfate, the lowering of the soil pH apparently did not induce manganese toxicity. Application of magnesium oxide raised the soil pH and the yield and decreased the manganese content of the crop to essentially the same extent as did calcium hydroxide. The combination of evidence provided by these different treatments thus indicates that the increase in yield from application of calcium hydroxide did not result from the calcium it contained, but from some other factor associated with the change in soil pH. Experiments of a similar nature have been conducted by Schmehl, Peech, and Bradfield (1950) and Heslep (1951). Schmehl et al. worked with a soil that contained 1.5 m.e. of exchangeable calcium per 100 g. and had a degree of calcium saturation of 11 per cent. Heslep used two soils containing 1.8 and 4.3 m.e. of calcium per 100 g. and having calcium saturation of 12 and 17 per cent, respectively.

Their results indicated that the soils were not deficient in calcium, although Heslep produced calcium deficiency symptoms in lettuce by additions of magnesium oxide.

The evidence at hand shows that calcium deficiency in crops grown on acid soils may occur under conditions of low calcium supply combined with a high crop requirement, or low calcium supply combined with a high proportion of other exchangeable cations. These conditions appear to be extreme. Substantial experimental verification is lacking for the view that calcium deficiency is a frequent and important cause of poor growth of crops on agricultural acid soils in general.

Phosphorus. Availability to plants of soil phosphorus tends to be greater in neutral soils than in acid soils. This behavior is illustrated in Table 7 by a summary of fifty-six experiments conducted in Kenya.

Table 7. Response of Different Crops to Application of Superphosphate to Soils Differing in Degree of Base Saturation

(Birch, 1951)

Base Saturation of Soils, %	Increase in Yield from Application of Superphosphate		
	Wheat, %	Grass, %	Millet, %
60 and below	111	26	125
61 to 70	44	11	27
71 and above	21	4	5

Application of limestone thus may have an effect similar to that of an application of phosphate fertilizers. In certain of the combined liming and phosphate fertilization experiments conducted currently by J. T. Pesek and co-workers of the Iowa Agricultural Experiment Station it appears that the effect of liming on the crop can be accounted for entirely on the basis of an increase in availability of soil phosphorus.

The cause of the relationship between soil acidity and availability of soil phosphorus appears to be primarily the increase in reactivity of iron and aluminum toward phosphate as the acidity increases. In many base-unsaturated soils the exchangeable aluminum alone probably is chemically equivalent to far more phosphorus than is added in the usual fertilizer application. In this connection note may be taken of the fact that application of phosphate may reduce or eliminate aluminum toxicity because of the low solubility of aluminum phosphate.

Micronutrients. Of the various micronutrients that are affected appreciably in availability by soil acidity, molydenum appears to be the only one that behaves like phosphorus. Availability of molybdenum is increased when acid soils are limed. Availability of boron, iron, zinc, and manganese, on the other hand, is decreased when acid soils are limed.

Activity of soil microorganisms

Organic matter decomposition.   Laboratory experiments in which carbon dioxide evolution and nitrate production are measured on un-limed and limed soils usually indicate that decomposition of organic matter is more rapid in limed soils than in unlimed soils.   The infer-ence has been made from such experiments that decomposition of or-ganic matter with the resulting release of nitrate is less rapid in acid soils than in neutral soils in general.

Work of Thompson, Black, and Zoellner (1954) indicates that the prevailing view may not be entirely correct.   These investigators de-termined the evolution of carbon dioxide, mineralization of nitrogen, and mineralization of organic phosphorus upon laboratory incubation of a group of fifty soil samples covering a range in pH from 5.2 to 8.1. Statistical analysis of the results showed that at a constant level of or-ganic carbon, the carbon mineralization did not increase with the pH of the soil; likewise at a constant level of organic nitrogen, the nitro-gen mineralization did not increase with the pH of the soil.   Since in these experiments the soil samples were not limed, the authors sug-gested that the effects of soil pH noted in experiments with unlimed and limed samples are relatively short-lived and do not represent the general state of affairs. With organic phosphorus, however, they found that mineralization increased with pH at a constant organic phosphorus content. Moreover, they found from analysis of the samples for total nitrogen and organic phosphorus that the nitrogen to organic phos-phorus ratio increased with the soil pH.   These results indicate that an increase in mineralization of soil organic phosphorus with increase in soil pH occurs in the field as well as in the laboratory.

Nitrogen fixation.   Laboratory experiments on nonsymbiotic nitro-gen fixation by the organism *Azotobacter* have shown that a pH value of 6 is critical.   *Azotobacter* will grow at pH values below 6 if sup-plied with fixed nitrogen, but little or no nitrogen is fixed under these conditions.   In the field, *Azotobacter* occurs mainly in soils having pH values above 6.   The importance of *Azotobacter* in fixing nitro-gen in such soils is not known; it is clear, however, that no nitrogen will be fixed by *Azotobacter* in strongly acid soils from which it is absent.

Symbiotic nitrogen fixation by leguminous plants usually decreases as the acidity increases (Horner, 1936).   Longevity of the rhizobia in the soil and inoculation of the host plant in soils differing in acidity are associated with the behavior of the host. Functioning of the organisms, however, is determined in part by the conditions in the soil and not entirely by the general welfare of the host. Pohlman (1946), for example, found that when different layers of an acid soil were limed, alfalfa roots developed many nodules in the limed layers and only a few in the unlimed layers.

Plant diseases. Development of various members of the microbial population of the soil is limited by the food supply; hence, there is competition between the different organisms present. Any change in conditions that affects the relative competitive ability will change the balance of the population toward the organisms whose relative competitive ability is favored by the change. In general the competitive ability of bacteria and actinomycetes relative to that of fungi decreases with an increase in soil acidity (Waksman, 1952). Occurrence of plant diseases caused by these different groups of organisms usually follows the general pattern for the group. One of the early practical applications of pH measurements in soils was made by Gillespie and Hurst (1918) in a survey of fields in the potato-growing area of Maine for infection by potato scab, produced principally by the actinomycete *Streptomyces scabies*. Of nineteen locations where the soil reaction was between pH 4.5 and 5.16, eighteen fields were not infected, and one was infected slightly. Infection varied from none to medium in nine areas having a reaction between pH 5.16 and 5.52. All but one of the nineteen locations having a reaction between pH 5.64 and 7.21 were badly infected. The one field that grew clean potatoes (pH 6.2) had just been cleared and was growing potatoes for the first time. Potato scab is controlled in practice by the application of sulfur. Sulfur undergoes microbiological oxidation in soils to sulfuric acid, which lowers the pH value. The effect of sulfur on potato scab, however, apparently is not accounted for by pH changes alone. Vlitos and Hooker (1951) found that upon application of sulfur, the numbers of actinomycetes in soil decreased before there was any detectable pH change. They attributed this effect to production of a small amount of hydrogen sulfide (which they demonstrated). Hydrogen sulfide is toxic to actinomycetes.

In contrast to diseases caused by actinomycetes, those caused by fungi usually are more prevalent in acid soils than in neutral soils. The reason for this seems to be not so much that fungi prefer acid conditions, but rather that they have a broader adaptability to changes in pH than do bacteria and actinomycetes. As a specific example, the "finger and toe" or "clubroot" disease of many brassicas is caused by the fungus, *Plasmodiophora brassicae*. This disease is most prevalent in acid soils, and is controlled by liming (Chupp, 1928). An exception to the usual behavior is found with the take-all disease of cereals, caused by the fungus, *Ophiobolus graminis*. According to Garrett (1942) attacks by this organism decrease with an increase in soil acidity. Garrett (1936, 1937) suggested that the cause of the exceptional effect of pH on *Ophiobolus graminis* is the sensitivity of the organism to carbon dioxide, and the increasing tendency of carbon dioxide to remain in solution in soils as the pH increases. A contributing condition no doubt is the fact that the organism is a relatively poor competitor. Between crops it lives in the soil mainly in dead tissue of the host crop.

Growth of different plants

Perhaps the most comprehensive field experiment that has been conducted to determine the growth of crop plants at different soil reactions is the legume-reaction experiment at the Ohio Agricultural Experiment Station (1938). The data from part of this experiment are shown in Table 8. All the crops produced the highest yield at pH

Table 8. Yield of Crops Grown in Corn, Small Grain, Legume or Timothy
Rotation at Different Soil Reactions

(Ohio Agricultural Experiment Station, 1938)

Crop	Relative Average Yield at pH Indicated				
	4.7	5.0	5.7	6.8	7.5
Corn	34	73	83	100	85
Wheat	68	76	89	100	99
Oats	77	93	99	98	100
Barley	0	23	80	95	100
Alfalfa	2	9	42	100	100
Sweet clover	0	2	49	89	100
Red clover	12	21	53	98	100
Alsike clover	13	27	72	100	95
Mammoth clover	16	29	69	100	99
Soybeans	65	79	80	100	93
Timothy	31	47	66	100	95

6.8 or 7.5. Among the grain crops, barley was most sensitive and oats were least sensitive to soil acidity. Sweet clover and alfalfa were the most sensitive of the legumes, and soybeans were least sensitive. Red, alsike, and mammoth clovers were intermediate.

Since the crops were grown in the common rotation of corn, small grain, and legume or timothy, the observed relationship between reaction and yield of a particular crop may not be independent of the other crops in the rotation. The response of corn in Fig. 9 provides

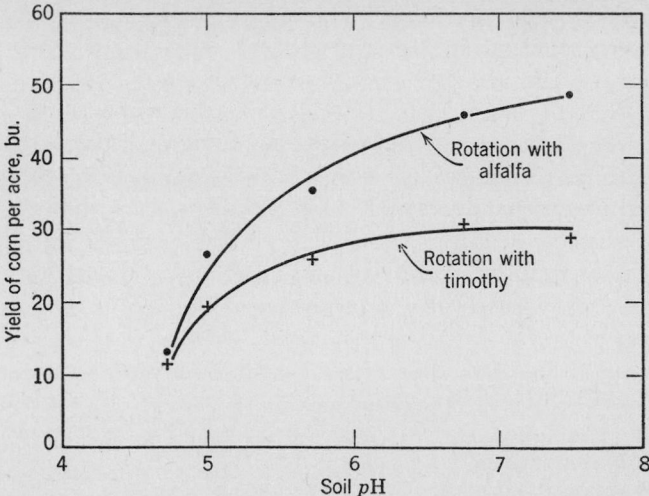

Fig. 9. Yield of corn grown in a rotation of corn, small grain, and alfalfa, and in a rotation of corn, small grain, and timothy on soil at various pH values. (Ohio Agricultural Experiment Station, 1938.)

an example. The yield of corn was about the same following alfalfa as following timothy at low pH values, but the yield after alfalfa was much the higher at high pH values. Presumably the extra nitrogen left in the soil at high pH values by the improved alfalfa crop was responsible.

With cultivated crops the adaptation to conditions at different degrees of acidity affects the yield of a crop and sometimes the stand. Where a choice of crops is available there is a natural tendency to plant the crops that make the best growth under the prevailing conditions. Although little scientific study has been made of the practice from the standpoint of soil acidity, the tendency to plant the best adapted crops causes the cropping pattern to vary somewhat with the acidity of the soil. The sensitivity of alfalfa to acid soil conditions, for example, is so well known that farmers seldom plant the crop without some assurance that the soil has a suitable reaction for the growth of the crop. Arrhenius (1926) made a survey of cropping practices in relation to soil pH in Sweden and found that crops such as oats and timothy occupied an important part of the acreage on strongly acid soils and that barley and alfalfa were not grown on such soils. The latter two crops, however, were important on neutral and alkaline soils.

In mixed plantings or under natural conditions, where the operator does not determine specifically which crop will be grown, competition between species results in a pattern of vegetation that varies with the acidity of the soil. A poor competitor may be eliminated entirely. Work of Pierre et al. (1937) on permanent pastures in West Virgina showed that as the pH of the soil increased, the prevalence of Kentucky bluegrass and white clover increased, and the proportion of weeds and bare space decreased. Table 9 gives the results of a survey

Table 9. Type of Vegetation on Pasture Sites Differing in pH Values, and Intensity of Grazing by Sheep and Cows

(Atkins and Fenton, 1930)

	pH Value of Soil								
	8.0–7.5	7.5–7.0	7.0–6.5	6.5–6.0	6.0–5.5	5.5–5.0	5.0–4.5	4.5–4.0	4.0–3.5
Number of sites examined	3	11	5	7	5	11	13	13	5
Number of sites exposed to grazing	3	11	5	7	5	11	9	11	5
Total number of sites grazed	3	11	5	6	5	8	1	1	0
Number of sites grazed only slightly	0	0	0	1	1	2	1	1	0
Number of sites containing indicated plant:									
Legumes									
Lotus corniculatus		2	1						
Medicago maculata		1	1						
Trifolium dubium	1	1							
Trifolium repens	1	3	4	2	1	2*			
Ulex europeans†						1	2	2	
Miscellaneous									
Calluna vulgaris†									2
Galium saxatile†						2	4	2	1
Potentilla tormentilla†						2			
Pteris aquilina†					1				
Rumex acetosella†							3	6	
Spergula arvensis†							2	2	
Vaccinium myrtillus†							1	1	3

* Both grazed; both sites had a reaction of pH 5.4.

† Plants of generally low palatability.

of seventy-three sites in pastures in Ireland reported by Atkins and Fenton (1930). An inspection of their data shows that the leguminous plants were found most frequently in pasture sites having a reaction between pH 5 and pH 8. These sites were grazed more heavily than those lacking legumes and having a reaction more acid than pH 5. Atkins and Fenton concluded that to all intents grazing ceased at pH 5 on the sites they examined.

LITERATURE CITED

Albrecht, Wm. A., and G. E. Smith. (1952) Soil acidity as calcium (fertility) deficiency. Int. Soc. Soil Sci., Comm. II and Comm. IV, Trans. 1:119–135.

Allaway, W. H. (1945) Availability of replaceable calcium from different types of colloids as affected by degree of calcium saturation. Soil Sci. 59:207–217.

Alway, Frederick J. (1940) A nutrient element slighted in agricultural research. Jour. Amer. Soc. Agron. 32:913–921.

Anonymous (1927) The study and determination of soil acidity. Int. Soc. Soil Sci., Trans. 2nd Comm. B:80–82.

Arnon, D. I., and C. M. Johnson. (1942) Influence of hydrogen ion concentration on the growth of higher plants under controlled conditions. Plant Physiol. 17:525–534.

Arrhenius, O. (1926) Kalkfrage Bodenreaktion und Pflanzenwachstum. Akademische Verlagsgesellschaft M.B.H., Leipzig.

Åslander, Alfred. (1952) Standard fertilization and liming as factors in maintaining soil productivity. Soil Sci. 74:181–195.

Atkins, W. R. G., and E. Wyllie Fenton. (1930) The distribution of pasture plants in relation to soil acidity and other factors. Sci. Proc. Royal Dublin Soc. (New Series) 19:533–547.

Bailey, Ernest H. (1944) Hydrogen-ion concentration of the important soils of the United States in relation to other profile characteristics: I. Pedocal soils. Soil Sci. 57:443–474.

Bailey, Ernest H. (1945) Hydrogen-ion concentration of the important soils of the United States In relation to other profile characteristics: II. Pedalfers and soils transitional between pedocals and pedalfers. Soil Sci. 59:239–262.

Birch, H. F. (1951) Relationship between base saturation and crop response to phosphate in acid soils. Nature 168:388–389.

Brady, N. C., and W. E. Colwell. (1945) Yield and quality of large-seeded type peanuts as affected by potassium and certain combinations of potassium, magnesium, and calcium. Jour. Amer. Soc. Agron. 37:429–442.

Bray, R. H., and F. M. Willhite. (1929) Determination of total replaceable bases in soils. Indust. Eng. Chem., Anal. Ed. 1:144.

Chupp, Charles. (1928) Club root in relation to soil alkalinity. Phytophathology 18:301–306.

Coleman, N. T., D. E. Williams, T. R. Nielsen, and H. Jenny. (1951) On the validity of interpretations of potentiometrically measured soil pH. Soil Sci. Soc. America Proc. (1950) 15:106–110.

Collison, R. C., and J. E. Mensching. (1932) Lysimeter investigations: II. Composition of rainwater at Geneva, N. Y., for a 10-year period. New York State Agr. Exp. Sta. (Geneva) Tech. Bul. 193.

Colwell, W. E., and N. C. Brady. (1945) The effect of calcium on yield and quality of large-seeded type peanuts. Jour. Amer. Soc. Agron. 37:413–428.

Crowther, Edward M. (1925) Studies on soil reaction. III. The determination of the hydrogen ion concentration of soil suspensions by means of the hydrogen electrode. Jour. Agr. Sci. 15:201–221.

Desai, S. V., and B. V. Subbiah. (1951) Nitrification in relation to cation absorption by plants. Proc. Indian Acad. Sci. 34B:73–80.

Fireman, Milton, and C. H. Wadleigh. (1951) A statistical study of the relation between pH and the exchangeable-sodium-percentage of western soils. **Soil Sci.** 71:273—285.

Garrett, S. D. (1936) Soil conditions and the take-all disease of wheat. **Ann. Appl. Biol.** 23:667—699.

Garrett, S. D. (1937) Soil conditions and the take-all disease of wheat. II. The relation between soil reaction and soil aeration. **Ann. Appl. Biol.** 24:747—751.

Garrett, S. D. (1942) The take-all disease of cereals. **Imperial Bur. Soil Sci. Tech. Commun.** 41.

Gillespie, Louis J., and Lewis A. Hurst. (1918) Hydrogen-ion concentration—soil type —common potato scab. **Soil Sci.** 6:219—236.

Hale, J. B., and S. G. Heintze. (1946) Manganese toxicity affecting crops on acid soils. **Nature** 157:554.

Harmsen, G. W., A. Quispel, and D. Otzen. (1954) Observations on the formation and oxidation of pyrite in the soil. **Plant and Soil** 5:324—348.

Harward, M. E., and N. T. Coleman. (1954) Some properties of H- and Al-clays and exchange resins. **Soil Sci.** 78:181—188.

Heslep, J. M. (1951) A study of the infertility of two acid soils. **Soil Sci.** 72:67—80.

Horner, Glenn M. (1936) Relation of the degree of base saturation of a colloidal clay by calcium to the growth, nodulation and composition of soybeans. **Missouri Agr. Exp. Sta. Res. Bul.** 232.

Jacobson, Louis, Roy Overstreet, H. M. King, and Raymond Handley. (1950) A study of potassium absorption by barley roots. **Plant Physiol.** 25:639—647.

Jenny, Hans, and Chester D. Leonard. (1934) Functional relationships between soil properties and rainfall. **Soil Sci.** 38:363—381.

Jenny, H., T. R. Nielsen, N. T. Coleman, and D. E. Williams. (1950) Concerning the measurement of pH, ion activities, and membrane potentials in colloidal systems. **Science** 112:164—167.

Jensen, H. L. (1927) Vorkommen von **Thiobacillus thiooxydans** im dänischen Boden. **Centbl. f. Bakt., Parasitenk. u. Infektionskr.** 72 (II):242—246.

Kipps, E. H. (1947) The calcium/manganese ratio in relation to the growth of lucerne at Canberra, A.C.T. **Jour. Council Sci. Indust. Res.** (Australia) 20:176—189.

Lehr, J. J. (1950) Seasonal variations in the pH value of the soil, as influenced by nitrification. **Fourth Int. Congr. Soil Sci. Trans.** 2:155—157.

Ligon, W. S., and W. H. Pierre. (1932) Soluble aluminum studies: II. Minimum concentrations of aluminum found to be toxic to corn, sorghum, and barley in culture solutions. **Soil Sci.** 34:307—321.

Low, Philip F. (1955) The role of aluminum in the titration of bentonite. **Soil Sci. Soc. America Proc.** 19:135—139.

Magistad, O. C. (1925) The aluminum content of the soil solution and its relation to soil reaction and plant growth. **Soil Sci.** 20:181—225.

Melsted, S. W. (1953) Some observed calcium deficiencies in corn under field conditions. **Soil Sci. Soc. America Proc.** 17:52—54.

Morris, H. D. (1949) The soluble manganese content of acid soils and its relation to the growth and manganese content of sweet clover and lespedeza. **Soil Sci. Soc. America Proc.** (1948) 13:362—371.

Morris, H. D., and W. H. Pierre. (1949) Minimum concentrations of manganese necessary for injury to various legumes in culture solutions. **Agron. Jour.** 41:107—112.

Mukherjee, J. N., B. Chatterjee, and B. M. Banerjee. (1947) Liberation of H^+, Al^{+++} and Fe^{+++} ions from hydrogen clays by neutral salts. **Jour. Colloid Sci.** 2:247—256.

Ohio Agricultural Experiment Station. (1938) Handbook of experiments in agronomy. Ohio Agr. Exp. Sta. Spec. Cir. 53.

Olsen, Carsten (1936) Absorption of manganese by plants. II. Toxicity of manganese to various plant species. Compt. rend. lab. Carlsberg, Sér. Chim. 21:129—145.

Peech, Michael, and Richard Bradfield. (1948) Chemical methods for estimating lime needs of soils. Soil Sci. 65:35—55.

Pierre, W. H. (1927) Buffer capacity of soils and its relation to the development of soil acidity from the use of ammonium sulfate. Jour. Amer. Soc. Agron. 19:332—351.

Pierre, W. H. (1928) Nitrogenous fertilizers and soil acidity: I. Effect of various nitrogenous fertilizers on soil reaction. Jour. Amer. Soc. Agron. 20:254—269.

Pierre, W. H. (1933) Determination of equivalent acidity and basicity of fertilizers. Indust. Eng. Chem., Anal. Ed. 5:229—234.

Pierre, W. H., J. H. Longwell, R. R. Robinson, G. M. Browning, Ivan McKeever, and R. F. Copple. (1937) West Virginia pastures: type of vegetation, carrying capacity, and soil properties. West Va. Agr. Exp. Sta. Bul. 280.

Pierre, W. H., and G. G. Pohlman. (1933) Preliminary studies of the exuded plant sap and the relation between the composition of the sap and the soil solution. Jour. Amer. Soc. Agron. 25:144—160.

Pierre, W. H., G. Gordon Pohlman, and T. C. McIlvaine. (1932) Soluble aluminum studies: I. The concentration of aluminum in the displaced soil solution of naturally acid soils. Soil Sci. 34:145—160.

Pohlman, G. G. (1946) Effect of liming different soil layers on yield of alfalfa and on root development and nodulation. Soil Sci. 62:255—266.

Rogers, H. T. (1948) Liming for peanuts in relation to exchangeable soil calcium and effect on yield, quality, and uptake of calcium and potassium. Jour. Amer. Soc. Agron. 40:15—31.

Russell, Sir E. John. (1932) Soil Conditions and Plant Growth. Sixth Edition. Longmans, Green and Co., London.

Schmehl, W. R., Michael Peech, and Richard Bradfield. (1950) Causes of poor growth of plants on acid soils and beneficial effects of liming: I. Evaluation of factors responsible for acid-soil injury. Soil Sci. 70:393—410.

Schofield, R. K., and A. Wormald Taylor. (1955) The measurement of soil pH. Soil Sci. Soc. America Proc. 19:164—167.

Schreiner, Oswald, and Edmund C. Shorey. (1909) The isolation of harmful organic substances from soils. U. S. Dept. Agr., Bur. Soils Bul. 53.

Shaw, W. M. (1952) Report on exchangeable hydrogen in soils: interrelationship between calcium sorption, exchangeable hydrogen and pH values of certain soils and subsoils. Jour. Assoc. Off. Agr. Chemists 35:597—621.

Shaw, W. M. (1953) Reaction of calcium carbonate with soils and determination of their calcium sorption capacities. Jour. Assoc. Off. Agr. Chemists 36:421—444.

Shaw, W. M., and W. H. MacIntire. (1951) Exchangeable hydrogen as determined by various procedures in relation to the soil's capacity for calcite decomposition. Jour. Assoc. Off. Agr. Chemists 34:471—492.

Small, James. (1946) pH and Plants. D. Van Nostrand Co., New York.

Teräsvuori, Armo. (1930) Über die Bodenazidität mit besonderer Berücksichtigung des Elektrolytgehaltes der Bodenaufschlämmungen. Valtion Maatalouskoetoeminnan Julkaisuja 29.

Thompson, L. M., C. A. Black, and J. A. Zoellner. (1954) Occurrence and mineralization of organic phosphorus in soils, with particular reference to associations with nitrogen, carbon, and pH.   **Soil Sci.** 77:185–196.

Truog, Emil, and M. R. Meacham.   (1919)   Soil acidity: Its relation to the acidity of the plant juice.   **Soil Sci.** 7:469–474.

Vlamis, James.   (1953)   Acid soil infertility as related to soil-solution and solid-phase effects.   **Soil Sci.** 75:383–394.

Vlitos, A. J., and W. J. Hooker.   (1951)   The influence of sulfur on populations of **Streptomyces scabies** and other streptomycetes in peat soil.   **Amer. Jour. Bot.** 38:678–683.

Waksman, Selman A.   (1952)   **Soil Microbiology.**   John Wiley & Sons, New York.

Walker, R. H., P. E. Brown, and A. W. Young.   (1932)   Some chemical and bacteriological effects of various kinds and amounts of lime on certain southern Iowa soils. Part 1.   Laboratory and greenhouse experiments.   **Iowa Agr. Exp. Sta. Res. Bul.** 148.

Whitney, Robert S., and Robert Gardner.   (1943)   The effect of carbon dioxide on soil reaction.   **Soil Sci.** 55:127–141.

6. SOIL SALINITY
AND ALKALINITY[1]

Soil acidity is a condition that results from prolonged leaching of soluble salts from soils, whereas soil alkalinity is found in the absence of such leaching.   Characteristically, most of the landscape is covered by acid soils in humid regions and by alkaline soils in arid regions.

Soil salinity is a condition that results from the accumulation of soluble salts in soils.   Although saline soils occur in humid regions in areas affected by sea water, the most extensive occurrences are in arid regions in which they usually are found in low-lying areas where evaporation concentrates the salts received from more elevated locations in surface water, ground water, or irrigation water.   Because these low-lying areas usually are the ones most easily cultivated and irrigated, and thus potentially of greatest agricultural value, the problems connected with soil salinity are of major importance in highly-developed agriculture in dry regions.   This chapter is concerned primarily with the soil conditions and plant production problems associated with the presence of excess soluble salts in soils and their removal from soils.   Only secondary attention is given to the matter of alkalinity as such.

SOLUBLE SALTS

The major cationic constituents of the soluble salts in saline soils are sodium, calcium, and magnesium.   The major anionic constituents are sulfate, chloride, and bicarbonate.   Minor ionic constituents include potassium, carbonate, and nitrate, numerous other ions occurring in smaller quantities.   One of these, borate, deserves particular

[1] The reviews by Magistad (1945) and Hayward and Wadleigh (1949) and the monographs by Kelley (1951) and the staff of the United States Salinity Laboratory (Richards, 1954) should be consulted for additional details and references to the literature.

159

mention because of its toxicity to plants at extremely low concentrations.

Weathering of primary minerals is the indirect source of nearly all the soluble salts in soils. The relative proportions of the different elements, however, are by no means the same in the soluble material as in the primary minerals. The tendency is for the soluble material to have the higher proportionate content of sodium and chloride and the lower proportionate content of calcium, magnesium, potassium, and sulfur. The cause of this change in ratio among the elements appears to be not so much a difference in rate of release from primary minerals as a difference in tendency to form secondary minerals of low solubility. Calcium, magnesium, potassium, and sulfur form a number of such minerals.

CLASSIFICATION OF SOILS ACCORDING TO CHEMICAL CONDITIONS

Criteria employed

After considerable experience with evaluation of conditions in salt-affected soils of the western United States, the staff of the United States Salinity Laboratory at Riverside, California, has proposed a classification of soils into four general categories. The separations are made on the basis of chemical properties that convey certain information with regard to the salt problem. The criteria are summarized in Table 1.

Table 1.   Classification of Salt-affected Soils According to Chemical Conditions
(Richards, 1954)

Soil Group	Conductivity of Saturation Extract at 25° C., millimhos/cm.	Saturation of Exchange Complex with Sodium, %
Saline soils*	>4	<15
Saline-alkali soils*	>4	>15
Nonsaline-alkali soils†	<4	>15
Nonsaline-nonalkali (normal) soils	<4	<15

  * A subdivision of the group of soils frequently termed "solonchak" or "white alkali."
  † A broader group than is included under the common term "solonetz."

As shown in Table 1, soils first are classified as saline or nonsaline according to the electrical conductivity of the saturation extract. The saturation extract is the solution removed from a water-saturated sample of soil by vacuum filtration. The electrical conductivity of the extract is the reciprocal of the electrical resistance. The figure reported represents the conductivity of 1 cm.[3] of the solution placed between two platinized electrodes, each having an area of 1 cm.^{2}, and placed 1 cm. apart. A conductivity of 4 millimhos per centimeter means that 1 cm.^{3} of the solution has an electrical conductivity of 0.004 mho or a resistance of 250 ohms. The significance of this criterion is that it is a measure of the salt content of the extract and is a function of the free energy of water. From analyses of the saturation extracts of samples from a number of soils, Campbell, Bower, and Richards (1949) found the average relationship between the milligram equivalents of salt per liter s and the conductivity in millimhos per centimeter c to be

$$s = 10.37c^{1.065}$$

The free energy of the water in atmospheres can be obtained by multiplying the conductivity in millimhos per centimeter by the factor —0.36 (Richards, 1954). For a saturation extract having an electrical conductivity of 4 millimhos per centimeter, the salt concentration thus is $10.37 \times 4^{1.065} = 45$ m.e. per liter, and the free energy of the water is $(4)(-0.36) = -1.44$ atmospheres. Experience has shown that yields of many crops are restricted if the conductivity of the saturation extract exceeds 4 millimhos per centimeter.

The second criterion employed in the classification is the percentage saturation of the exchange complex with sodium. The percentage sodium saturation provides an index of dispersion and certain nutritional conditions that either exist in the soil or may develop upon removal of the soluble salts.

Limitations

The United States Salinity Laboratory classification makes for a clean separation of soils into four categories and provides a convenient frame of reference for discussion. It must be recognized, however, that the classification is arbitrary in nature and that it has distinct limitations.

One limitation arises from the fact that the criteria employed do not classify soils into sharply different categories. The reason is the gradational nature of the properties measured. This difficulty is common to soil classification schemes in general and hence is not unique with the United States Salinity Laboratory classification.

A second limitation lies in the fact that although the criteria were devised to provide an index to plant response and soil physical behavior, these two are not defined by the criteria employed. More information is needed.

A third limitation lies in the criteria themselves. The saturation extract has been chosen as a basis for evaluating the salt status of soils, because saturation is a fairly reproducible condition that is related to the water-retaining properties of soils (the saturation percentage is for many soils about twice the field capacity percentage and four times the permanent wilting percentage), and because it is about the lowest water content at which a quantity of solution can be obtained conveniently for analysis. The osmotic component of the free energy of soil water under field conditions is different, of course, from that of the saturation extract. The lower the water content of the soil, the more concentrated are the salts, and the greater is the decrease in free energy of the water from osmotic effects. Unfortunately, the concentration of salts and the osmotic effects at a particular water percentage are not related in a simple manner to the respective conditions in the saturation extract. The phenomenon of negative adsorption results in a greater concentration of salts in the portion of the solution extracted from the soil than is present in the solution as a whole in the soil. The magnitude of this effect varies with the nature of the soil and with the nature and concentration of the salts (Bower and Goertzen, 1955). Negative adsorption causes some uncertainty in estimates of osmotic effects and also in the degree of sodium saturation, since determination of the degree of sodium saturation involves subtraction of the water-soluble sodium from the sum of the exchangeable and water-soluble sodium. Additional sources of uncertainty arise from the fact that (*a*) greater quantities of certain constituents of limited solubility, like calcium sulfate, may be present in the saturation extract than are present in dissolved form in the soil under natural conditions, and (*b*) the quantity of sodium in exchangeable form decreases as the dilution increases because of exchange with divalent cations.

Saline soils

Saline soils contain soluble salts in quantities great enough to interfere with the growth of most crop plants. According to the United States Salinity Laboratory classification, the saturation extract of saline soils has a conductivity greater than 4 millimhos per centimeter at 25° C. The degree of sodium saturation of the exchange complex is less than 15 per cent. Sodium seldom comprises more than half of the soluble cations. The *p*H value usually is less than 8.5. A white crust of salts often occurs on the surface in dry weather. When the salts are removed by leaching to the point where the saturation extract has a conductivity less than 4 millimhos per centimeter, the soils are classified as "normal."

Saline-alkali soils

Saline-alkali soils contain soluble salts and exchangeable sodium in quantities great enough to interfere with the growth of most crop plants. The saturation extract has a conductivity greater than 4 millimhos per centimeter at 25° C. The degree of sodium saturation is greater than 15 per cent. Sodium usually comprises more than half of the total soluble cations. Probably the usual cause of the excess of sodium is the preferential removal of calcium and magnesium by precipitation as calcium sulfate and as calcium and magnesium carbonates. This process of precipitation may or may not have taken place within the soil where the salts are found. As long as the soluble salts are present in excess, the appearance and properties of saline-alkali soils are similar to those of saline soils. Usually the pH value is below 8.5. Because of the excess of sodium in exchangeable form, however, removal of soluble salts causes these soils to revert to "non-saline-alkali" soils instead of "normal" soils.

Nonsaline-alkali soils

Nonsaline-alkali soils contain enough exchangeable sodium to interfere with the growth of most crop plants, but they do not contain appreciable quantities of soluble salts. The saturation extract of non-saline-alkali soils has a conductivity less than 4 millimhos per centimeter at 25° C. The degree of sodium saturation is greater than 15 per cent. Nonsaline-alkali soils probably develop most frequently as a result of removal of excess salts from a saline-alkali soil, but they may originate in other ways as well. Ordinarily the pH value is in the range between 8.5 and 10. The absence of excess salts permits the exchangeable sodium to hydrolyze in part to sodium hydroxide, which thereupon reacts with carbon dioxide to produce a mixture of sodium bicarbonate and sodium carbonate. The pH value is not necessarily above 8.5, however, and may even be below 7 in soils that sometimes are termed "degraded alkali" soils. Because of the low salt content and the relatively high percentage of sodium among the exchangeable cations, the inorganic and organic colloids tend to disperse and move with the water in the soil. Some of the organic matter may migrate to the surface of the structural units and of the soil as a result of evaporation of water. The color of the soil is darkened in this way, giving rise to the term "black alkali," which sometimes is used to describe the soils. Movement of organic matter seems to take place more easily and in a different direction from movement of clay, perhaps because of the difference in size of the dispersed particles. With sufficient time, nonsaline-alkali soils may develop a B horizon having a well-developed prismatic structure and a clay content higher than that of the A horizon. They may then be called "solonetz" soils.

Nonsaline-alkali soils may contain calcium sulfate, in which case leaching with water low in sodium salts will cause gradual solution of the calcium sulfate and replacement of the sodium, which is removed from the soil. The end result is to change the soil from the nonsaline-alkali to the normal category. For soils originally containing too little calcium sulfate, the calcium-for-sodium exchange may be hastened by applying calcium sulfate in the form of gypsum. Sometimes applications of sulfur are made as a means of replacing the exchangeable sodium. The sulfuric acid derived from oxidation of the sulfur brings about a hydrogen-for-sodium exchange. If the soil contains calcium carbonate, the sulfuric acid reacts with it to produce calcium sulfate, which can then bring about a calcium-for-sodium exchange. Calcium carbonate alone is an ineffective source of calcium in soils having high pH values because of its low solubility under these conditions. Richards (1954) gives equations to illustrate the mode of action of various soil amendments intended to cause replacement of exchangeable sodium.

The reclamation process is easiest to carry out in coarse-textured soils, because they have lower cation-exchange capacity and because they commonly retain greater permeability to water than do the finer-textured soils. Some fine-textured, nonsaline-alkali soils are essentially impermeable to water, so that applications of gypsum or other amendments are of little or no avail. Such soils are nonreclaimable under present economic conditions.

SOIL-PLANT RELATIONSHIPS

Saline conditions

Osmotic effects. Plants grown on saline soils often are relatively small in size and dark bluish-green in color. The foliage color results from a high content of chlorophyll and an unusually thick coating of wax. Since these same characteristics are found in plants growing on soils that differ considerably in salt composition, the plant response apparently is caused by some characteristic effect of salt per se rather than the presence of one or more particular ions.

Experimental evidence indicates that the "salt effect" described above is essentially a water deficiency induced in the plants by the osmotic properties of the salts. The plant symptoms are consistent with this view. To test the water-deficiency hypothesis, Hayward and Spurr (1944) grew corn plants in a nutrient solution and then transferred them to other solutions in which the kind and concentration of solute were varied. Measurements of the rate of water absorption by the roots were made over a short period of time just after transference of the plants to the new solutions. The rate of water intake was found to decrease with increasing concentration of each solute and to be essentially independent of the nature of the solute when the additions were expressed on an osmotic basis, that is, in terms of the specific free energy of the water (Fig. 1). This is the type of results one would expect if the "salt effect" were merely an osmotic effect.

The study of osmotic effects was carried further by Wadleigh and Ayers (1945), who grew bean plants in cultures of soil that were treated with different quantities of sodium chloride and allowed to dry to different degrees before watering. They found that the growth of the plants decreased with both increasing water tension and increasing salt content, but that it could be expressed as a unique func-

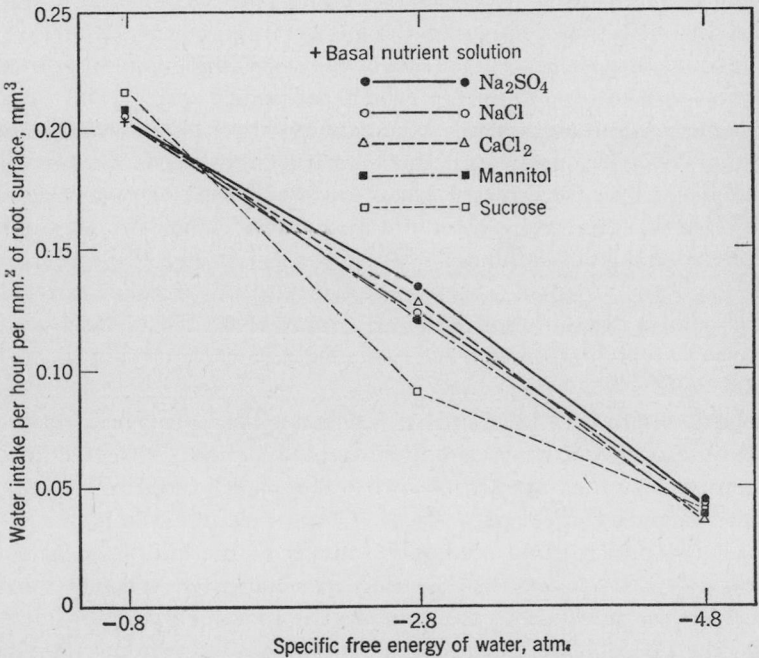

Fig. 1. Rate of entry of water into corn roots versus specific free energy of water in solutions containing different kinds and concentrations of solutes. (Hayward and Spurr, 1944.)

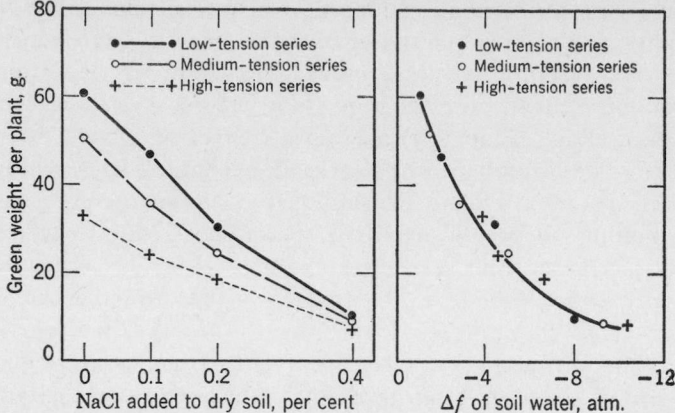

Fig. 2. Yield of red kidney beans in soil treated with different quantities of sodium chloride and subjected to different water regimes. (Wadleigh and Ayers, 1945.)

tion of the specific free energy of the water in the soil, as estimated by adding the osmotic and tension components (Fig. 2). These results indicate not only that the salt effect was in this case a water-availability effect, but also that the plant response was a function of the specific free energy of the soil water, independent of the relative magnitude of the osmotic and tension components.

Osmotic versus ionic effects. The experiment of Hayward and Spurr in Fig. 1 evidently dealt with the primary effect of solutes on water absorption. The time that elapsed during the absorption measurements was too short to permit much internal change in the plant in response to the various kinds and concentrations of solutes in the external solution. Over a somewhat longer period of time, absorption of the solutes and differential loss of water from the plants by transpiration would have changed the specific free energy of water in the plants. The associated change in water absorption might be termed a secondary effect of the solutes. Over a still longer period of time, these differences in water supply would have been reflected in the amount of dry matter produced by the plant, and this would be another secondary effect.

If all the primary and secondary effects of the various solutes are traceable to the variations in specific free energy of the water occasioned by the presence of the solutes, the functional relationship between the yield of the plant and the specific free energy of the water will be independent of the nature of the solute. The results of an experiment to investigate this question are shown in Fig. 3. In this experiment, red kidney beans were grown in a complete nutrient solution, with and without additions of various salts. The yield of dry matter per plant is plotted against the specific free energy of the water. The response curves obtained with additions of sodium chloride, sodium sulfate, and calcium chloride are similar, although the curve for sodium sulfate is consistently a little below that for sodium chloride. These results thus provide no evidence for the existence of major differences in effects between salts, which is the type of experimental finding one would expect if the effects of the various salts on the growth of the plant were attributable entirely, or almost entirely, to the effect on the specific free energy of the water in the external medium. The substantially lower yields obtained with magnesium chloride and magnesium sulfate, however, show that these salts have effects that in some way are different from those brought about by the other three salts.

Thus there is evidence that the effect of excess salts on plant growth cannot in all cases be expressed as a unique function of the specific free energy of the water in the nutrient medium. From this it is inferred that certain salts or ions have additional or secondary effects beyond their influence on water availability. Existence of such effects is evidenced further by occurrence in some instances of foliage symptoms other than the nonspecific bluish-green color that is simply an indication of the presence of excess salts.

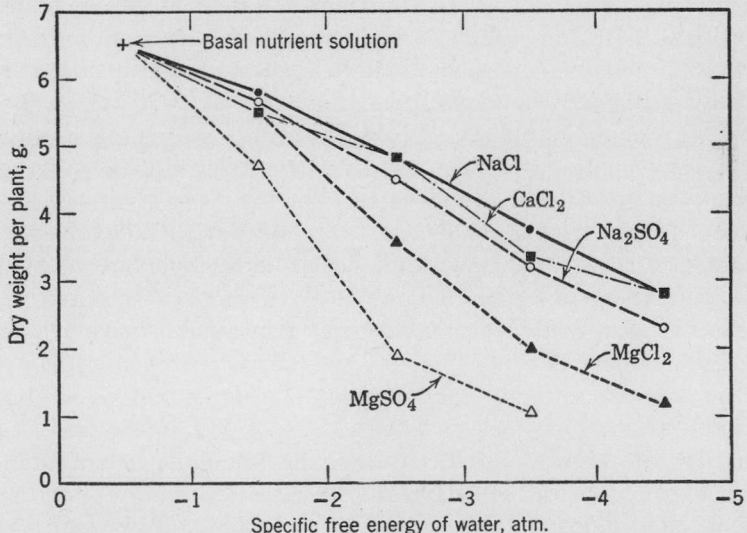

Fig. 3.   Yield of bean plants versus specific free energy of water in a nutrient solution with and without addition of various salts.   (Gauch and Wadleigh, 1944.)

Ionic effects. Having determined that one or more salts have a detrimental effects not shared by others when the specific free energy of the water in the external medium is equal, the next question is the reason or reasons behind the observations. Because of the difficulties of experimentation and interpretation, research in this area has been limited, and the results are largely inconclusive.

The experiment of Gauch and Wadleigh (1944) in Fig. 3 may be considered for purposes of illustration. Perhaps the simplest explanation for the behavior of the plants with respect to magnesium chloride and magnesium sulfate is that magnesium had some specific detrimental effect that was not shared equally by sodium and calcium. The reasoning behind this interpretation is that magnesium was present in the salts that produced the lower yields and was absent from the salts that produced the higher yields. The reverse was true of calcium and sodium. Chloride and sulfate were present in both groups of salts.

The foregoing interpretation involves the assumption that all factors and conditions aside from magnesium operate in the same way in the presence as in the absence of the excess magnesium. This assumption may be incorrect. Thus Fig. 3 shows that the difference in yield between cultures supplied with excess chloride and excess sulfate was greater when the associated cation was magnesium than when it was sodium. According to Hayward and Wadleigh (1949), the apparent specific effect of magnesium may be merely a deficiency of calcium induced by partial exclusion of calcium from the plant in the presence of excess magnesium. The "toxic" symptoms of excess magnesium may disappear upon addition of more calcium to the nutrient medium. Calcium deficiency may have been involved also in the differential action of chloride and sulfate observed in Fig. 3. Since calcium sulfate is of limited solubility, an excess of sulfate would reduce the concentration of calcium in solution.

In some instances, differential plant response to salts having a common ion actually may be attributable to the common ion. For example, Brown, Wadleigh, and Hayward (1953) grew various stone-fruit trees in sand cultures supplied with a nutrient solution to which was added calcium or sodium chloride in concentrations to produce osmotic effects equal to 2 atmospheres. The growth was much poorer in the cultures salinized with calcium chloride than in those salinized with sodium chloride, from which one might expect a specific toxic effect of the calcium. The chloride content of the leaves, however, was much greater in the calcium chloride cultures than in the sodium chloride cultures. The excess uptake of chloride was presumed to be largely responsible for the unfavorable effect of the calcium chloride since the limited information obtained on calcium indicated that the calcium content of the leaves was not increased enough to account for the injury.

From the examples discussed above, it is apparent that the rôle of a particular ion in bringing about the specific effect of a salt is not known without adequate supplementary information. The meager evidence on toxicity of individual ions was reviewed by Hayward and Wadleigh (1949), whose paper should be consulted for citations to the original papers. There is some indication of specific toxic effects of each of the ions (sodium, calcium, magnesium, potassium, chloride, sulfate, bicarbonate, and nitrate) that may accumulate in quantity in salty soils. The effects vary with the nature of the plant.

There is no reason to doubt that part of the unfavorable effect of soil salinity on plant growth in individual instances is attributable to specific ionic effects. Chloride is blamed more frequently than any other specific ion for poor growth of plants on salty soils. This tendency carries over to fertilizer practice, where potassium sulfate usually is preferred over potassium chloride from the standpoint of crop quality. Chloride often increases succulence, which probably accounts for the claim of some truck-crop growers that tomatoes and other fruits are more firm with potassium sulfate than with potassium chloride and that cabbage and lettuce are more succulent (and hence of higher quality in this case) with potassium chloride than with potassium sulfate. The general impression of the magnitude of specific ionic effects in salty soils perhaps is exaggerated, however, because in experimental work single salts are added in increasing quantities, whereas in practice the excess soluble salts are mixtures.

Crop tolerance. According to the review of Hayward and Wadleigh (1949), the salt tolerance of individual plant species or varieties apparently increases with their capacity to absorb salt from the nutrient medium and decreases with their sensitivity to the salt that has been accumulated internally. Accumulation of salt by the plant aids in maintaining the specific free energy of water in the plant below that in the surrounding medium, a condition prerequisite to water absorption. Plants native to a saline environment possess both high capacity for salt absorption and limited sensitivity to the absorbed salt. Crop plants seem to have considerable capacity for salt absorption, but they are sensitive to accumulated salt.

The United States Salinity Laboratory staff has classified many crop plants according to their tolerance to salt (Richards, 1954). Their classification is based for the most part on observations made upon addition of different quantities of salt to nonsaline soil in the field

after the seedlings were established. The conductivity of the saturation extract was measured in the laboratory, and by graphical methods
the conductivity associated with a 50 per cent decrement in yield
was determined. The resulting value for electrical conductivity provides a reasonable way to compare diverse crops when they are grown
under uniform conditions.

Classifications of crops on the basis of salinity tolerance are necessarily subject to revision for local conditions, not only because of
possible differences in specific ionic effects, but also because of interaction between crop tolerance and location. The latter is illustrated
in Table 2. The data in Table 2 were obtained by growing plants

Table 2. Salinity of Nutrient Medium Corresponding to a 25 per cent Reduction
in Yield of Three Crops Grown in Sand Cultures at Two Locations
(Magistad et al., 1943)

	Salinity of Solution Corresponding to a 25% Yield Reduction at Indicated Location, atm.	
Crop	Torrey Pines	Indio
Bean pods	1.4	1.1
Garden beet roots	4.0	2.4
Onion bulbs	4.5	1.2

in large out-of-door sand cultures with complete nutrient solutions
adjusted to different degrees of salinity. The basal nutrient solution
had a salinity corresponding to 0.4 atmosphere. The level of salinity
at which the reduction in yield below that of the control amounted
to 25 per cent of the control yield was determined graphically. The
tolerance was in the order, onions > beets > beans at Torrey Pines
and beets > onions > beans at Indio. The environment at Torrey
Pines was relatively cool and humid, whereas at Indio, it was relatively
hot and dry. These results serve as a reminder of the fact that the
growth response of plants is a function of the total environment.

On a local basis, one condition that confuses the question of salt
tolerance is the distribution of the root system of the plant in relation
to the distribution of salts. The response of the plant may be conditioned materially by the existence of local areas that contain more
or less salt than the remainder of the soil. Under otherwise equal
conditions, plants absorb water more readily from low-salt than from
high-salt locations, as noted by Eaton (1941) and others. Thus an
alfalfa plant may appear to be extremely salt tolerant, as inferred from
measurements of salinity of the surface 6 inches of soil, simply because

most of the salt is present in that layer and because deeper portions of the root system are absorbing water from a solution that is only slightly saline. The converse, of course, may be found if the subsoil is salty and the concentration of salt in the surface soil has been reduced to a low level by irrigation.

Seed germination also is affected by the distribution of salt in the soil. This problem is of particular practical interest with row crops that must be irrigated after planting to promote germination. In normal irrigation practice, the irrigation furrow is placed midway between the rows. The salt moves with the water from the irrigation furrow into the rows, causing a local concentration in the vicinity of the seed. Heald, Moodie, and Leamer (1950) found that germination of sugar beet seed in saline soil was improved considerably by opening an irrigation furrow near the row and throwing up a ridge on the side of the furrow away from the row. The ridge was about midway between rows. The irrigation water then carried the salt away from the seed and into the ridge.

Alkali conditions

Exchangeable-sodium-percentage. Following the terminology of the United States Salinity Laboratory (Richards, 1954), an alkali soil is "a soil that contains sufficient exchangeable sodium to interfere with the growth of most crop plants, either with or without appreciable quantities of soluble salts." In practice the quantity of sodium has been found to be of lesser value than the ratio of sodium to the total cations in predicting the occurrence of detrimental effects. This is the reason for the use of the exchangeable-sodium-percentage as a criterion for distinguishing between alkali and nonalkali soils. The exchangeable-sodium-percentage is simply the percentage of the exchange positions occupied by sodium.

Whether or not the exchangeable-sodium-percentage is invariably the most suitable criterion for distinguishing between soils that do and soils that do not have enough sodium to interfere with crop growth is not certain, as pointed out by Richards (1954). The exchangeable-sodium-percentage probably is of greatest diagnostic value in non-saline-alkali soils. These soils are low in soluble salts, and most of the sodium is in exchangeable form. Where soluble salts are present in quantity, most of the sodium may be in soluble form. In such soils, determination of exchangeable sodium involves a somewhat questionable correction for the soluble sodium. Moreover, use of the derived exchangeable-sodium-percentage for diagnostic purposes takes no account of the quantity of sodium present in soluble form. Usually the exchangeable-sodium-percentage is much lower than the soluble-sodium-percentage, and depends on both the total concentration of soluble cations and the ratio of sodium to other soluble cations. According to Richards (1954), the exchangeable-sodium-percentage can be calculated approximately from the soluble cations by the relationship

$$\text{Exchangeable-sodium-percentage} = \frac{1.47x - 1.26}{0.0147x + 0.99}$$

where $x = \text{Na}/\sqrt{(\text{Ca} + \text{Mg})/2}$, and Na, Ca, and Mg are the concentrations of the cations in milligram equivalents per liter of saturation extract. With further research, additional refinements probably will be made in methods for characterizing the sodium status of soils. One refinement that might offer some advantage would be to confine the use of the exchangeable-sodium-percentage to characterization of physical effects and to introduce the "soluble-sodium-percentage" for characterization of nutritional effects.

Physical effects. The relative effects of sodium and calcium are illustrated by data of Mattson (1928) in Table 3. This table shows

Table 3.   Physical Properties of the Colloidal Fraction of a Soil with Different Degrees of Saturation with Sodium and Calcium

(Mattson, 1928)

Degree of Saturation of Exchange Capacity with Indicated Cation		Volume per gram of Material after Imbibition of Water, c.c.	Dispersibility, %	Electrical Migration per Second per Volt per Centimeter, μ
Sodium, %	Calcium, %			
0	100	1.9	2	1.7
5	95	2.0	3	1.9
10	90	2.0	2	1.7
20	80	2.1	13	2.9
30	70	2.3	53	3.0
40	60	3.2	88	3.3
50	50	5.1	97	3.5
75	25	6.5	99	3.5
100	0	7.1	99	3.5

the results of certain physical measurements made on samples of the colloidal material extracted from soil. The third column shows the volume attained by 1 g. of the dry material after it had been allowed to absorb water. The fourth column shows the percentages of the material that remained in suspension after it had been moistened, shaken with 100 ml. of water, and allowed to stand 31 hours in cylinders in which the depth of the suspension was 10 cm. The marked effect of sodium in increasing swelling and dispersion may be explained on the basis that the degree of dissociation from the soil particles is greater with sodium than with calcium. A greater density of positive charges thus exists in the solution surrounding a particle bearing exchangeable sodium than exchangeable calcium. Adjacent particles are repelled by the proximity of their respective ion atmospheres if these are developed strongly. The last column in the table shows the rate of horizontal movement of individual particles in water when an electrical potential of 1 volt was applied across 1 cm. of extremely dilute suspension. Uncharged particles show no horizontal movement under these conditions. Charged particles, however, move at a rate that depends on their size and charge. Particles of a given size move at a rate that increases with the charge. The increase in rate of movement with the increasing degree of sodium saturation thus may be attributed to the greater charge, which is associated with the greater dissociation of exchangeable sodium than calcium.

The charge of the particles decreases as the salt concentration of the solution increases. In the presence of excess salt, even sodium-saturated colloids are virtually uncharged and are flocculated. If the salt content is reduced sufficiently by leaching or dilution, however, the floccules will disperse. One of the important reasons for distinguishing two classes of salty soils on the basis of their sodium status is the fact that, upon removal of the salt, high-sodium soils tend to disperse, whereas low-sodium soils do not. Upon removal of excess salt by leaching with water, saline-alkali soils become nonsaline-alkali soils, whereas saline soils become nonsaline-nonalkali or normal soils.

The primary physical difficulty associated with the dispersion that takes place in nonsaline-alkali soils is that fine soil particles clog the larger pores. Several other problems then arise indirectly. Because of the reduction in volume percentage of large pores, the permeability of the soil to water is decreased. An example of such effects is provided by Fireman and Reeve (1949), who obtained permeabilities of 1.9 and less than 0.01 cm. of water per hour in two adjacent samples from the surface horizon of a silty clay loam soil from Idaho. The exchangeable-sodium-percentages of the samples from the respective areas were 4 and 54. The low-sodium, permeable area was carrying a good crop, and the high-sodium, impermeable area was bare. The factors responsible for the absence of a crop from the one area are a matter of conjecture. Clearly, however, the bare area is unsuitable for production of dry-land crops because of impermeability to water, if for no other reason. A permeability of 0.01 cm. per hour is equivalent to only 34 inches per year. Thus the soil would have to be flooded for perhaps 5 months before enough water could be absorbed to produce a good crop. Once such an impermeable soil becomes wet, the aeration probably will be too poor for the production of dry-land crops since the soil will remain essentially saturated with water over a long period of time. And finally, reclamation will be difficult or perhaps impracticable because of the difficulty of introducing calcium into the soil and removing sodium from it.

Nutritional effects. As the exchangeable-sodium-percentage increases, there is a concomitant increase in the soil pH. Fireman and Wadleigh (1951) investigated the relationship between these two properties using samples of many soils from the western United States. Since the soil pH and exchangeable-sodium-percentage increase together, one may inquire whether the unfavorable nutritional effects of alkali soils on plant growth actually are sodium effects, or whether in fact they may be pH effects. Different types of evidence indicate that excess exchangeable sodium has unfavorable nutritional effects that are independent of pH changes. In an experiment of Bower and Wadleigh (1949), for example, different plants were grown in cultures of ion-exchange resins. The yield of the plants decreased as the exchangeable-sodium-percentage increased, despite the fact that the pH value of all cultures was about 6.5. In other work of Bower, Moodie, et al. (1954), a multiple regression analysis was made to find the association between soil properties and the yield of sugar beets on individual plots located on a heterogeneous area of saline-alkali soil. Statistical tests showed that exchangeable sodium and pH taken singly were both related significantly to the yield of beets. When taken together, however, only exchangeable sodium was of significant independent value in predicting yield. Thus the apparent effect of pH taken alone was attributable to its correlation with exchangeable sodium and not to any independent effect. The pH range involved in this work was from 7.8 to 9.6, and the pH value was measured on the saturated soil paste.

In both the instances mentioned in the preceding paragraph, the unfavorable effects of exchangeable sodium appeared to be nutritional rather than physical in nature. The manner in which sodium produces nutritional disturbances, however, is not entirely clear. The best answer seems to be that the sodium induces deficiencies of other cations, deficiencies of calcium being of greatest importance in practice. The data of Bower and Turk (1946) in Table 4 illustrate the results obtained in an experiment with variously treated samples of a nonsaline-alkali soil. The marked increases in yield and percentage content of calcium and magnesium from applications of the chlorides

Table 4. The Yield and the Calcium and Magnesium Content of Alfalfa
Grown on a Nonsaline-Alkali Soil with Different Treatments
(Bower and Turk, 1946)

Soil Treatment	pH	Exchangeable Sodium Percentage	Yield of Dry Matter per Culture, g.	Content in Dry Matter	
				Ca, %	Mg, %
Control	9.6	46	0.1	0.6	0.3
Leached with water	9.8	45	0.1	...	...
CaCl₂, 12 m.e. per 100 g., followed by leaching with water	8.6	6	2.0	1.5	0.3
CaCl₂, 9 m.e., plus MgCl₂, 3 m.e. per 100 g., followed by leaching with water	8.7	8	3.7	1.5	0.5

indicate that the alfalfa was deficient in both calcium and magnesium
on this particular soil. Reference may be made also to other evidence
on calcium deficiency given earlier in Table 9 of the chapter on exchangeable bases.

The action of sodium in inducing deficiencies of calcium and magnesium appears to be twofold. First, there is the complementary-ion
principle that was discussed in the chapter on exchangeable bases.
Second, the excess of sodium tends to bring about precipitation of
soluble and exchangeable calcium and magnesium in the form of carbonates. At high pH values, the soil solution contains bicarbonate
and carbonate ions that react with the calcium and magnesium. The
saturation extract of the soil used in the experiment described in
Table 4, for example, contained 19.5 m.e. of bicarbonate and 8.8 m.e.
of carbonate, and only 1.5 m.e. of calcium and 0.3 m.e. of magnesium
per liter of solution.

Physical versus nutritional effects. There is little evidence upon
which one can base a judgment of the relative importance of the physical and nutritional effects of sodium on plant growth. Figure 4 shows
the results of an experiment of Chang and Dregne (1955) in which
the nutritional effects appeared to be the more important. In this experiment, alfalfa and cotton were grown on cultures of a "normal"
clay loam soil that had been treated with different quantities of sodium
carbonate to obtain various exchangeable-sodium-percentages. Half
of the cultures were treated with a synthetic soil aggregant to improve
the physical properties, and the others were employed as controls.

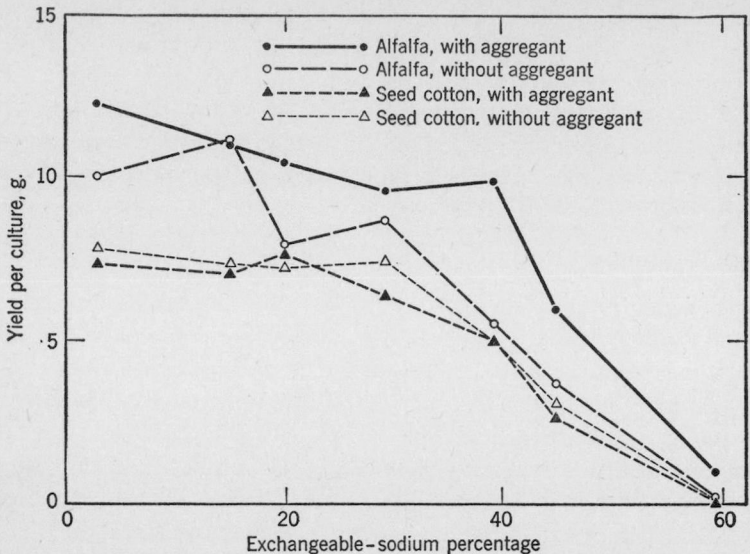

Fig. 4. Yield of alfalfa and seed cotton on cultures of clay loam soil at different exchangeable-sodium percentages with and without synthetic soil aggregant. (Chang and Dregne, 1955.)

The failure of the soil aggregant to alleviate the unfavorable effect of high exchangeable-sodium-percentages indicates that poor physical properties of the soil were not primarily responsible for the decrease in yield; hence the nutritional effects presumably were the cause. In other instances the physical effects apparently are the more important. Allison's (1952) experiment reported in Table 5 represents such a case. The data in Table 5 were obtained from comparable plots of

Table 5. Stand and Yield of Sweet Corn on Comparable Plots of Normal and Nonsaline-Alkali Soil, with and without Synthetic Soil Aggregant

(Allison, 1952)

| | Normal Soil | | Nonsaline-Alkali Soil | |
	Control	Aggregant Added	Control	Aggregant Added
Exchangeable-sodium-percentage	3	3	29	29
Percentage stand of corn	100	100	30	100
Yield of ear corn, g.	3700	3820	760	4050

"normal" and nonsaline-alkali, fine sandy loam soil. Half of each plot was treated with a synthetic soil aggregant; the other half, used as a control, was similarly treated except that no aggregant was added. In this experiment, the yield of corn was decreased by the nonsaline-alkali condition in the absence of soil aggregant but not in its presence. These results indicate the absence of substantial unfavorable nutritional effects and the existence of major physical effects. Prevention of seedling emergence by the hard surface crust apparently was the most important of the physical effects. The stand was poor on the nonsaline-alkali control; most of the plants that emerged came up through cracks in the crust.

Alkaline conditions

Quite apart from the effects of sodium and the possible direct effects of hydroxyl ions, soil alkalinity has indirect effects on the availability of various nutrients. Phosphorus and iron seem to present the most common problems in practice. Both tend to have low availability under alkaline conditions.

The availability of such nutrients as manganese, zinc, and boron is lower under alkaline conditions than under slightly acid conditions. Deficiencies of these elements, however, are seldom found in naturally alkaline soils, except when these soils occur in humid regions. Usually the native supply is ample. Nitrogen deficiency, on the other hand, is common when irrigation is practiced in dry regions because ordinarily the native supply of nitrogen is small. In this case, the alkaline conditions are not responsible for the deficiency but are merely associated with it. Both the alkaline conditions and the low native supply of soil nitrogen result from the limited rainfall under which the soils have been developed.

_____LITERATURE CITED

Allison, L. E.   (1952)   Effect of synthetic polyelectrolytes on the structure of saline and alkali soils.   Soil Sci. 73:443–454.

Bower, C. A., and J. O. Goertzen.   (1955)   Negative adsorption of salts by soils. Soil Sci. Soc. America Proc. 19:147–151.

Bower, C. A., C. D. Moodie, P. Orth, and F. B. Gschwend.   (1954)   Correlation of sugar beet yields with chemical properties of a saline-alkali soil.   Soil Sci. 77:443–451.

Bower, C. A., and L. M. Turk.   (1946)   Calcium and magnesium deficiencies in alkali soils.   Jour. Amer. Soc. Agron. 38:723–727.

Bower, C. A., and C. H. Wadleigh.   (1949)   Growth and cationic accumulation by four species of plants as influenced by various levels of exchangeable sodium.   Soil Sci. Soc. America Proc. (1948) 13:218–223.

Brown, J. W., C. H. Wadleigh, and H. E. Hayward.   (1953)   Foliar analysis of stone fruit and almond trees on saline substrates.   Proc. Amer. Soc. Hort. Sci. 61:49–55.

Campbell, R. B., C. A. Bower, and L. A. Richards. (1949) Change of electrical conductivity with temperature and the relation of osmotic pressure to electrical conductivity and ion concentration for soil extracts. **Soil Sci. Soc. America Proc.** (1948) 13:66–69.

Chang, C. W., and H. E. Dregne. (1955) Effect of exchangeable sodium on soil properties and on growth and cation content of alfalfa and cotton. **Soil Sci. Soc. America Proc.** 19:29–35.

Eaton, Frank M. (1941) Water uptake and root growth as influenced by inequalities in the concentration of the substrate. **Plant Physiol.** 16:545–564.

Fireman, Milton, and R. C. Reeve. (1949) Some characteristics of saline and alkali soils in Gem County, Idaho. **Soil Sci. Soc. America Proc.** (1948) 13:494–498.

Fireman, Milton, and C. H. Wadleigh. (1951) A statistical study of the relation between pH and the exchangeable-sodium-percentage of western soils. **Soil Sci.** 71:273–285.

Gauch, Hugh G., and Cecil H. Wadleigh. (1944) Effects of high salt concentrations on growth of bean plants. **Bot. Gaz.** 105:379–387.

Hayward, H. E., and Winifred B. Spurr. (1944) Effects of isosmotic concentrations of inorganic and organic substrates on entry of water into corn roots. **Bot. Gaz.** 106:131–139.

Hayward, H. E., and C. H. Wadleigh. (1949) Plant growth on saline and alkali soils. **Adv. Agron.** 1:1–38.

Heald, Walter R., C. D. Moodie, and Ross W. Leamer. (1950) Leaching and preemergence irrigation for sugar beets on saline soils. **Washington Agr. Exp. Sta. Bul.** 519.

Kelley, W. P. (1951) **Alkali soils—their formation, properties and reclamation.** Reinhold Publishing Corp., New York.

Magistad, O. C. (1945) Plant growth relations on saline and alkali soils. **Bot. Rev.** 11:181–230.

Magistad, O. C., Alvin D. Ayers, C. H. Wadleigh, and H. G. Gauch. (1943) Effect of salt concentration, kind of salt, and climate on plant growth in sand cultures. **Plant Physiol.** 18:151–166.

Mattson, S. (1928) The influence of the exchangeable bases on the colloidal behavior of soil materials. **First Int. Congr. Soil Sci. Proc. Papers, Comm.** 2:185–198.

Richards, L. A. (Editor) (1954) Diagnosis and improvement of saline and alkali soils. **U. S. Dept. Agr. Handbook** 60.

Wadleigh, C. H., and A. D. Ayers. (1945) Growth and biochemical composition of bean plants as conditioned by soil moisture tension and salt concentration. **Plant Physiol.** 20:106–132.

7. NITROGEN

Plant growth probably is limited more often by deficiency of nitrogen than of any other nutrient. Nitrogen occupies a unique position among the nutrient elements derived from the soil: combined nitrogen occurs only in trace quantities in igneous rocks but is required by plants in relatively large quantities. Most plants derive their supply of nitrogen from forms in the soil. Soils and plants have a particularly intimate relationship with respect to nitrogen since the build-up of the supply of soil nitrogen, on which most plants are dependent, itself has resulted from the growth of plants. The traces of nitrogen found in igneous rocks appear to be in ammonium form. The much larger quantities of nitrogen found in soils are largely in organic forms.

CONTENT IN SOILS

The plowed layer of the majority of cultivated soils contains between 0.02 and 0.4 per cent nitrogen. How much is present in a particular case is determined largely by the general influence of climate and the type of vegetation determined thereby, as these are modified by local influences of parent material, topography, and activities of man, and by the length of time these different factors have been in operation.

Climatic effects

Climate plays a dominant part in determining the nitrogen content of soil through the influence of temperature and water supply on the activities of plants and microorganisms. The classical investigation of the relationship between climate and soil nitrogen content is that made by Jenny (1930). His results in Fig. 1 show a marked decrease in soil nitrogen content with an increase in annual temperature from 32° F.

179

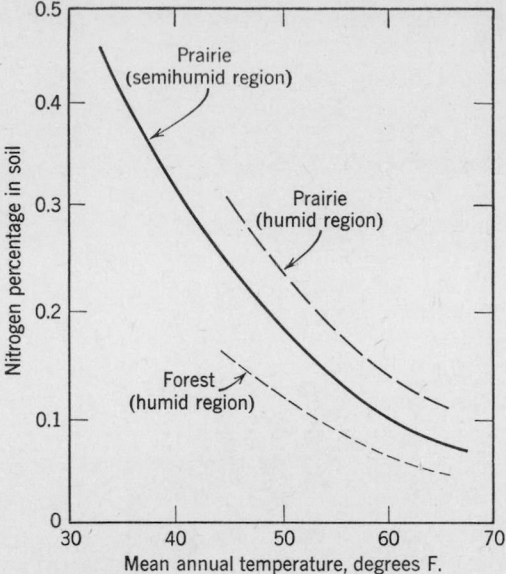

Fig. 1. Soil nitrogen versus temperature relationships for soils of the United States developed under different conditions of climate and vegetation.   (Jenny, 1930.)

in Canada to 70° F. in the southern United States. He considered (Jenny, 1941, p. 213) that the effect of temperature on microbial activity is primarily responsible since, as indicated by the similarity of the yields of prairie hay over the area in question, there apparently was no pronounced effect of temperature on the quantity of organic material that was added to the soil each year prior to cultivation. In fact his examination of the literature (Jenny, 1941, pp. 166 to 170) showed that some of the highest nitrogen percentages in mineral soils are found where the annual yield of vegetation is extremely low as a result of the low temperature.

Other factors remaining the same, the content of soil nitrogen increases with the water supply. The vertical displacement of the nitrogen-temperature curves in Fig. 1 for the soils of semihumid and humid grasslands is an indication of this relationship. The cause lies partly in the rate at which vegetation is produced and partly in the rate at which it is decomposed. Up to a limit both the rate of production of vegetation and the content of soil nitrogen increase with the water supply. Presumably the increase in content of soil nitrogen in this range may be attributed primarily to the rate of production of vegetation and not to a decrease in the rate of decomposition. When the water supply exceeds that corresponding to the maximum rate of production of vegetation, however, the further increase that occurs in content of soil nitrogen may be attributed to the effect of water supply in decreasing the rate of decomposition. Organic soils, which develop in a water environment, represent the extreme condition.

Jenny (1930) expressed the combined effects of temperature and water supply in the equation

$$N = 0.55e^{-0.08T} \; (1 - e^{-0.005H})$$

where N is the nitrogen percentage of the surface soil, e is the base of natural logarithms, T is the mean annual temperature in degrees centigrade, and H is the "humidity" factor. The humidity factor is the ratio of annual precipitation in millimeters to the absolute saturation deficit of the air in millimeters of mercury. It is a measure of effective precipitation. The values of the constants in the equation are those for grass vegetation on upland soils of sandy loam, loam, and silt loam texture. The equation states that with any given humidity factor the nitrogen content decreases with increase in annual temperature and approaches zero as a limit. At any given temperature the nitrogen content increases with increase in humidity factor and approaches a limit fixed by the temperature.

Local effects

Vegetation might be considered either a general or a local factor, depending on the point of view. Although vegetation is related to climate, local differences exist that are not related to climate. These are associated with differences in content of soil nitrogen. As illustrated by Fig. 1, for example, the nitrogen content at a particular temperature and under a given climatic regime is greater in soils developed under prairie than under forest vegetation.

Marked variations in nitrogen content of soils occur within local areas as the result of topographic changes. In effect, the local climate is modified by direction and degree of slope. The difference between north and south slopes may be ascribed primarily to temperature, whereas the lower nitrogen content of soils on the steeper slopes of a given exposure results primarily from the drier local climate and greater loss by erosion. At the other extreme, restriction of drainage in depressions may increase the content of nitrogen and organic matter to the point of peat formation. These relationships have been discussed and illustrated schematically by Ellis (1938).

Soil texture also affects the nitrogen content of soil in local areas. Table 1 shows results of analyses on soils differing in texture in north-

Table 1.   Average Nitrogen Content of Upland Soils Differing
in Texture in Northeastern Iowa
(Walker and Brown, 1936)

Soil Texture	Nitrogen in Soil, %
Sand	0.027
Fine sand	0.042
Sandy loam	0.100
Fine sandy loam	0.107
Loam	0.188
Silt loam	0.230

eastern Iowa.   The nitrogen content increases as the texture becomes finer.   Probably differences in water-holding characteristics, aeration, fertility, and tendency of the mineral portion of the soil to combine with organic matter all are responsible in part for the change in nitrogen content with texture.

Profile distribution

Figure 2 shows the nitrogen content versus depth relationship for three soil profiles from Iowa.   Although the nitrogen content is at a maximum in the surface layer of all these soils, the distribution with depth differs among soils.   Weller silt loam, developed under forest vegetation, has a greater relative concentration of nitrogen near the surface than do the other two soils, both developed under grass.   This difference probably results from the addition of a greater proportion of the organic matter on the surface of the Weller profile.   The irregular curve in the Edina silt loam profile is connected with occurrence of a gray A_2 horizon and a B horizon high in clay.

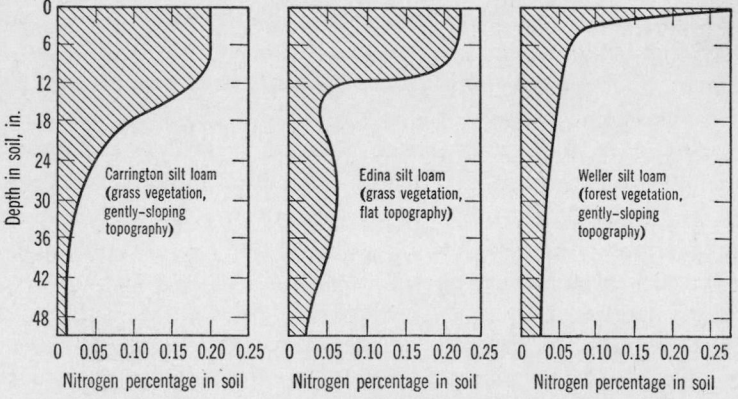

Fig. 2.   Vertical distribution of nitrogen in three soil profiles.   (Pearson and Simonson, 1939.)

The depth of accumulation of nitrogen varies in accordance with the accumulation of organic matter. In soils of arid and semiarid regions where water penetration is shallow, the depth to which organic matter and nitrogen have accumulated also is shallow. In most soils, however, the bulk of the organic matter and nitrogen is found in the surface 2 feet of the profile.

FORMS IN SOILS

Nitrogen occurs in many different forms in soils. Elemental nitrogen is present in gaseous form in the soil atmosphere and dissolved in the soil water. In dry soils it is present in adsorbed form on the solid surfaces. Elemental nitrogen ordinarily is neglected from consideration, however, because it is not of direct significance to nonleguminous crops and is present in ample supply for both symbiotic and nonsymbiotic nitrogen fixation.

In inorganic combined form, nitrogen occurs in soils as nitrous and nitric oxide, ammonium, nitrite, and nitrate. The first two of these are gases and are present only in traces. The last three are ionic forms found in the soil solution. The ionic forms are of qualitative importance because they may be absorbed and utilized by plants. The amount present, however, usually constitutes less than 2 per cent of the total nitrogen, the balance being in organic forms. Nitrogen makes up about 5 to 6 per cent of the soil organic matter by weight.

The nature of the nitrogenous fraction of soil organic matter is still something of a puzzle. The organic nitrogen added to soils in the form of plant and animal residues is largely proteinaceous in nature. The microbial attack to which these materials are subjected in soils probably results in nearly complete disappearance of the original protein and its partial replacement by microbial protein, with the remaining nitrogen being changed to inorganic or elemental forms. To what extent the microbial protein remains as such or is transformed to still other forms is not known.

Proteins as such have not been isolated from soils. If more are present beyond the amount found in undecomposed residues and viable microbial tissue, they apparently are attached firmly to other substances in such a way that their extraction is prevented. One indication that proteins are present, however, is provided by the fact that many amino acids can be identified in the extracts obtained upon partial hydrolysis of the organic matter of soils. For the most part these amino acids are liberated by hydrolysis from combined form. Although soils apparently contain free amino acids (Bremner, 1952; Simonart and Peeters. 1954). these free acids are decomposed rapidly by microorganisms and, hence, probably do not occur in more than trace amounts. Bremner (1950) identified twenty different amino acids in the acid hydrolysate of each of ten soils. In work with six soils he found that about one-third of the organic nitrogen was liberated as α-amino nitrogen (Bremner, 1949). Work of other investigators has produced similar results. Since hydrolysis of proteins yields α-amino acids, this evidence indicates the existence of a third or more of the organic nitrogen in protein form.

In addition to amino acids, soil hydrolysates contain amino sugars. Bremner (1952) reported that from 6 to 14 per cent of the total nitrogen in samples of six soils was in the form of 2-amino sugars. Amino acids and amino sugars constitute the identified portion of the organic nitrogen in soil hydrolysates. Much of the organic nitrogen in these hydrolysates remains unidentified. The same is true of the organic nitrogen that is not changed to soluble form by hydrolysis, although Mattson and Koutler-Anderson (1943) obtained evidence suggesting that this residual organic nitrogen is present in the form of oxidized residues of lignin and ammonia.

The acid hydrolysis used to liberate the amino acids and amino sugars from soil organic matter causes considerable ammonium nitrogen to appear in soluble form. This nitrogen may result in part from decomposition of organic nitrogen-bearing compounds and in part from the inorganic portion of the soil. Rodrigues (1954) found that treatment of soil with a mixture of 50 per cent sulfuric acid and hydrofluoric acid caused the release of much ammonium nitrogen, even when the soil had been treated previously with hydrogen peroxide or a mixture of chromic and sulfuric acids. This observation suggests that much ammonium nitrogen may be present in relatively stable inorganic forms that are not determined by ordinary methods for ammonium.

STABILITY IN SOILS

Although a substantial proportion of the organic nitrogen in soils may be proteinaceous in nature, the behavior of soil nitrogen is by no means analogous to that of protein nitrogen. When proteins are added to soils, much of the nitrogen is changed to inorganic forms in a short time. Soil nitrogen, on the other hand, resists microbial attack and is changed to inorganic forms at the rate of only 1 or 2 per cent annually. Several different theories have been advanced to account for the relatively low rate of mineralization of soil nitrogen.

One possible mechanism of stabilization is a reaction between protein and lignin. Waksman and Iyer (1932) found that proteins and lignin may interact in such a way as to reduce the rate of nitrogen mineralization. Table 2 shows the results obtained with lignin and

Table 2. Mineralization of Carbon and Nitrogen during 30 Days' Incubation of Soil Treated with Lignin, Casein, or Lignin-Casein Complex

(Waksman and Iyer, 1932)

Treatment*	Carbon Mineralized, mg.	Nitrogen Mineralized, mg.
Soil alone	41	9
Soil + 6 g. lignin	73	6
Soil + 0.95 g. casein	399	110
Soil + 6 g. lignin-casein complex	112	11

* 200 g. of soil in each case; nitrogen added in casein = 137 mg.; nitrogen added in lignin-casein complex = 134 mg.

casein applied individually or together as a complex prepared by mixing alkaline solutions of the two substances and adding acid to bring about their coprecipitation. Only about one-tenth as much nitrogen was mineralized in the presence as in the absence of lignin, and most of this could be accounted for by the control. Other work showed that reduction in mineralization of casein nitrogen was much greater with the lignin-casein complex prepared by solution in alkali and precipitation in acid than it was in mechanical mixtures of lignin and casein. Since there is evidence for the occurrence of both lignin and protein in soils, the existence of a lignin-protein complex that aids in stabilization of the nitrogen is a definite possibility. The interaction of ammonia and lignin to produce resistant complexes (Mattson and Koutler-Anderssen, 1943) represents a means of stabilizing in organic form the ammonia resulting from mineralization of organic compounds. Although the mechanism of this reaction probably is different from that of the lignin-protein reaction, both are dependent on lignin. Still another possibility is the reaction between nitrous acid and lignin that results in binding some of the nitrogen in organic form (Bremner, 1952).

A second possible stabilization mechanism is interaction of nitrogenous substances and clays. Demolon and Barbier (1929) found that when a mixed suspension of ammonium "humate" and ammonium clay was treated with enough potassium chloride to flocculate the clay, some of the organic matter was carried down with the clay. The proportion of the organic matter carried down increased with decreasing pH of the medium. In the absence of clay the ammonium "humate" remained in suspension. Other observations lend supporting evidence. The addition of proteins to expanding-lattice type clays results in an increase in distance between lattice layers (Ensminger and

Gieseking, 1939; Pinck, Dyal, and Allison, 1954), a decrease in cation exchange capacity (Ensminger and Gieseking, 1941), and a decrease in the rate of decomposition (Pinck, Dyal, and Allison, 1954). Ensminger and Gieseking (1942) found that enzymatic hydrolysis of proteins is decreased to a greater extent in the presence of bentonite, having high cation-exchange capacity, than in the presence of kaolinite, having low exchange capacity. Allison, Sherman, and Pinck (1949) found that the rate of decomposition of plant residues is less in sand plus clay than in sand alone. The tendency,of the nitrogen content of soils to increase with the clay content probably is atributable in part to stabilization of the nitrogenous compounds by interaction with the clay.

Broadbent and Norman (1947) proposed an entirely different cause of stability. They suggested that the stability is "more apparent than real" and results largely from the absence of enough energy material to support a large microbial population. They found that the increase in carbon and nitrogen mineralized as a result of adding tracer-labeled organic materials to soil was derived in part from the soil organic matter itself. The greater enzyme activity associated with the larger microbial population in the organic-matter-treated soils presumably was responsible. Some of their results are shown in Table 3.

Table 3. Mineralization of Carbon and Nitrogen from Soil Organic Matter and Added Organic Matter Sources as Determined in Experiments with Isotopic Carbon and Nitrogen

(Broadbent and Norman, 1947)

	Carbon Mineralized in 11 Days per 100 g. of Soil			Nitrogen in Sudan Grass Grown on Soil		
Soil Treatment	From Soil Organic Matter, mg.	From Added Organic Matter, mg.	Total, mg.	From Soil Organic Matter, mg.	From Added Organic Matter, mg.	Total, mg.
None	49	. . .	49	5.6	. . .	5.6
Organic matter*	215	418	633	8.2	6.6	14.8

* Sudan grass in the carbon experiment and oat straw in the nitrogen experiment.

Each of the various theories described above is supported by experimental evidence. None has been disproved. As far as is known, therefore, the overall explanation for stability of soil organic nitrogen must take into account all three, and perhaps additional ones yet to be proposed.

A fourth stabilization mechanism involves plants. This mechanism is more properly one of regeneration than of stabilization, however, because it involves the formation of organic nitrogen from the mineral nitrogen in the soil. Evidently the mineral nitrogen is stabilized temporarily in the soil if it remains below the surface of the soil after reconversion from mineral to organic forms as a result of the presence of roots. If conditions should be such that the capacity of the crop to generate organic nitrogen in the soil exceeds the nitrogen mineralized in the soil, the application of fertilizer nitrogen may actually cause the soil organic nitrogen to increase. The appropriate combination of conditions is found frequently where perennial grasses are grown on soil low in nitrogen but with an ample supply of minerals and water. Soils under perennial grass vegetation characteristically contain only traces of mineral nitrogen. Probably the principal reason for this is that the fibrous root system permeates the soil throughout the year, and thus is in position to absorb the mineral nitrogen rapidly. Much of the nitrogen is carried over from one season to the next in living tissue. The nitrogen in the dead roots changes to the mineral form slowly because of the deficiency of mineral nitrogen in the soil for decomposition (the explanation for the slow decomposition will be elaborated in the next section). Perennial grasses thus may get enough nitrogen from the soil the first year or two after planting but have a tendency to become deficient in nitrogen, or "sod bound."

MINERALIZATION AND IMMOBILIZATION

The nitrogen utilized by nonleguminous plants is derived primarily from the mineral forms of nitrogen in soils and not from the organic forms that constitute the bulk of the soil nitrogen. In unfertilized soils the mineral forms of nitrogen arise almost entirely from decomposition of the organic nitrogenous compounds. The various steps in the process occur in the order, organic nitrogen → ammonium → nitrite → nitrate. In general the rate-controlling step is the conversion of organic nitrogen to ammonium rather than the conversion of ammonium to nitrite and thence to nitrate. In consequence, nitrate usually is the most abundant form of mineral nitrogen in soils, and is the principal form of mineral nitrogen utilized by plants.

The organic nitrogen → ammonium nitrogen transformation is an unspecialized process. That is to say, it is carried out by a wide variety of microorganisms. The change of nitrogen from ammonium to nitrate, on the other hand, apparently is brought about by only a few organisms. Certain organisms specialize in oxidation of ammonium to nitrate, and others specialize in oxidation of nitrite to nitrate. Free energy is released in both these reactions. The most important organisms that carry on these processes are autotrophs that have the capacity to synthesize organic compounds using carbon dioxide as the source of carbon. The necessary energy is derived from the oxidation of nitrogen.

The production of mineral nitrogen in soil is accompanied by the reverse process in which nitrate and other mineral forms of nitrogen are converted back into organic forms. This reverse process is unspecialized and is the consequence of nitrogen assimilation in the metabolism of the microorganisms present. Hence when the rate of mineral nitrogen production is calculated from the difference between the amounts of mineral nitrogen present in the soil at two different times, the figure obtained actually represents the net result of two opposing processes and not the total production of mineral nitrogen. Under some circumstances the rate of production of mineral nitrogen is exceeded by the rate of production of organic nitrogen.

The voluminous literature on this general subject was reviewed by Harmsen and Van Schreven (1955). Literature on the more restricted subject of production of nitrate from ammonium was reviewed by Meiklejohn (1953) and Delwiche (1956).

The present discussion will be undertaken from the point of view of the factors that control the rate of production of mineral nitrogen from organic nitrogen and the reverse, together with relationships to plant growth. First, however, brief mention of the significance of the terms used for describing the different processes is in order since in the earlier literature the use of some of these terms was not entirely consistent.

Terms

"Nitrogen mineralization" refers to the change of organic nitrogen to mineral form. As generally employed, unspecified biological mechanisms are implied. The exact definition depends on the method of measurement. The term "nitrification," widely used in the older literature, sometimes was used in the same sense as "mineralization" and occasionally had a more restricted meaning, namely, the transformation of ammonium to nitrate. When the restricted meaning was used, the transformation of organic nitrogen to ammonium form was denoted by the term "ammonification." The term "nitrate production" refers to the formation of nitrate in soil without reference to the source of the nitrogen. If ammonium and nitrite are present in relatively small amount, as is usually the case, the net increase of nitrate over a given length of time is essentially equal to the net increase of mineral nitrogen.

"Nitrogen immobilization" refers to the change of inorganic combined nitrogen to organic form. In the usual usage of the term, unspecified biological mechanisms are implied. Immobilization thus is the reverse of mineralization. The term "denitrification" sometimes was used in the older literature to denote any disappearance of nitrate that took place in the absence of leaching or absorption by crops. In this sense, immobilization is one kind of denitrification. At present, however, the term denitrification is used to represent only the reduction of nitrate or nitrite nitrogen that culminates in liberation of nitrogen in gaseous forms. In this sense, immobilization and denitrification are distinct processes. The term immobilization is distinct from nitrogen fixation. Although nitrogen fixation involves a change of nitrogen to organic form, the nitrogen involved is present initially in elemental form rather than mineral or inorganic combined form. Ammonium fixation is excluded from immobilization to the extent that it involves reaction with the inorganic part of the soil. Ammonium fixation by lignin may or may not be classified as immobilization, depending on the definition of the latter. If immobilization is restricted to conversion of mineral to organic nitrogen by microbial assimilation, ammonium fixation by lignin is not immobilization but is a separate process.

Total nitrogen

The total nitrogen content of soils provides a measure of the quantity of substrate undergoing decomposition. Experience has shown that when samples of different soils are allowed to incubate uniformly under conditions of temperature and water content favorable for microbiological activity, the net quantity of nitrogen mineralized usually is approximately proportional to the total quantity of nitrogen. The total quantity of nitrogen (or substrate) is not the sole controlling factor, however, as exemplified by the finding of Allison and Sterling (1949) that in different phase of an investigation of the association of these two variates, the coefficients of correlation ranged from 0.59 to 0.84. The principal reason for the failure of such correlation coefficients to approach unity apparently is that conditions in the different soils are not sufficiently similar. The analytical measurements can be carried out in a reasonably accurate and precise manner.

Substrate composition

With a constant quantity of nitrogen in different substrates, the rates of nitrogen mineralization and immobilization may vary because

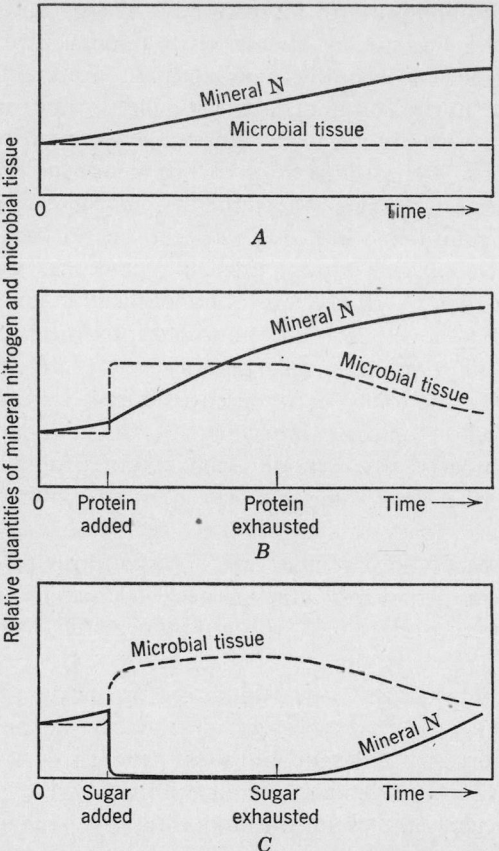

Fig. 3. Schematic representation of changes in content of mineral nitrogen and microbial tissue with time in fallow soil, with and without additions of protein and sugar. (A. No organic matter added; B. protein added; C. sugar added.)

of differences in the nature of the substrate. The schematic diagrams in Fig. 3 illustrate the effect of three types of substrates on the mineral nitrogen-organic nitrogen balance in soils. Section *A* of Fig. 3 shows the situation in fallow soils that remain in warm, moist condition without addition of organic material or loss of mineral nitrogen by leaching. The content of mineral nitrogen gradually increases, because the net quantity of nitrogen tied up in microbial tissue remains approximately the same while the organic compounds of the soil organic matter are undergoing gradual decomposition. Section *B* of Fig. 3 shows how the course of events is changed by the addition of proteinaceous material. The microbial population increases rapidly to a limiting value determined by the environment. The content of

mineral nitrogen continues to increase beyond the time when the protein is exhausted because of liberation of mineral nitrogen from the
soil and the shrinking microbial population. Eventually the mass of
microbial tissue in the soil approaches its initial value, and the content
of mineral nitrogen in the soil remains above that of case A. In
section C of Fig. 3, the addition of carbonaceous material provides an
unbalanced diet of another type, that is, one deficient in nitrogen.
The microbial population increases as before, but at the expense of the
mineral nitrogen initially present in the soil, together with the mineral
nitrogen subsequently produced. The content of mineral nitrogen
remains at a low level until the carbonaceous material is exhausted
and the microbial population decreases in size. If the length of time
is long enough, the content of mineral nitrogen will surpass that
present initially. Eventually the content of mineral nitrogen will
approach and surpass that in case A because of the secondary effects
of carbohydrate addition on soil nitrogen availability and nitrogen
fixation.

Changes of the type described above depend on the relative availability of carbonaceous and nitrogenous food material for the microorganisms. If the nitrogenous material is in excess, nitrogen is mineralized, and if the carbonaceous material is in excess, nitrogen is
immobilized. The relative availability of the two ordinarily is represented by the ratio of carbon to nitrogen in the original material.
The data of Jensen (1929) in Fig. 4 may be cited as an example of
the effects produced when organic materials differing in ratio of carbon to nitrogen are allowed to decompose in soil. In Jensen's experiment the organic materials were added to soil in containers. A

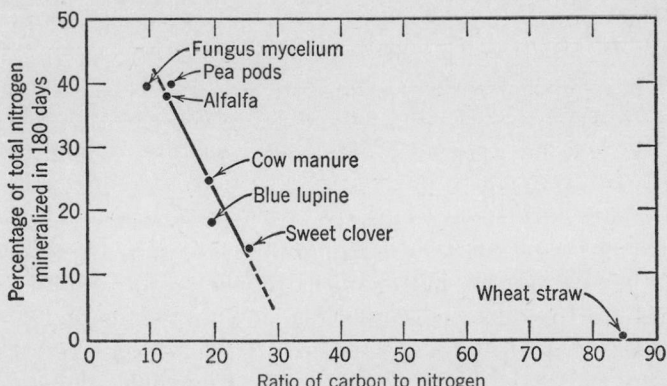

Fig. 4. Mineralization of nitrogen in organic materials differing in ratio of carbon
to nitrogen. (Jensen, 1929.)

6-month period of decomposition was allowed before the analysis for mineral nitrogen was performed.

In general, soil nitrogen is immobilized if the carbon to nitrogen ratio of the added material is in excess of about 33 to 1, or if the nitrogen content is below about 1.2 per cent. Added nitrogen is mineralized if the carbon to nitrogen ratio is below about 15 to 1, or if the nitrogen content is in excess of about 2.6 per cent. These values are approximations. The actual critical points depend on the length of time allowed before analysis of the soil and on the nature of the organic material undergoing decomposition. Carbon to nitrogen ratios or nitrogen percentages are not sufficient to predict precisely the behavior of individual materials.

The manner in which nitrogen mineralization is related to the character of the organic material undergoing decomposition is understood only slightly. Preliminary work of Peevy and Norman (1948) indicates that, with a given carbon to nitrogen ratio, nitrogen mineralization decreases with increasing content of lignin in the material.

Carbon to nitrogen ratios of organic matter in the plowed layer of soils of temperate regions are mostly in or near the range of 10 or 11 to 1. Ordinarily the ratio narrows as the depth in the soil profile increases and as the mean annual temperature increases. Carbon to nitrogen ratios of soils thus are in the range where nitrogen mineralization occurs in decomposing organic materials.

Although the ratio of carbon to nitrogen frequently is calculated for soil organic matter, the values obtained have been demonstrated in only a few instances to be of value for predicting nitrogen mineralization. Perhaps the main reason is that usually the ratio is not the critical factor. An important limitation in the use of carbon to nitrogen ratios of soil organic matter is the fact that nitrogen mineralization in soil can be changed markedly by additions of decomposable organic matter too small to influence the ratio appreciably. When the added organic matter constitutes a substantial part of the total, a relationship can be found. Richer and White (1946) found that nitrate production decreased with increasing carbon to nitrogen ratio of soil organic matter in a field experiment involving heavy organic matter additions. Nye (1951) reported that in Ghana, response to nitrogen fertilization was greatest in soils having high ratios of carbon to nitrogen (13 to 17). The soils having the high ratios were low in organic matter (0.39 to 0.91 per cent organic carbon) and had been in bush for a long period of time. The organic matter apparently contained much carbonaceous material. Perhaps the same is true in the situation described by Hardy (1945) for certain soils of Queensland. "Bolting" of cotton, which may result from an excessive supply of mineral nitrogen, was found to be associated with low carbon to nitrogen ratios (4 to 6) in the soil organic matter. The soils that produced good cotton had higher carbon to nitrogen ratios and had been under cultivation only 1 to 4 years.

Soil reaction

Differences in soil reaction frequently are cited as a cause of the failure of nitrogen mineralization to be strictly proportional to the content of total nitrogen. Allison and Sterling (1949) and others have noted that nitrogen mineralization usually increases when acid soils are limed. Presumably, therefore, in an assembly of unlimed soils of constant total nitrogen content and variable pH, the quantity of nitrogen mineralized should increase with pH. Thompson, Black, and Zoellner (1954) made a test of this type by statistical methods on a group of fifty samples of unlimed soils, but found no significant change in nitrogen mineralization with pH at constant total nitrogen content. In their results, therefore, pH was not an important factor. They suggested that the absence of a pH effect in their results might be accounted for on the basis that the effect of liming usually found in laboratory studies is only temporary.

Water supply

Nitrogen mineralization is limited by both wet and dry soil conditions, although at high temperatures it apparently occurs at a substantial rate even in air-dry soils (Drouineau, Lefèvre, and Blanc-Aicard, 1953). It proceeds most rapidly in moist soils where the water content is suitable for plant growth. Table 4 shows the relative produc-

Table 4. Production of Ammonium and Nitrate Nitrogen in Soils Incubated at Different Percentages of the Water-holding Capacity

(Greaves and Carter, 1920)

Percentage of Water-holding Capacity	Relative Quantities of Mineral N Produced during Incubation	
	Ammonium	Nitrate
10	2	11
20	9	17
30	32	31
40	67	62
50	81	86
60	100	100
70	78	40
80	56	10
90	48	...
100	44	...

tion of ammonium and nitrate nitrogen at different percentages of the
water-holding capacity of samples of twenty-one soils that were incubated with dried blood. Since the production of ammonium is a
prerequisite to the formation of nitrate, the results for nitrate are not
necessarily independent of those for ammonium. It may be noted,
nevertheless, that the rapid decrease in nitrate production with the
increase in water supply above the optimum is characteristic of the
ammonium → nitrate transformation. This process is aerobic. Production of ammonium nitrogen, however, takes place under both
aerobic and anaerobic conditions.

Soil dryness often limits the yield of crops relatively more than the
yield of nitrogen in the crops. It may be inferred that in such cases
the rate of mineralization is less limiting in relatively dry than in moist
soils. This behavior is illustrated by the data for oats in Table 5.

Table 5.   Yield and Nitrogen Content of Grain of Oats and Wheat
Grown with and without Irrigation*

(Greaves and Carter, 1924)

	Oats			Wheat		
	Unirri-gated (A)	Irri-gated (B)	A/B	Unirri-gated (A)	Irri-gated (B)	A/B
Yield of dry matter per acre, lb.	1460	2580	0.57	2250	2240	1.00
Nitrogen in dry matter per acre, lb.	40.2	55.2	0.73	53.8	45.0	1.20
Nitrogen percentage in dry matter	2.75	2.14		2.39	2.01	

* The results with oats and wheat were obtained in separate experiments and are
not directly comparable.

The nitrate content of plants occasionally is so high under conditions
of drought and high soil nitrate as to poison livestock. In extreme
cases as much as 20 per cent of the dry weight of forage has been
reported to be potassium nitrate, the crystals of which may be observed in the dried tissue (Gilbert, Eppson, Bradley, and Beath, 1946).

In some instances soil dryness limits the yield of nitrogen in crops
relatively more than the yield of dry matter; that is, dryness induces
nitrogen deficiency. The appropriate conditions are found when the
subsoil supplies water but little nitrogen, and the surface soil supplies
nitrogen but little water. The decrease of dry matter production attributable to water deficiency is relatively less than the limitation of
nitrogen uptake brought about by the curtailment of root activity in
the surface soil where most of the mineral nitrogen is located. Onset

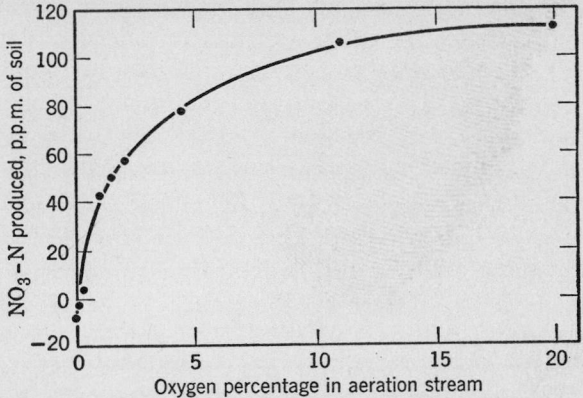

Fig. 5. Production of nitrate nitrogen in Carrington silt loam incubated with added ammonium sulfate and aerated continuously with air-nitrogen mixtures differing in oxygen percentage. (Amer.[1])

of drought thus may cause the plant to exhibit symptoms of nitrogen deficiency instead of water deficiency. This behavior has been used as an argument for deep placement of nitrogen fertilizers in parts of the humid region affected by summer droughts.

Nitrogen deficiency often develops in crops grown in soils that receive much water. The data for wheat in Table 5 indicate that irrigation decreased nitrogen availability; this is evidenced by the decrease in nitrogen content without a corresponding decrease in yield. Restricted nitrogen mineralization, however, is only one of several causes of low nitrogen availability under such conditions. The combined effects of limited root development and loss of mineral nitrogen by leaching and denitrification probably are more important.

Aeration

Although some production of ammonium from organic nitrogen occurs under anaerobic conditions, production of nitrate in soil requires the presence of free oxygen, as was indicated by the data in Table 4 in the preceding section. More direct evidence is provided by the work of Amer[1] in Fig. 5. This figure shows the production of nitrate in soil that was treated with ammonium sulfate and aerated with different mixtures of nitrogen and air. The aeration stream was passed directly through the soil. Indications from these data are that the optimum oxygen concentration is approximately that found in the

[1] Amer, Fathi Mohamed. (1949) Influence of oxygen percentage and moisture tension on nitrification in soils. M. S. Thesis, Iowa State College, Ames, Iowa.

atmosphere, but that oxygen deficiency has little effect until the concentration in the aeration stream is below 10 per cent. Meyerhof (1916) found that *Nitrosomonas* (a bacterium that oxidizes ammonium to nitrite) exhibits similar sensitivity to oxygen supply in vigorously aerated liquid culture.

In the experiments of Amer and Meyerhof, ammonium was added in ample quantity so that the supply of ammonium was not critical. Under natural conditions in soils, however, the rate of nitrate production appears usually to be controlled by the rate of ammonium production. In practice, therefore, the effect of aeration on nitrate production usually reflects the effect of aeration on the organic nitrogen → ammonium nitrogen transformation and not on the ammonium → nitrate transformation. The former transformation is less sensitive to poor aeration than the latter.

A number of instances have been reported in which the nitrate content of soil in field experiments was lower in compact soil than in loose soil. Work of Albrecht (1937) in Missouri may be cited as an example. Current indications are that the relatively low nitrate content in compacted soils is the consequence of a low rate of ammonium production, that the low rate of ammonium production is the consequence of a low oxygen concentration at the surface of the soil particles, and that the low oxygen concentration, in turn, results from the thick water films in the more compact soils. Analyses of soil air usually show little difference in oxygen content between treatments, as was pointed out earlier in the chapter on aeration.

Temperature

Nitrogen mineralization is limited at low soil temperatures because of the restricted biological activity. Work of Russel, Jones, and Bahrt (1925) and others shows that when soils are incubated at different temperatures, nitrate production increases with temperature up to about 35° C., and then decreases with further increase in temperature. Here again, however, the requirements of specific organisms are involved. Thompson[2] found maximum production of ammonium nitrogen from soil organic matter at 60° to 70° C. The true optimum may have been higher, since possible loss of ammonia by volatilization was not prevented.

The rate of nitrogen utilization by plants also varies with temperature. Plants will absorb nitrate at low temperatures. Both translocation and assimilation are limited under these conditions, however, so

[2] Thompson, Louis M. (1950) The mineralization of organic phosphorus, nitrogen and carbon in virgin and cultivated soils. Ph.D. Thesis, Iowa State College, Ames, Iowa.

that the rate of utilization is low.   As temperature increases, utilization increases, reaches a maximum at some temperature characteristic of the plant, and then decreases.   Since the rates of nitrogen mineralization in soils and nitrogen utilization by plants are different functions of temperature, the sufficiency of soil nitrogen for plant development may vary with temperature.   Many different results may be obtained, depending on the absolute and relative rates of nitrogen mineralization and utilization with particular soil-plant combinations, and the change therein with temperature.

From experiments conducted over a period of several years in England, Blackman (1936) concluded that temperature was the factor that limited the growth of pasture herbage when the soil temperature was below 42° F. at the 4-inch depth.   Added nitrogen was absorbed, but no growth occurred below this temperature.   At temperatures of 42° to 47° F., the herbage grew, but the rate was limited by the supply of soil nitrogen; evidence for this is the fact that herbage production was much increased by the application of nitrogen fertilizer.   Above 47° F. the rate of increase in herbage production with soil temperature was accelerated.   Blackman interpreted this behavior as a result of increased soil nitrogen mineralization.   He thought that above a soil temperature of 47° F., the supply of soil nitrogen no longer controlled growth.   Whether or not this was true cannot be determined from the data given; however, it is clear that the supply of soil nitrogen was deficient from 42° to 47° F., and that the greatest increase in earliness from nitrogen fertilization was obtained when the soil temperature rose slowly through this range.   Blackman's work was mainly on pastures having perennial rye grass as the dominant species.

Quite a different result was obtained in unpublished work of Roger McHenry, J. W. Fitts, L. T. Alexander, and H. F. Rhoades on nitrogen fertilization of blue grama grass pasture in western Nebraska. Nitrogen topdressing in early spring produced a rank growth of wild lettuce but had little effect on the grass.   In this case, the growth of wild lettuce apparently was controlled mainly by nitrogen supply, whereas the growth of grass was controlled mainly by temperature. Blue grama is a "warm-season" grass that makes little early spring growth.   The perennial rye grass in Blackman's work is a "cool-season" grass.

Drying and freezing

Mineralization of nitrogen usually takes place more rapidly in soil that is incubated in a moist condition after air-drying than in soil that has been maintained continuously in a moist condition.   This behavior

Table 6.   Nitrate-Nitrogen Produced during 8 Weeks' Incubation of Soil
Samples, with and without Previous Drying
(Landrau, 1953)

| | Nitrate-nitrogen Produced during Incubation* | |
Date of Sampling	Soil Maintained Continuously Moist, p.p.m.	Soil Air-dried Previous to Incubation, p.p.m.
May 29	23	31
July 3	22	29
July 28	17	29
August 17	15	24
October 29	13	25

* Average of eight field treatments.

is illustrated in Table 6, which represents the nitrate-nitrogen produced during laboratory incubation of samples taken at different dates during a given season from a silty clay loam soil in Nebraska.

Originally the effect of drying on nitrogen mineralization was attributed to a "partial sterilization" whereby certain types of organisms that inhibited the activity of others were destroyed. If this were true it would be expected that (a) the organisms remaining after drying would be more efficient than an equal number before drying, (b) the number of organisms would be decreased by drying and would remain at a relatively low level for several weeks, (c) the effect of drying would disappear if the dried soil were reinoculated with organisms from the moist soil before incubation, and (d) the effect of drying would disappear if, before drying, the soil were partially sterilized using some other method. Khalil (1929) examined each of these consequences of the partial sterilization hypothesis, and obtained negative results in each case. The partial sterilization hypothesis thus was shown to be incorrect. Khalil's opinion was that drying increases the susceptibility of some of the soil organic matter to decomposition.

Evidence in favor of Khalil's view was obtained by Achromeiko (1928). Achromeiko measured the quantity of water-soluble organic matter in terms of milligrams of oxygen from permanganate required to oxidize the organic matter in a liter of a 1 to 2 soil to water extract. He found that the oxygen equivalent was increased from 46 to 241 mg. when a soil was dried three times by exposure to the sun. During a subsequent 7-month incubation in a moist condition, the oxygen equivalent dropped to 27 mg. and 36 mg. in the continuously moist and air-dried samples, respectively.

Freezing the soil has an effect similar to that of drying. Lyon and Bizzell (1913) kept samples of two soils in unfrozen condition in a greenhouse and kept duplicate samples in an unheated building from

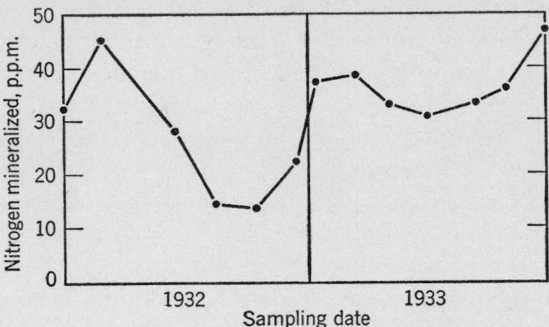

Fig. 6. Nitrogen mineralized in soil samples taken at different dates and incubated in the laboratory under standard conditions. (Richardson, 1938.)

December 28 to February 28. The samples in the unheated building were frozen most of the time but thawed occasionally. On February 28 the frozen samples were brought into the greenhouse. Analyses made on March 4 showed that the nitrate-nitrogen content was 16 and 25 p.p.m. in the unfrozen samples, and 21 and 35 p.p.m. in the respective previously frozen samples. Presumably the susceptibility of part of the nitrogen to mineralization was increased by freezing. When the soil temperature became favorable for mineralization, the nitrogen thus affected was mineralized more rapidly than the originally corresponding nitrogen in the unfrozen soil.

The effect of freezing probably contributed to the cyclic fluctuation of mineralizable soil nitrogen (Fig. 6) recorded by Richardson in England in work on soil samples taken from the field at intervals covering a period of 2 years. Similar evidence covering a shorter period of time was obtained in Nebraska by Landrau (1953), who found that the mineralizable nitrogen in samples taken from field plots gradually decreased from spring to fall (Table 6). The fact that the nitrate production in Landrau's previously dried samples exceeded that in the continuously moist samples by a smaller margin at the beginning of the season than at the end suggests that the effects of freezing and drying are not additive and that the susceptibility of at least one source of nitrogen to mineralization is increased by both processes.

Plant growth

Mineral nitrogen is produced in soils as a byproduct of microbial metabolism. Higher plants are not known to bring about mineralization of soil nitrogen. Instead they are presumed to depend on the nitrogen mineralized microbiologically. Accumulated evidence nevertheless indicates that nitrogen mineralization and plant growth are not entirely independent processes. Goring and Clark (1949), for example, maintained samples of soil in fallow condition in the greenhouse and grew various crops in comparable samples of the same soil. At intervals they analyzed the fallow and cropped soils for mineral nitrogen and analyzed the tops and roots of plants in the cropped soil for their content of nitrogen. They represented the sum of the nitrogen in the plants and in mineral form in the soil as the total nitrogen mineralized. A summary of their results in Fig. 7 shows that after about 6 weeks, more nitrogen was mineralized in the fallow soil than in the cropped soil. At the end of 13 weeks about twice as much nitrogen had been mineralized in the fallow soil. The presence of the crops thus decreased the nitrogen mineralization.

Statistical analysis of the data on the various crops showed that nitrogen mineralization was correlated negatively with total root weight and with bacterial numbers contributed by the crop roots. Since the increase in number of microorganisms around the roots undoubtedly resulted from the liberation of organic materials by the roots, it appears that at least part of the depression of nitrogen mineralization by plants may be described more properly as plant-induced immobilization. This mechanism accounts qualitatively for the various kinds of evidence indicated above. Quantitative verification is provided by the fact that during 16 weeks of incubation in the

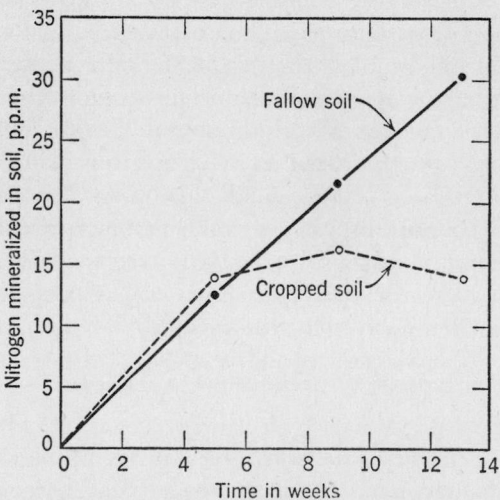

Fig. 7. Mineralization of nitrogen in cropped and fallow soil over different lengths of time. (Goring and Clark, 1949.)

laboratory after completion of the experiment described in Fig. 7, nitrogen mineralization in previously cropped soil exceeded the mineralization in previously fallowed soil. The increase in mineralization after the majority of crops was approximately equal to the apparent decrease in mineralization observed while the crops were growing (Clark, 1949).

A different type of relationship between plant growth and nitrogen mineralization is presumed to occur in mycorrhizae, which are found widely in the plant kingdom (Kelley, 1950). The word "mycorrhiza" means "fungus root," and refers to the symbiotic association of certain fungi with roots of plants.

Evidence for the connection of mycorrhizae and the nitrogen nutrition of plants is of two types. The first type is illustrated in Table 7,

Table 7. Yield and Nitrogen Content of Coniferous Tree Seedlings Grown on an Infertile Soil with and without Inoculation with Mycorrhizal Fungi
(Finn, 1942)

	Control* (A)	Inoculated (B)	B/A
Yield of dry matter per plant, mg.	155	223	1.44
Yield of nitrogen per plant, mg.	1.17	2.05	1.75

* Some inoculation occurred in control plants.

which records the effect of inoculation with mycorrhizal fungi on the yield and nitrogen content of coniferous tree seedlings grown on an infertile soil. The greater relative increase in nitrogen content than in yield of dry matter with inoculation indicates that the increase in nitrogen content resulted at least in part from a specific effect of the mycorrhizae on nitrogen availability. The second type of evidence is that some of the nitrogen absorbed by the fungus from sources external to the plant is transferred to the plant; this process was demonstrated by tracer nitrogen (Melin and Nilsson, 1952). Presumably the fungus mineralizes some of the organic nitrogen in the soil, absorbs the mineral nitrogen thus produced, and transfers some of it to the plant root. In turn, the root is a source of carbohydrates and, perhaps, of other growth factors for the fungus.

ESTIMATION OF NITROGEN AVAILABILITY

The mineral forms of nitrogen in soils constitute the bulk of the nitrogen present in available form at a given moment. In general, however, the content of mineral nitrogen does not provide a good estimate of the availability of soil nitrogen to crops. The reason is that the mineral nitrogen present at a given moment usually represents a small and variable proportion of the total amount of mineral nitrogen that will be at the disposal of a crop throughout a season. To considerable extent, the variability occurs because the content of mineral nitrogen in soils is influenced strongly by the recent history of the soil. This situation is recognized generally. In consequence, measurements of mineral nitrogen seldom are made for the purpose of estimating the availability of soil nitrogen to agronomic crops. Such measurements are more common with greenhouse crops where fertilizer nitrogen is added frequently and serves as the main source of nitrogen for the plants.

Three different types of measurements have been used in an attempt to improve on the nitrogen availability estimates provided by the content of mineral nitrogen present in the soil at a given moment. The first is measurement of the content of total nitrogen or organic matter; the second is measurement of the quantity of nitrogen changed to the mineral form as a result of some chemical treatment; the third is measurement of the quantity of nitrogen mineralized in a fixed length of time during incubation under uniform conditions in the laboratory. With all three types of measurements the figures obtained are assumed to be proportional to the nitrogen availability. (The proportionality factor varies with the circumstances and, hence, must be found by trial for the particular combination of conditions for which the estimates are to be made.)

Munson and Stanford (1955) investigated the comparative value of these different types of measurements in an experiment in which the yield of nitrogen was measured in a test crop grown on samples of twenty-one soils in the greenhouse. Their results are summarized in Table 8. The correlation coefficients in this table were calculated

Table 8. Correlation between Yield of Nitrogen in a Test Crop Grown on Samples of 21 Soils and Different Measurements Made on the Soils in the Laboratory

(Munson and Stanford, 1955)

Soil Measurement Correlated with Yield of Nitrogen	Correlation Coefficient
Total N in soil	0.84
Initial NO_3—N in soil	0.95
Initial NO_3—N in soil + NH_4—N distilled from soil with alkaline permanganate according to unpublished method of Truog et al.	0.95
Initial NO_3—N in soil + NO_3—N produced during 2-week incubation in the laboratory	0.97

in part from original data not shown in the published paper. The correlation coefficients show that the best estimate of the yield of nitrogen was provided by the sum of initial nitrate and nitrate produced during a 2-week incubation in the laboratory; the poorest estimate was provided by total nitrogen. The correlation between yield of nitrogen and nitrate-nitrogen initially present in the soil in this experiment probably is higher than would be found in many instances, because no loss of mineral nitrogen by leaching was permitted, and because the initial nitrate content of the soils was relatively high (12 to 71 p.p.m.). The initial nitrate content is partly responsible also for the relatively small differences among the last three correlation coefficients in Table 8 since the initial nitrate averaged 39 per cent of the sum of the initial nitrate and the nitrate produced during incubation and 92 per cent of the sum of the initial nitrate nitrogen and the ammonium nitrogen distilled from the soil by the alkaline permanganate method.

AMMONIUM FIXATION

Nitrate does not react with soil constituents to produce insoluble combinations, but this is not true of ammonium. Certain soils react with added ammonium and change it to nonexchangeable forms. Chaminade and Drouineau (1936) found that when they ground soil in a ball mill, the content of exchangeable ammonium increased greatly. The increase was greater in soil that had received ammonium-bearing fertilizer over a period of 7 years than in corresponding unfertilized soil. These observations indicate that much nonexchangeable ammonium was present in the soil that was investigated and that the content of nonexchangeable ammonium had been increased by ammonium fertilization. Laboratory experiments have shown that in extreme cases, over 500 p.p.m. of ammonium-nitrogen may be fixed in nonexchangeable form on addition of an ammonium salt to a moist soil (Allison, Kefauver, and Roller, 1953).

The property of ammonium fixation is exhibited more strongly by subsoils than by surface soils. It seems to be associated with clay minerals, such as illite and vermiculite, that are capable of fixing potassium in nonexchangeable form. In fact, Stanford and Pierre (1947) found that ammonium and potassium were fixed almost interchangeably. When the two ions were added consecutively, fixation of the one that was added second decreased with the increase in quantity of the other that had been fixed previously. The total amount of the two ions fixed was essentially constant when results were expressed on the basis of chemical equivalents.

In addition to reaction with the mineral portion of the soil, ammonium may react with lignin via the mechanism of Mattson and

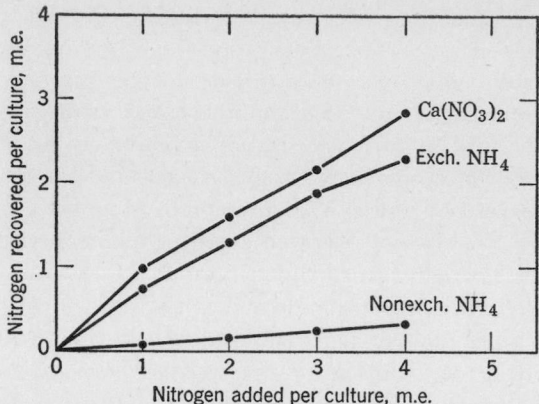

Fig. 8. Recovery by barley plants of nitrogen added in different forms to soil. (Bower, 1951.)

Koutler-Anderssen (1943). Such a mechanism has not been demonstrated to occur in soil. Perhaps the lignin that will react in this way has reacted previously with ammonium.

Fixation of ammonium in nonexchangeable form greatly reduces its susceptibility to nitrification and its availability to plants. Figure 8 shows the results obtained in an experiment with barley as the test crop. The availability of the nonexchangeable ammonium relative to that of exchangeable ammonium in this particular soil may be estimated at 0.13, which is the approximate ratio of the slopes of the respective lines in the figure.

NITROGEN BALANCE

Most of the organic nitrogen in soils probably remains in the same state of combination over a long period of years. Nitrogen in this form nevertheless constitutes a reservoir for continual removals and additions in the nitrogen cycle. Over each annual cycle, some nitrogen is mineralized, and some is immobilized. Some is removed by plants, and some is returned in the form of plant residues. Some is lost to the atmosphere, and some is returned. Some may be lost by leaching, and some added by fertilization. Some may be lost by erosion or added by deposition.

In a given environment, the amount of nitrogen present in available form at any particular time tends to increase with the supply of nitrogen in the reservoir. It is therefore of concern whether the total nitrogen content is low or high and whether current management practices in a particular instance are causing a decrease or an increase.

Losses

Crop removal. The loss of nitrogen by crop removal from the harvested crop land of the United States was estimated by Lipman and Conybeare (1936) to be 25 lb. per acre for the year 1930. The figure of 25 lb. refers to the nitrogen content of the portion of the crop that is harvested and not to the total. The total probably was about 35 to 40 lb. Taking Lipman and Conybeare's estimate of 2840 lb. per acre as the average nitrogen content of the plowed layer of soil on which these crops were grown, a removal of 40 lb. is seen to be equal to 1.4 per cent of the total nitrogen in the plowed layer.

Leaching. Usually most of the mineral nitrogen lost by leaching is in the nitrate form. Collison and Mensching (1930) found that more than 99 per cent of the nitrogen in the leachate from lysimeters in New York was present as nitrate. Less than 1 per cent was present as ammonium, and only a trace was present as nitrite. The relatively low losses of ammonium and nitrite nitrogen may be attributed to the low initial concentration and, in the case of ammonium, to retention by the soil.

Nitrogen present in nitrate form is soluble in the soil water and does not form insoluble compounds with soil constituents; hence it is transported readily by water movement in the soil. When soil water rises and is lost by evaporation, the nitrate tends to concentrate at the surface of the soil, as illustrated in Fig. 9. Conversely, when a rain causes downward movement of soil water, nitrate moves deeper in

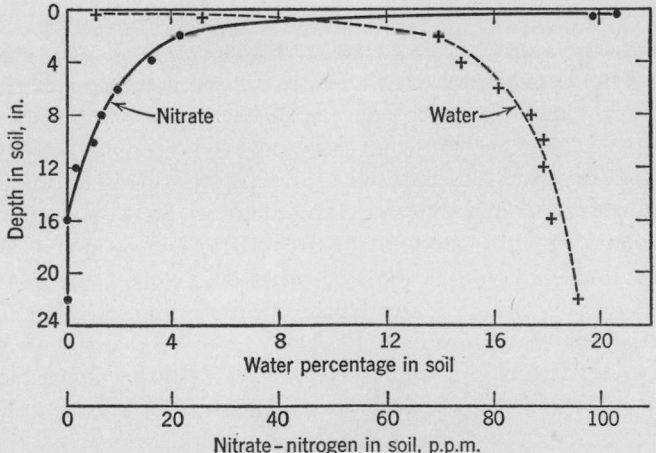

Fig. 9. Vertical distribution of nitrate-nitrogen and water in soil after a period without rainfall. (Scarseth, Cook, Krantz, and Ohlrogge, 1943.)

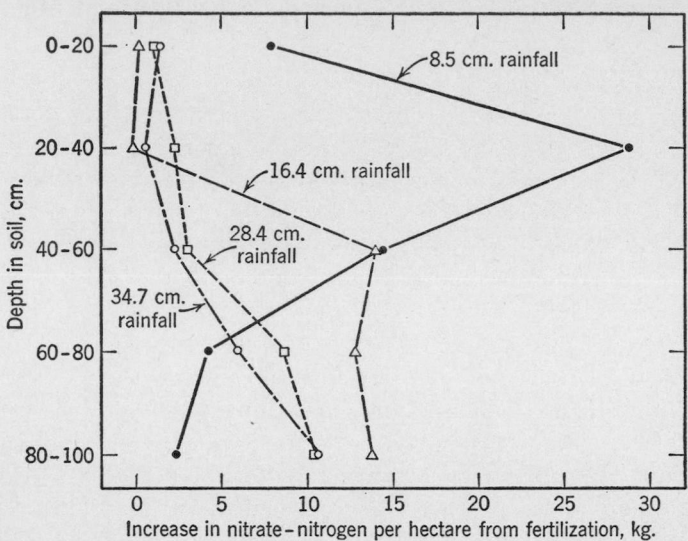

Fig. 10. Increase in content of nitrate-nitrogen at different depths in a fallow sandy loam soil as a result of fertilization with calcium nitrate at a rate equivalent to 60 kg. of nitrogen per hectare. (The measurements recorded for cumulative totals of 8.5, 16.4, 28.4, and 34.7 cm. of rainfall after fertilization were obtained 34, 66, 107, and 153 days after fertilization, respectively. The total recovery of added nitrogen at the respective times of measurement amounted to 58, 41, 25, and 21 kg. per hectare.) (Soubies, Gadet, and Maury, 1952.)

the soil, and may be carried beneath the root zone. This behavior is illustrated in Fig. 10.

Nitrate is lost more rapidly from coarse than from fine-textured soils because of greater water loss. In addition, it is removed more readily. The percentage of the total nitrate leached per inch of leachate is greater in coarse than in fine-textured soils (Morgan and Street, 1939). The lower water-holding capacity of coarse-textured soils no doubt is related to this behavior.

Loss of nitrate by leaching increases with nitrate concentration and loss of water. Loss usually is greater from fallow soil than from cropped soil because of the absence of a crop to absorb nitrate and water. In New York, Lyon, Bizzell, Wilson, and Leland (1930) recorded an average annual loss of 22 inches of water by percolation from fallow lysimeters and 16 inches from cropped lysimeters. Corresponding losses of nitrogen in pounds per acre annually were 68 and 5. The actual time at which the loss occurs depends on the water regime in the soil and the soil depth employed. In some situations the actual loss may not take place until the year after the nitrate is produced. Such a case was reported by Collison and Mensching (1930).

Loss of nitrate by leaching is an important factor in crop production in humid regions. In northern Europe, for example, it is recognized that yields of winter wheat decrease with increasing rainfall the preceding autumn. This relationship was the subject of statistical investigations by Shaw (1906) in England and Lehr and Veen (1952) in the Netherlands. The cause of the relationship presumably is that the loss of nitrate by leaching increases with the rainfall, so that less nitrate remains for absorption by the crop.

Leaching evidently may modify the potency of nitrogenous fertilizers applied at different times. When the soil is dry, the time of application of nitrogenous fertilizer before planting has little effect on the results. Under wetter conditions, however, much of the value of nitrogenous fertilizer applied in the fall may be dissipated by spring. Figure 10 shows the losses of fertilizer nitrogen recorded in a series of experimental measurements made in France. Under otherwise equal conditions, loss of fall-applied nitrogen by leaching is reduced by employing ammonium rather than nitrate, by placing the ammonium fertilizer in bands instead of applying it broadcast, and by absence of warm weather after application. These conditions minimize the increase in nitrate content of the soil.

Winter cover crops offer an effective means of reducing loss of nitrogen by leaching and erosion during the fall, winter, and early spring in areas where the soil is not frozen during the winter. As indicated by the data of Jones (1939) in Table 9, however, the benefit

Table 9. Nitrogen Lost by Leaching, and Nitrogen Absorbed by a Summer Crop of Sudan Grass from Different Soils with and without Winter Cover Crops in Alabama
(Jones, 1939)

Cover Crop during Winter	Nitrogen Lost by Leaching per Acre		Nitrogen in Sudan Grass per Acre	
	Norfolk Sandy Loam, lb.	Decatur Clay Loam, lb.	Norfolk Sandy Loam, lb.	Decatur Clay Loam, lb.
None	46	6	8	37
Oats	11	0	11	19
Vetch	37	3	66	73

to the following crop from the presence of a nonlegume during the winter may be considerably smaller than the benefit anticipated from the nitrogen saved. No doubt the reason for this is that much of the nitrogen is retained in organic form in residues of the cover crop.

With a leguminous cover crop, the benefit may exceed the saving because of the nitrogen fixed.

Change to gaseous forms. Numerous experiments have demonstrated the existence of a negative nitrogen balance in soils (Allison, 1955). That is to say, the sum of the nitrogen removed from the soil by cropping, leaching, and erosion, and the nitrogen residual in the soil, is less than the sum of the nitrogen added and the nitrogen present initially in the soil. For example, Table 10 shows the nitrogen

Table 10. Nitrogen Balance in a Soil Culture Experiment with Different Additions of Nitrogen Fertilizer

(Pinck, Allison, and Gaddy, 1948)

Nitrogen Added as Urea per Acre, lb.	Total Yield of Dry Matter per Culture in 5 Crops, g.	Nitrogen Gain or Loss per Acre, lb.
0	33	+ 50
200	91	+ 4
400	133	− 19
800	181	− 31
1200	180	−153

balance in a soil culture experiment in which different additions of nitrogen fertilizer were made. The balance was positive under conditions of marked nitrogen deficiency (indicating some fixation) but negative when the supply was adequate. The nitrogen that cannot be accounted for in experiments of this sort is presumed to be lost in gaseous forms.

Three different mechanisms have been proposed to account for the loss. The first of these is denitrification. Denitrification is a type of nitrate reduction in which the nitrogenous products are gases. The principal products are elemental nitrogen (N_2) and nitrous oxide (N_2O); nitric oxide (NO) is of relatively minor importance. Denitrification is a microbiological process that takes place when a deficiency of free oxygen is accompanied by a supply of nitrate or nitrite and a source of decomposable organic matter. The process occurs because nitrate or nitrite can be substituted for oxygen as a hydrogen acceptor in oxidation reactions carried out by certain organisms. Transformation of nitrate to forms such as ammonium or nitrite that remain in the soil may be termed nitrate reduction but not denitrification.

Nitrous oxide occurs in the atmosphere to the extent of about 0.00005 per cent (Slobod and Krogh, 1950). Adel (1951) presumed that atmospheric nitrous oxide arises from denitrification in soils. He visualized the existence of a cycle, in which elemental atmospheric nitrogen is fixed in combined form in soils, and nitrous oxide is released from soils to the atmosphere. The nitrous oxide accumulates in the atmosphere until the rate of photochemical decomposition to nitrogen and oxygen is equal to the rate of accumulation.

Denitrification undoubtedly occurs in rice culture where conditions favorable to reduction alternate with those permitting oxidation. Loss of nitrogen from nitrate by denitrification probably is one reason why nitrate is inferior to ammonium as a nitrogen source in fertilizers applied to rice.

Some difference of opinion still exists regarding the extent to which denitrification occurs in soils that are thought to be well aerated. Indications are that some denitrification occurs under these conditions. Such loss of nitrogen might result from denitrification under anaerobic conditions present temporarily or in local areas or from denitrification under aerobic conditions. With respect to the former possibility, it is known that at temperatures favorable for plant growth, soils may become anaerobic within a period of 10 hours after they have become saturated with water. Hence even a "well-aerated" soil may be anaerobic for a short time after a heavy rain. Moreover, nitrate present in an aerobic surface soil may be leached downward to an anaerobic subsoil where denitrification occurs. Denitrification may occur also in anaerobic islands within a matrix of aerobic soil. An example demonstrating the existence of such islands was noted by M. B. Russell (1952). Although evidence for denitrification under aerobic conditions is provided by Meiklejohn's (1940) demonstration that certain organisms cause denitrification in aerated solution cultures, Delwiche (1956) pointed out that the observed "aerobic" denitrification could have occurred within cell clumps where the oxygen level was low. His question is in order, in view of the fact that obligate anaerobes sometimes can be grown on "aerobic" substrates if vigorously growing aerobic bacteria are present simultaneously; this question is a particularly difficult one on which to obtain evidence. Delwiche's (1956) view is that truly aerobic denitrification does not occur. Oxygen is the preferred hydrogen acceptor, and nitrate can compete as a hydrogen acceptor only when free oxygen is present in minimal concentration.

A second means of gaseous loss of nitrogen is the interaction of nitrous acid and amines or ammonium. This reaction likewise yields elemental nitrogen, of which half comes from each source. For example,

$$C_2H_5NH_2 + HNO_2 = C_2H_5OH + H_2O + N_2$$

In the presence of glacial acetic acid and an atmosphere of nitric oxide this reaction goes to completion and is the basis for a quantitative measurement of amino nitrogen. Certain other nitrogenous compounds undergo a similar reaction with nitrous acid. Lignin also reacts with nitrite to release gaseous nitrogen (Bremner, 1952). Wilson (1943) reviewed the literature on this subject and emphasized particularly the possibility of loss from plants. He found that water droplets that were exuded from the leaves of plants commonly contained nitrite in concentrations up to 2 p.p.m. When they contained ammonia also, both nitrite and ammonia disappeared concurrently on collection and standing in the laboratory, supposedly as a result of interaction to produce gaseous nitrogen. Corbet and Wooldridge (1940) found a significant loss of nitrogen from ammonium nitrite in neutral soil under nonsterile conditions but not under sterile conditions. This observation indicates that the loss of nitrogen was caused by microorganisms and was not the result of an inorganic chemical reaction between nitrite and ammonium. Experiments in which soil was incubated with alfalfa meal and tagged nitrate (Wijler and Delwiche, 1954) showed that the abundance of N^{15} in the N_2 produced by denitrification was virtually identical with that in the nitrate. If the reaction of nitrite with ammonium or amino forms of nitrogen had been the source of the N_2, the N^{15} content would have been half or less than half that of the tagged nitrate. Moreover in addition to N_2, a loss of N_2O and NO was observed in this experiment (all the gases had virtually the same abundance of N^{15} as the nitrate). Therefore, in this instance, at least, there is no evidence for a significant loss of nitrogen from soil by the reaction of nitrite with ammonium or amino forms of nitrogen.

Volatilization of ammonia represents a third mechanism of gaseous loss of nitrogen from soils. The ammonia may be that formed in the process of organic nitrogen mineralization or the ammonia added in fertilizers. Such losses have been thought to be the cause of the lesser efficiency of ammonium than of nitrate sources of fertilizer nitrogen observed with certain alkaline soils. Under laboratory conditions at room temperature, volatilization of as much as 87 per cent of the ammonia added as ammonium sulfate has been reported (Jewitt, 1942). In general, however, losses have been much less. The properties of soils are such that considerable ammonia can be held. Application of even anhydrous ammonia as fertilizer results in little loss if the application is made several inches below the soil surface with good covering. Conditions favoring rapid volatilization are the presence of the ammonia in the surface layer of soil, soil pH values above 7, high temperature, and rapid loss of water by evaporation. Literature on ammonia volatilization was reviewed by Harmsen and Van Schreven (1955).

The significance to plants of gaseous losses of nitrogen from soils is mostly a matter of conjecture. Although the quantities normally involved in soils may be large enough to be of importance to plants, the measurement of such losses under natural conditions has not been feasible experimentally except in instances where relatively large amounts of nitrogen were involved (as with anhydrous ammonia).

Erosion. Precise information on erosion losses is lacking except for small experimental areas that do not represent an unbiased sample of the landscape as a whole. On the basis of available data, however, Lipman and Conybeare (1936) estimated the annual loss of nitrogen by erosion from the crop land of the United States to be 4,994,636 tons. This figure corresponds to an estimated removal of 4,611,210 tons of nitrogen in harvested crops. The ratio, thus, is about 1 to 1.

In estimating the loss of nitrogen by erosion, Lipman and Conybeare assumed that the material lost has the same composition as the soil. This supposition is only approximately correct. Erosion is a selective process. Although the degree of selectivity varies, the percentage content of nitrogen and other nutrients in solids lost by erosion generally exceeds the corresponding percentage content in the soil from which they were eroded. Massey and Jackson (1952) found that in 177 measurements of erosion made at different locations and different times in Wisconsin, the percentage content of nitrogen in the eroded solids averaged 2.7 times greater than the percentage content of nitrogen in the original soil. The estimates of erosion losses made by Lipman and Conybeare thus appear to be a considerable underestimate of the true losses.

Erosion losses of nitrogen are more serious than those of other nutrients because nitrogen is concentrated in the upper part of the soil profile (Fig. 2) to a greater extent than are other nutrients. Thus as the surface portion of the soil is removed by erosion, losses of nitrogen are not compensated appreciably by nitrogen brought into the root zone from beneath.

Gains

If there were no natural processes by which the content of combined nitrogen in soils could be increased at the expense of elemental nitrogen, crop production on unfertilized soils eventually would cease for lack of available nitrogen. The fact that long-continued removal of nitrogen from unfertilized soils does not exhaust, but merely reduces, the nitrogen content of the soil to a low and stable level indicates that processes of combined nitrogen addition are in operation.

Soils may gain combined nitrogen by four generally recognized processes. These are nonsymbiotic fixation, symbiotic fixation, addition in rainfall, and fertilization. Nonsymbiotic fixation is the process by which certain free-living organisms change elemental nitrogen into organic combination. Symbiotic fixation is the process by which elemental nitrogen is changed to organic forms by the symbiosis or association between certain plants and the bacteria found in nodules on their roots. In addition to these processes, some fixation of nitrogen at the soil surface may occur by photochemical action.

Nonsymbiotic fixation. Burris (1953) classified the nonsymbiotic nitrogen-fixing organisms as follows:

Plants
  Nostoc, Calothrix (blue-green algae)
Bacteria
  Aerobic
    Azotobacter
  Anaerobic
    Nonphotosynthetic
      Clostridium (heterotrophic)
      Desulfovibrio (autotrophic)
    Photosynthetic
      Rhodospirillum (purple nonsulfur bacteria)
      Chromatium (purple sulfur bacteria)
      Chlorobacterium (green sulfur bacteria)

Shields (1953) summarized the literature regarding claims that nitrogen is fixed by many other organisms.

Attention of research workers has been centered on the bacteria, *Clostridium* and *Azotobacter*. *Clostridium* was isolated by Winogradsky (1893). He found that it is capable of fixing nitrogen under only anaerobic conditions in pure culture, but that it can act under aerobic conditions as well if certain other bacteria are present. Ammonium salts inhibit fixation. *Clostridium* has been found in considerable numbers in soils distributed widely over the world. The reaction most favorable for the development of the organism is near neutrality, although it can be found in soils as acid as pH 5.

Azotobacter was isolated by Beijerinck (1901). *Azotobacter* fixes nitrogen under aerobic conditions in pure culture and under semi-anaerobic conditions when in symbiosis with certain other bacteria. Nitrogen fixation is not an essential process, since *Azotobacter* uses combined nitrogen if offered in available form. As little as 5 p.p.m. of ammonium or nitrate nitrogen inhibit fixation. *Azotobacter* is distributed widely but is more sensitive to soil conditions than *Clostridium*. It is sensitive to phosphorus deficiency, and the common types are of limited occurrence in soils having pH values below 6. Certain species are more tolerant, however. A species of *Azotobacter* described by Starkey (1939) developed and fixed nitrogen in cultures as acid as pH 3.1.

Substantial amounts of nitrogen may be fixed nonsymbiotically in soils when the supply of mineral nitrogen is deficient and the supply of decomposable carbohydrate is ample. An outstanding instance was described by Koch et al. (1907) and Koch (1909). An instance of a small amount of nonsymbiotic fixation is shown in Table 10.

Nonsymbiotic nitrogen fixation no doubt occurs under field conditions, but experimental verification that it does is inconclusive. The addition of nitrogen by nonsymbiotic fixation under field conditions has been variously estimated at 0 to 50 pounds per acre annually (Jensen, 1940). The more recent estimates, however, are closer to 0 than to 50 pounds. Because of the inhibitory effect of mineral nitrogen, it appears that nonsymbiotic nitrogen fixation is not normally of much importance in cultivated soils except where soil nitrogen has fallen to levels of marked deficiency. Where soils are returned to grass or native vegetation, however, nonsymbiotic fixation may make an important contribution in the accumulation of soil nitrogen since mineral nitrogen usually is maintained at a low level under such conditions.

Circumstantial evidence that *Azotobacter* fixes nitrogen in the soil when nitrogen is naturally present therein is provided by the fact that the critical pH for the natural occurrence of *Azotobacter* in field soils is the same as the critical pH value for the fixation of atmospheric nitrogen in synthetic media in the laboratory. In the laboratory, *Azotobacter* can be grown at pH values below 6 in media well supplied with available nitrogen and free of competition with other soil organisms.

There has been considerable interest in the possibility of inoculating seeds of nonlegumes with *Azotobacter* to increase crop yields. In the U.S.S.R., large acreages of crops have been inoculated by an *Azotobacter* preparation. Allison (1947) reviewed the experimental evidence on such inoculation. He concluded that if the practice was beneficial, the effects probably were not the result of nitrogen fixation. Usually *Azotobacter* is present naturally if conditions are favorable for its occurrence.

Nonsymbiotic fixation is thought to be of special significance in soils that are flooded for rice production. Some rice fields have been under cultivation for centuries and still have a moderate supply of nitrogen. Fixation by photochemical means, by algae, and by bacteria have been proposed as possibilities. Species of *Azotobacter* have been isolated from wet tropical soils, and a new genus of nitrogen-fixing bacteria (*Beyerinckia*) has been found to be distributed widely in soils and waters of the humid tropics. Literature on this subject was reviewed by Harmsen and Van Schreven (1955).

Symbiotic fixation. Discovery of the cause of the anomalous behavior of legumes with respect to nitrogen nutrition was the objective of a number of unsuccessful researches in the nineteenth century. Hellriegel and Wilfarth (1891) finally connected this behavior with the root nodules present on leguminous plants. They demonstrated that the growth of nonlegumes depends upon the quantity of mineral nitrogen supplied, but that this is not necessarily true of legumes (Table 11). They found that when a medium free of combined ni-

Table 11. Yield of Oats and Peas, and Nitrogen Balance in Quartz Sand Variously Inoculated or Fertilized with Nitrogen
(Hellriegel and Wilfarth, 1891)

Nitrogen Added as Nitrate, mg.	Inoculation	Dry Weight of Plants		Nitrogen in Plants Gained (+) or Lost (−)*	
		Oats, g.	Peas, g.	Oats, mg.	Peas, mg.
0	Not inoculated	0.6	0.8	−20	− 25
0	Inoculated but sterilized	...	0.9	...	− 23
0	Inoculated	0.7	16.4	−19	+386
112	Not inoculated	12.0	12.9	−49	+ 38
112	Inoculated	11.6	15.3	−47	+107

* Relative to nitrogen added in seed, medium, and nitrate.

trogen was inoculated with soil and when nodules formed on the roots, leguminous plants grew well and gained considerable nitrogen. On the other hand, when the soil inoculum was added, but subsequently was sterilized, the leguminous plants did not have nodules. These plants made poor growth and did not gain nitrogen. Hellriegel and Wilfarth hypothesized from these experiments that the bacteria in the root nodules assimilate elemental nitrogen from the air and that the plants then use some of the nitrogenous compounds fixed by the bacteria. Schloesing and Laurent (1892) found that the gain in nitrogen by the plants is balanced by a corresponding loss of nitrogen from the atmosphere, thus verifying Hellriegel and Wilfarth's hypothesis about the source of the nitrogen. More recently, verification has been obtained of the long-accepted view that the root nodules are the site of the fixation process. Magee and Burris (1954) found that nodules will fix nitrogen for a short time after being cut from the plant. Beijerinck (1888) isolated the root-nodule organism, which he called *Bacillus radicicola*. Later the genus name was changed to *Rhizobium*.

Most of the leguminous plants that have been examined are known to bear root nodules. A few apparently do not form such nodules. A few nonlegumes have nodules resembling those of legumes and fix nitrogen symbiotically (Shields, 1953). The cultivated annual legumes usually have relatively large nodules grouped about the tap root or the first laterals. The nodules of biennial and perennial species are smaller and are distributed more widely over the root system; new nodules form throughout the growing season.

The number of nodules per plant may vary from few up to hundreds or even thousands. The number of nodules, however, is not a reliable index of nitrogen fixation. The nature of the organisms present in the nodules is of greater importance. Several species of *Rhizobium* are recognized. Within each species are individual strains that may differ considerably in action. No one species or strain is effective in nodulating all legumes and producing nitrogen fixation. A given culture of organisms may be highly effective in both respects on one legume and yet fail to produce nodules on another. On a third legume, the same culture may produce many nodules without bringing about much nitrogen fixation.

Fred, Baldwin, and McCoy (1932) and others have arranged various legume species into groups, in each of which the members are effectively nodulated by a single organism. The more recent trend in research is away from this type of classification. Specificities between certain species or varieties of *Rhizobium* and certain species of leguminous plants exist, but these are not so well defined as they were once thought to be (Allen and Baldwin, 1954). In developing a satisfactory inoculum for a given legume, the best practice is to increase a culture obtained from an effectively inoculated plant of the same species. The culture must be tested before use, since the efficiency of the organisms may differ among nodules on the same plant.

The reasons for regularly inoculating legume seed before planting are two. First, although rhizobia may live in the soil for many years in the absence of the host legume, they are not necessarily present in sufficient numbers. Second, although the legume may be inoculated by soil rhizobia in the absence of added inoculum, the soil strain may be inefficient. Inoculating the seed serves as insurance against both these eventualities.

When the symbiosis is running smoothly, minerals and carbohydrates needed by the microorganisms are supplied by the plant. Nitrogen needed by the plant is supplied in combined form by the microorganisms. Considerable importance has been attached to the balance between the supplies of carbohydrate and nitrogen, since it has some bearing on the results obtained. For example, invasion of the host plant by rhizobia takes place in response to a high carbohydrate to nitrogen ratio in the plant (Wilson and Fred, 1939). If, however, the inoculation is delayed until definite nitrogen deficiency has set in, development of the nodules may be limited by the nitrogen supply. This relationship accounts for the observation that application of small quantities of nitrogenous fertilizer sometimes results in improved legume stands. Extension of the same idea indicates that maintenance of a low carbohydrate to nitrogen ratio during growth by means of a high level of soil nitrogen will result in limited fixation because the carbohydrate supply to the nodules is low. Decreasing nitrogen fixation with increasing nitrogen fertilization has been observed experimentally by many investigators. Table 12 represents an

Table 12.   Net Gain of Nitrogen in Presence of Legumes with Different Applications of Fertilizer Nitrogen

(Chapman and Liebig, 1947)

Nitrogen Added per Acre Annually, lb.	Net Gain of Nitrogen per Acre Annually	
	Purple Vetch, lb.	*Melilotus indica*, lb.
0	106	118
100	103	50
200	68	37

example. Although the observations are in accord with the carbohydrate-deficiency hypothesis, such experiments do not provide a particularly critical experimental test of the hypothesis because the results can be explained in other ways. One of these is competitive inhibition. Existence of such inhibition is well known; its cause appears to be (*a*) that nitrate absorbed from the soil is reduced by the plant to ammonium, (*b*) that ammonium is the end-product of the nitrogen fixation process, and (*c*) that the plant assimilates ammonium from the two sources in proportion to the quantities present. No choice between these two hypotheses can be made with respect to Table 12.

The carbohydrate-nitrogen balance is connected further with the response of legumes to nitrogen fertilization. Umbreit and Fred (1936) pointed out that nitrogen fertilization might be expected to increase the yields of inoculated legumes under conditions of a high carbohydrate to nitrogen ratio.

Another practical problem associated with the carbohydrate to nitrogen ratio is the benefit derived by nonlegumes from association with legumes. Table 13 shows the results of an experiment in which

Table 13. Yield and Nitrogen Content of Peas and Oats Grown in Association, and the Excretion of Fixed Nitrogen in Sand Culture
(Virtanen, von Hausen, and Laine, 1937)

	Dry Weight, g.		Nitrogen Content, mg.			Fixed Nitrogen Excreted, %
	Peas	Oats	Peas	Oats	Sand	
Peas not inoculated	0.6	0.4	12	3	9	...
Peas inoculated	2.9	1.4	45	16	26	48

oats grown with peas contained more nitrogen where the peas were inoculated than where they were not. The sand in which the two plants were grown likewise contained more nitrogen where the peas were inoculated. Apparently nitrogen fixed by the peas was excreted in part into the sand culture from which it was removed by the oats.

The behavior shown in Table 13 is not observed regularly. According to the hypothesis of Wilson and Wyss (1937), excretion of fixed nitrogen is most likely when photosynthesis is rapid enough to insure a fairly high rate of nitrogen fixation but is not rapid enough to cause utilization of all the fixed nitrogen. A relatively high concentration of fixed nitrogen then accumulates in the nodules, and part of it is excreted into the surrounding soil as aspartic acid (an amino acid). Excretion does not occur with a high rate of photosynthesis because the plant then utilizes all the fixed nitrogen. Excretion does not occur with a low rate of photosynthesis because fixation is too limited. Wilson and Wyss thought that excretion probably is common in regions with cool, cloudy weather but not in regions with sunny weather and little rainfall.

The importance of the transfer of nitrogen from a legume to an associated nonlegume crop under field conditions has been shrouded with uncertainty. If a nonlegume contains more nitrogen per acre when it is associated with a legume than when it is grown alone, as in an instance reported by Johnstone-Wallace (1937), there is little doubt that a transfer has occurred. If, on the other hand, the nonlegume contains less nitrogen per acre when it is associated with the legume than when it is grown alone, as frequently is the case, it is possible that a transfer has occurred, but the evidence is not clear. A way to estimate the transfer of nitrogen despite such complications has been worked out by T. W. Walker et al. (1954). Their procedure will be discussed in the last section of this chapter. At the moment, note will be made only of their conclusion that in several field experiments with grass-legume mixtures, the portion of the yield of nitrogen in the above-ground parts of the grass that could be attributed to transfer was equal to approximately two-thirds the yield of nitrogen in the above-ground parts of the legume.

Giöbel (1926) made a summary of nitrogen fixation data reported in the literature and found a range from 50 to 288 lb. per acre annually. Two different methods have been used to determine the total amount of nitrogen fixed by legumes under field conditions: analysis of the crop with and without inoculation and "balance-sheet" measurements involving soil analysis. The former method is unsatisfactory for use with many soils because rhizobia already present in the soil will cause some inoculation. Another limitation of this method is the questionable validity of the implied assumption that the inoculated and noninoculated plants have absorbed equal amounts of soil nitrogen. In the latter method the precision is limited by the relatively large quantity of nitrogen usually present initially. Moreover, the data obtained represent only net changes. Possible gains from nonsymbiotic fixation and losses from formation of gaseous products are included as part of the changes attributed to the legumes. Because of these experimental difficulties, it is probable that there are no accurate data on fixation in the field. There is no doubt, however, that legumes fix nitrogen in quantities great enough to affect the nitrogen supply of succeeding crops.

Rainfall. Small amounts of nitrogen are brought down each year in the rainfall. Lightning discharges unite nitrogen and oxygen to form oxides of nitrogen. The latter may decompose or unite with water and reach the soil in rain or snow. In addition, a small amount of nitrogen is added in ammoniacal and organic forms present in the atmosphere in dust and gaseous contaminations. The amounts brought down vary with seasonal conditions and proximity to factories and cities. The many available data were reviewed by Eriksson (1952). He found that the range reported was from 1 to 69 lb. per acre annually, and that most values were below 10 pounds.

Seasonal fluctuations

In most instances the seasonal changes in content of organic and total nitrogen are within the experimental errors of measurement because the differences are small in relation to the amount present initially. The amount of mineral nitrogen, however, is relatively small and may show pronounced seasonal fluctuations. Such fluctuations are in part the result of increases or decreases in the total content of

nitrogen (that is, changes in nitrogen balance) and in part only transformations of nitrogen from one form to another in the soil.

Published data usually have shown that the content of mineral nitrogen in soils is lower in winter than in summer (Batham and Nigam,
1930). Winter temperatures limit the biological activity that results
in nitrogen mineralization. The greater leaching that often occurs in
winter months removes previously accumulated nitrate and keeps the
supply low. In the absence of a crop, the rate of accumulation of
mineral nitrogen usually is greatest in the early part of the summer,
and the accumulated content usually is greatest in the latter part.

Many types of departures from the foregoing generalizations may
occur in individual instances because of different combinations of conditions. If the winter were dry and the spring moist, for example,
the mineral nitrogen accumulated in the soil during the summer would
remain through the winter until removal by spring rains. In the presence of a crop, the seasonal pattern of mineral nitrogen content may
be modified further. With a spring-planted crop the maximum content of mineral nitrogen in the soil often occurs early in the summer
because the rate of removal exceeds that of accumulation when the
crop is making rapid growth. With a perennial crop like grass or a
fall-planted crop like winter wheat, seasonal fluctuations may be less
marked, with a lower maximum content of mineral nitrogen. In
some cases the seasonal trend is opposite to that indicated above, that
is, the mineral nitrogen content is higher in winter than in summer.
Albrecht (1937) reported the results of an extensive investigation of
the seasonal pattern of nitrate content of soil under different crops and
with different management conditions.

Slow changes

If environmental conditions and soil treatments remain approximately the same over a long period of years, there is opportunity for
the nitrogen cycle to approach a steady state wherein annual rates of
gain and loss are equal and the total nitrogen content is constant. On
the other hand, when the conditions are modified, as by changing the
management practices, the balance is disturbed. After the change,
the rate of loss exceeds the rate of gain, or vice versa, as a new equilibrium is approached. Figure 11 represents an example of an excess of
losses over gains when virgin soils were brought into cultivation. Figure 12 represents an example of an excess of gains over losses when a
previously cultivated soil was allowed to remain in grass vegetation.
From the figures it is evident that many years are required to change
from one equilibrium level to another.

Dawson (1950) expressed the foregoing generalities in mathematical terms by the differential equation

$$\frac{dN}{dt} = -aN + bN + k_1$$

where N is the organic nitrogen in the soil, t is the time in years, a is the fraction of the organic nitrogen that changes to mineral form each year, b is the annual addition of organic nitrogen by resynthesis from the mineral nitrogen liberated by decomposition expressed as a fraction of the total organic nitrogen, and k_1 is the organic nitrogen produced annually from the fixed nitrogen added from all sources.

Since b must be equal to or less than a, because of possible drainage and volatilization losses, the quantity $(b - a) \lessgtr 0$. The quantity $(b - a)$ represents the fraction of the organic nitrogen present at the beginning of the year that is lost and not resynthesized during the year. If this quantity is set equal to k the foregoing equation may be written:

$$\frac{dN}{dt} = -kN + k_1$$

The integral of this equation between the limits of time zero and time t is

$$N_t = \frac{k_1}{k} - \left[\frac{k_1}{k} - N_0\right] e^{-kt}$$

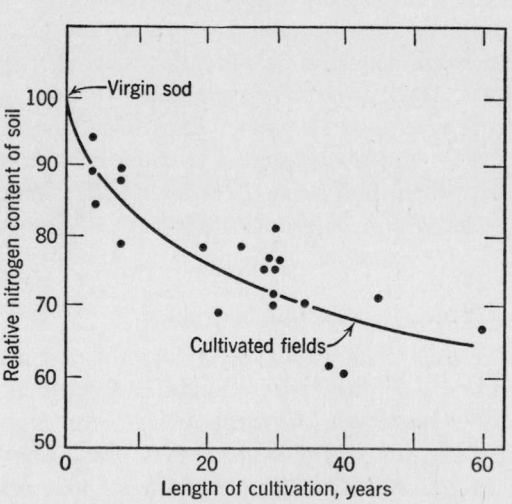

Fig. 11.   Relative nitrogen content of soil versus length of cultivation in the midwestern United States.   (Jenny, 1933.)

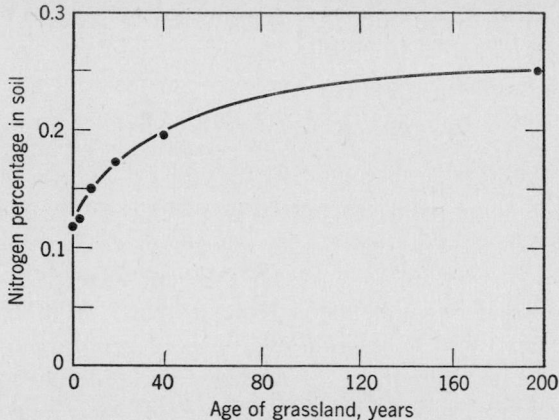

Fig. 12. Nitrogen percentage in soil under grassland vegetation maintained for different lengths of time. (Richardson, 1938.)

where N_t and N_0 represent the nitrogen content of the soil at times t and zero, respectively, and where e is the base of natural logarithms. The second term on the right-hand side of this equation approaches zero as the time approaches infinity. Thus the equilibrium value of N_t is given by the ratio k_1/k, which may be represented by N_∞ :

$$N_t = N_\infty - [N_\infty - N_0]e^{-kt}$$

The resulting equation contains two parameters, N_∞ and k. As an example of the use of the equation, Dawson found that over a period of 9 years the relative nitrogen content of a soil cropped continuously to alfalfa increased from an initial value of 100 to a value of 106. The latter value represents N_t. In this instance the equation predicted that N_∞ was 111. With a cropping system of rye, oats and peas, wheat and vetch, corn, and wheat, the observed value of N_t after 9 years was 92 relative to a value of 100 for N_0. The predicted value of N_∞ was 59.

FUNCTION IN PLANTS

Nitrogenous compounds make up a significant part of the total weight of plants. In a plant that contains 1.6 per cent nitrogen, for example, about 10 per cent of the plant weight is contributed by nitrogenous compounds. Nitrogen occurs in both inorganic and organic forms in plants. The inorganic forms of combined nitrogen make up only a small proportion of the total. Nitrate is the principal form in which plants absorb nitrogen from the soil, and it is the only inorganic form that can and does accumulate in quantity in the plant without injurious effects. Nitrate is assimilated by reduction to ammonium, followed by incorporation into organic forms. Ammonium and nitrite usually are found only in small quantities, if at all.

With respect to both numbers of compounds and the amount of nitrogen involved, the organic forms predominate. Most of the organic nitrogen of plants is found in proteins. Proteins are high-molecular-weight compounds made up of amino acids that are linked together through the amino ($-NH_2$) group. Some 22 amino acids have been found as components of plant proteins. With the exception of water, proteins are the main constituents of protoplasm. From the standpoint of the functioning of nitrogen, protoplasmic proteins are important because, acting together, they synthesize not only themselves but also the other organic nitrogenous compounds of plants.

The proteins of cells of the vegetative parts of plants are thought to be primarily functional in nature. Many of them are enzymes; others are nucleoproteins, some of which are present in chromosomes. Nitrogen is present in both the protein and nucleic acid portions of nucleoproteins. Proteins thus serve both as catalysts and directors of metabolism. Functional proteins are not stable substances; rather, they exist in a continuous state of flux, being both broken down and reformed again. The amino acid links used for repair may be newly formed or they may have come from hydrolysis of some other protein, like a reserve protein. Much of the protein in seeds, for example, may be classified as reserve protein, because during germination it is hydrolyzed and not reformed and, hence, appears to serve only as a source of amino acids for the development of other proteins in the seedling.

In addition to its function in proteins, nitrogen plays a part in other processes. Nitrogen is a component of the chlorophyll pigments which give plants their green color. Since chlorophyll is necessary for the process of photosynthesis, nitrogen may be said to play an essential part in photosynthesis. Nitrogen is found in some of the vitamins that serve as functional groups in enzymes. It is a component of the respiration-energy carrier, adenosine triphosphate, which will be discussed in the next chapter.

Further reading on this subject will be found in the book by Bonner (1950).

NITROGEN SUPPLY AND PLANT BEHAVIOR

Deficiency symptoms

Under conditions of nitrogen deficiency the leaves are small, the stems are thin and upright, and lateral shoots are few; hence the growth has a sparse appearance. The leaves usually have a pale, yellowish-green color in the early stages of growth and may develop yellow, red, or purple colors as they grow older. Symptoms are most pronounced on older leaves.

Specific symptoms may differ somewhat from one kind of plant to another. In corn the leaf tip becomes yellow, and the yellowing follows the midrib toward the base of the leaf. The edges of the leaf remain green for a longer period of time. With potato, on the other hand, the color of the margins of the lower leaflets fades to a yellow. In the case of tomato and apple, the yellowish-green of the nitrogen-deficient foliage is associated with the production of purple anthocyanin pigments. Acute nitrogen deficiency in peach trees results in leaf colors varying from a yellowish green at the tip of long current-season twigs to a reddish yellow with numerous red and brown spots at the base of the twigs. The leaf symptoms on nitrogen-deficient citrus trees vary with the point of time in the season during which they appear. If a nitrogen shortage occurs when growth begins, the young leaves are a light, yellowish-green color, and the color of the veins is slightly lighter than that of the tissue between. If a nitrogen shortage occurs during the summer and fall while the fruit of the tree is maturing, the leaves develop a mottled green and yellow pattern. Under conditions of severe deficiency, the leaves ultimately become yellow and are shed.

The books by Kitchen (1948), Hambidge (1941), and Wallace (1951) should be consulted for further information. Reproductions of color photographs of nitrogen-deficient plants appear in the last two of these books.

Carbohydrate utilization

Kraus and Kraybill (1918), and subsequently many others, have noted that plant behavior may be modified considerably by the nitrogen supply through the controlling influence of nitrogen on carbohydrate utilization. When the supply of nitrogen is curtailed to the point where carbohydrate utilization does not keep pace with photosynthesis, the carbohydrates accumulate. On the other hand, with an abundant supply of nitrogen, the tendency is for carbohydrate to be utilized to produce nitrogenous compounds.

The nitrogen-carbohydrate balance has many indirect effects on plant behavior, some of which are described in subsequent sections. It is of direct importance in the culture of sugar-producing crops. Gardner and Robertson (1942) and others have found that the sucrose percentage in sugar beets decreases with the increasing content of nitrate in the beets. Usually the maximum yield of sugar is reached at a lower nitrogen level than is the maximum yield of the plant as a whole. This behavior is illustrated in Table 14 by the results of an

Table 14. Yield and Sugar Content of Sugar Beets Fertilized with Different Applications of Nitrogen as Ammonium Nitrate

(Walker, Hac, Ulrich, and Hills, 1950)

Nitrogen Applied per Acre, lb.	Yield of Beets per Acre, ton	Sucrose in Beets, %	Yield of Sucrose per Acre, ton
0	20	18	3.6
80	24	17	4.1
160	26	16	4.2
240	27	15	4.0

experiment on nitrogen fertilization of sugar beets conducted in California. The depressing effect of nitrogen on the sugar percentage may not be found with low rates of application (Haddock, 1952) because of early depletion of added nitrogen from the soil and growth response to the extra nitrogen absorbed.

Succulence

An abundance of available nitrogen promotes vegetative growth. When all factors including nitrogen are favorable to rapid growth, the tendency is for utilization of carbohydrate to form more protoplasm rather than for deposition of carbohydrate to thicken the cell walls. Cells produced under such conditions tend to be large and to have thin walls. Since protoplasm is largely water, the high-nitrogen plant contains a relatively high proportion of water and a low

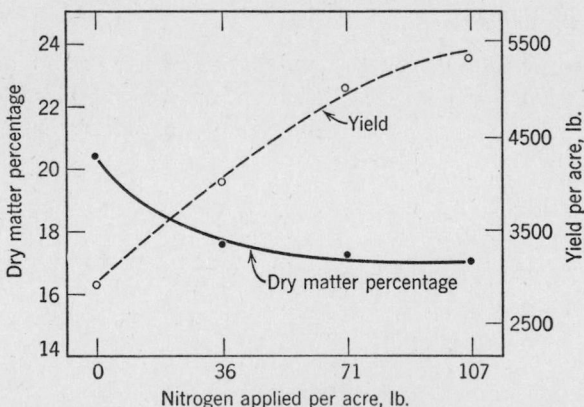

Fig. 13. Dry matter percentage and yield of sudan grass with different applications of nitrogen. (Siebert, 1939.)

proportion of dry matter and is said to be succulent. Figure 13 shows the effect of nitrogen supply on yield and dry matter content of sudan grass.

The characteristic succulence of high-nitrogen plants is of special significance in the production of fiber crops. With hemp, for example, the fiber cells are larger and have thinner walls when the plant is grown with high nitrogen than with low nitrogen (Scheel, 1936). Such hemp fiber is of low mechanical strength. Table 15 shows the

Table 15.   Yield and Fiber Content of Hemp Grown with Different Applications of Nitrogen Fertilizer

(Unpublished data, Iowa Agricultural Experiment Station, 1944)

Nitrogen Applied per Acre, lb.	Yield of Green Plants per Acre, ton	Yield of Fiber as Percentage of Green Weight, %	Yield of Fiber per Acre, lb.		
			Line	Tow	Total
0	10.3	4.0	694	135	829
50	13.1	3.8	742	260	1002
100	14.4	3.6	614	426	1040

behavior of hemp fertilized with different levels of nitrogen. The fiber percentage decreased with increasing nitrogen supply; hence the fiber yield did not keep pace with the total yield. The main effect of the nitrogen supply on the fiber was to increase the yield of the fraction classified as tow. Since tow is the short, commercially undesirable fiber, fiber quality evidently deteriorated with the increase in nitrogen supply in this experiment. Similar observations have been made for other crops. Gulati and Ahmad (1947) reported that strength of the cotton fiber decreased with increasing nitrogen supply. Nitrogenous fertilization of plants grown for fiber requires, therefore, a consideration of the response of the plant in terms of both fiber yield and fiber quality if the best results are to be obtained.

Root growth

Within the range of practical interest, an increase in the supply of nitrogen causes the growth of the above-ground portion of plants to increase relatively more than the growth of the roots. Figure 14 shows the results of an experiment with oats. One reason that can be given for the behavior exhibited in this figure is that with the increasing supply of nitrogen, the proportion of the carbohydrate used in the aerial portion increases, and the proportion translocated to the roots decreases. A second reason is that the production of auxin in the plant increases with the nitrogen supply (Avery et al., 1936), presumably because the principal plant auxin, β-indoleacetic acid, contains nitrogen and apparently is formed by alteration of tryptophane, an

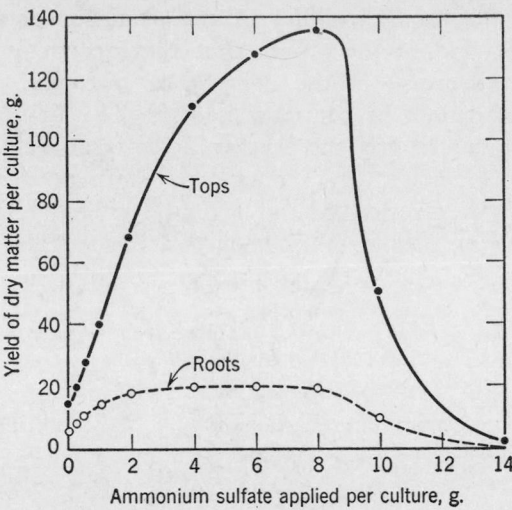

Fig. 14. Yield of oat tops and roots in sand cultures with different applications of ammonium sulfate.   (Meyer and Storck, 1927.)

amino acid found in plants.   The concentration of tryptophane probably increases with the nitrogen supply.   In both the tops and roots of plants, the processes of cell division and elongation are promoted by low concentrations of auxin and inhibited by high concentrations. Hence for both tops and roots there is a critical concentration of auxin, below which growth increases and above which it decreases with increasing auxin concentration.   The critical concentration of auxin is much lower with roots than with tops, so that between these two critical values, an increase in concentration of auxin tends to inhibit root growth and to promote top growth.   Variations in nitrogen supply apparently cause changes in the auxin concentration within the range between the two critical concentrations.   Work of Bosemark (1954) supports this view.   The results of his experiments indicate that the tendency of roots of high-nitrogen plants to be short and thick compared with those of low-nitrogen plants results at least in part from the inhibitory effects of high auxin concentration on the division and elongation of cells in the roots.

The increase in ratio of tops to roots with increase in nitrogen supply should not be allowed to obscure the fact that nitrogen is essential for the growth of roots, and that nitrogen is an important fertilizer for root crops grown on soils of low nitrogen availability. The first objective in nitrogen fertilization of root crops is to obtain rapid elaboration of leaves in the early part of the growth cycle.

Without this, the total capability of the plant for photosynthesis is diminished. Second, at the proper time the growth of leaf must be checked by a decrease in the content of nitrogen, or otherwise. Growth of leaf cannot be continued too long, because, with a growing-season of given length, the time available for development of the storage organ decreases with increase in length of time the carbohydrate supply is diverted to top growth. These relationships are exemplified by the data of Woodman and Paver (1944) for turnips supplied with different levels of nitrogen at different times. Table

Table 16. Yield of Turnip Tops and Roots with Nitrogen Applied at Different Rates and Times
(Woodman and Paver, 1944)

Nitrogen in Culture Solution in Growth Period Indicated, p.p.m.			Yield of Dry Matter, g.	
Early	Intermediate	Late	Tops	Roots
4	4	4	0.4	1.4
66	4	4	1.1	6.6
66	66	4	2.3	14.4
66	66	66	2.8	13.1
4	66	66	2.6	9.7
4	4	66	1.5	4.0

16 shows that the best root growth was obtained when the high nitrogen level was applied early rather than late.

Fruiting

With reference to the tomato, Kraus and Kraybill (1918) recognized that high-nitrogen plants were unfruitful or excessively vegetative even though conditions were favorable for carbohydrate synthesis. With some reduction in nitrogen supply, vegetative growth decreased and fruitfulness increased. With further reduction in nitrogen supply, both vegetation and fruitfulness were diminished.

The behavior described by Kraus and Kraybill is characteristic of many plants. With the small grains, for example, the straw usually is more responsive to nitrogen fertilization than the grain (although the reverse may obtain if the nitrogen is applied late; see Fig. 15). The level of nitrogen required to produce the maximum yield is greater with the straw than the grain. Where the deficiency of nitrogen is extreme, many plants become barren; under these conditions nitrogen fertilization may cause greater relative response of grain than of straw. This greater response of grain probably is rare in the field because the nitrogen supply seldom is low enough. It has been observed in experiments in which the plants were grown in sand supplied

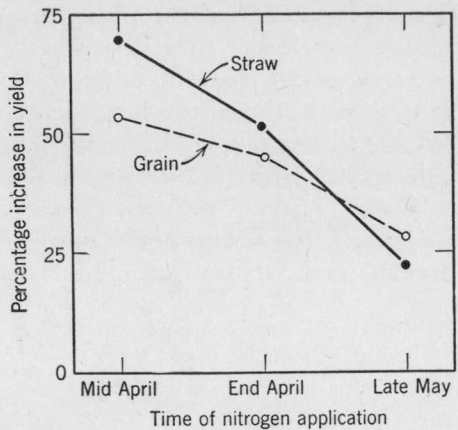

Fig. 15. Response of grain and straw of oats to a constant application of nitrogen fertilizer at different dates in England. (Halliday, 1948.)

with only a small quantity of nitrogen (Hellriegel et al., 1898). In other words, there is an intermediate nitrogen-carbohydrate condition at which the plant is most fruitful per unit of vegetative tissue. Maximum total fruitfulness lies at a much higher nitrogen level. Maximum vegetative growth occurs at a still higher nitrogen level.

Some plants do not follow the behavior described by Kraus and Kraybill. With table beets, for example, Mann (1951) found that the proportion of plants that produced seed the first year was increased from 3.1 per cent without nitrogen to 7.2 and 9.0 per cent with 4 and 12 cwt. of ammonium sulfate per acre, respectively. The higher of these applications is excessive with respect to plant response in terms of yield and must have resulted in high-nitrogen plants. Corn, which behaves in a manner analogous to that of table beets, is subject to barrenness under conditions of low nitrogen availability. Augmenting the nitrogen supply increases the relative yield of grain more rapidly than that of stover. Although the trend probably would be reversed if the nitrogen supply were high enough, the reversal apparently does not occur within the range normally encountered in practice. In an experiment reported by Krantz (1949), where different quantities of nitrogen fertilizer were applied, the corn yield per acre was increased from 23 bushels without nitrogen to 102 bushels with 160 lb. of nitrogen per acre. At the same time, the ratio of stover to grain gradually decreased from 2.83 to 0.93 with the respective rates of application. The yield of 102 bushels appeared to be near the maximum that could have been produced by adding nitrogen under the experimental conditions since a yield of 100 bushels was obtained with 120 lb. of nitrogen. With these two crops, therefore, it appears that fruitfulness, as expressed by fruit produced per unit of vegetative tissue, increases with nitrogen supply throughout the range of practical interest. Stated another way, high nitrogen availability apparently does not result in excessive vegetative growth of these two crops.

From the fact that variations in nitrogen supply affect fruiting of different plants in different ways, it may be inferred that the control mechanism is not the nitrogen supply as such. Rather it is something that is affected by the nitrogen supply and by other factors as well.

Lodging

Lodging is the inelastic displacement of the plant from the vertical or initial position. Usually wind provides the force that produces the lateral displacement. The moment of force, however, is determined not only by wind pressure but also by the height and weight of the plant and the weight of rain that may be adhering to the plant.

Figure 16 illustrates the results obtained in an experiment with wheat in which lodging increased linearly with the content of nitrogen in the crop. The common experience that susceptibility of crops to

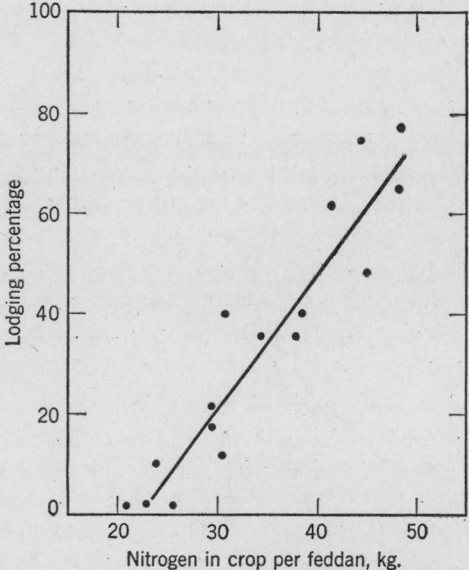

Fig. 16. Lodging of wheat versus nitrogen content of crop in an experiment with different applications of nitrogen. (Crowther, Tomforde, and Mahmoud, 1937.)

lodging increases with nitrogen supply may be attributed to the action of nitrogen in increasing the force exerted on the basal parts of the plant relatively faster than it increases the strength of these parts. Nitrogen fertilization frequently increases plant height, weight, and leaf area, and, hence, increases the moment of force. Observations on the basal portion of the stem of wheat and other small grain crops (in which lodging is an important problem) indicate that nitrogen fertilization does not bring about an increase in the diameter, wall thickness, and weight per unit length of the stem in proportion to the increase in weight of the plant; in fact decreases sometimes occur. The increase in tillering associated with nitrogen fertilization is an important facet of the problem, since with an increasing number of shoots per unit area the competition for light increases, and the individual stems tend to become thinner. Literature on this subject was reviewed by Mulder (1954).

In some instances the stem remains intact, and lodging results from partial uprooting of the plant. Such lodging may occur, for example, with corn affected by rootworms. Hill, Hixson, and Muma (1948) found that lodging of corn associated with rootworm injury was decreased by the application of nitrogen fertilizer. The apparent explanation for this observation is that the damaged roots were replaced to a greater extent by the nitrogen-fertilized plants than by the plants without supplemental nitrogen.

Time of maturity

Applications of considerable quantities of nitrogen fertilizer often have been observed to delay the time of maturity of plants, and this delay may be of importance in certain crops. Thus Stakman and Aamodt (1924) found that excessive applications of nitrogen fertilizer to wheat delayed the maturity date 7 to 10 days in one experiment and 4 to 8 days in another. These delays in maturity were associated with increased lodging and stem rust infection. In New York, Boynton (1948) noted that peaches attain their best market quality when they ripen in relatively warm weather. Fruit matures more slowly on trees fertilized heavily with nitrogen than on low-nitrogen trees. In the southern Hudson Valley where peaches ripen late in August during warm weather, the delay in maturity is no particular disadvantage. In western New York near Lake Ontario, however, peaches do not ripen until late in September when the weather is likely to be cool. Under these conditions a delay in ripening may have important consequences because the best market quality may never be attained.

Nitrogen application does not invariably delay the maturity date.

In some instances it has no measurable effect, and in others it may cause the crop to mature earlier.   In considering the effect of nitrogen on maturity, at least four factors must be taken into account: (1) the degree of nitrogen deficiency, (2) the quantity of nitrogen applied, (3) the time of nitrogen application, and (4) the nature of the crop.

The connection between the degree of nitrogen deficiency, the quantity of nitrogen applied, and the effect on maturity is illustrated in Figs. 17 and 18. In Fig. 17 the effect of nitrogen fertilizer on

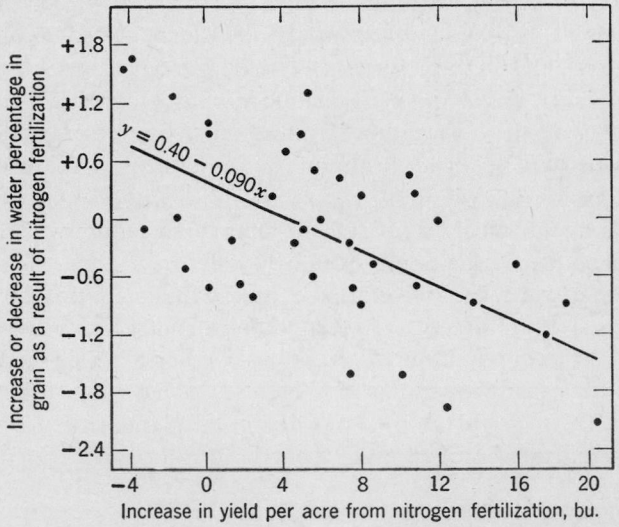

Fig. 17.   Change in water percentage in corn grain at harvest versus change in yield of corn from fertilization with 40 lb. of nitrogen per acre in experiments conducted in Iowa in 1944.   (Unpublished data, Iowa Agricultural Experiment Station, 1944.)

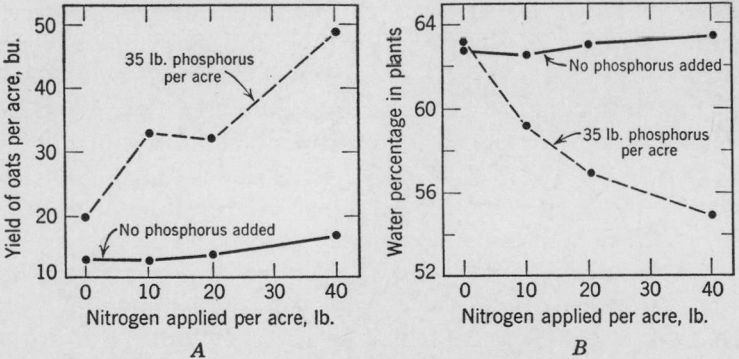

Fig. 18.   Response of oats to different levels of nitrogen at two levels of phosphate fertilization: A. Yield of Grain; B. Water content of oat plants one week before harvest. (Unpublished data, Iowa Agricultural Experiment Station, 1947.)

maturity is measured in terms of the change in water percentage of corn grain at harvest. Each point represents the result of a separate experiment in which nitrogen fertilizer was applied at a rate equivalent to 40 lb. of nitrogen per acre. The regression equation shows the change in water content of the grain resulting from fertilization as a function of the increase in yield from fertilization. The greater the increase in yield from fertilization, the earlier was the maturity of the nitrogen-fertilized corn in comparison with that of the unfertilized corn. In Fig. 18 the effect of nitrogen fertilizer on maturity is measured in terms of the water content of oat plants a week before harvest. The results in this figure were obtained in a single experiment with oats in which nitrogen was applied at different rates in the presence of two levels of phosphorus. Where no phosphorus was applied, nitrogen applications had little effect on either yield or maturity; where phosphorus was applied, the yield was increased considerably by nitrogen, and maturity became progressively earlier with increasing rates of nitrogen application.

The observations in Figs. 17 and 18 may be combined to yield the diagram in Fig. 19 which represents a schematic picture of the sig-

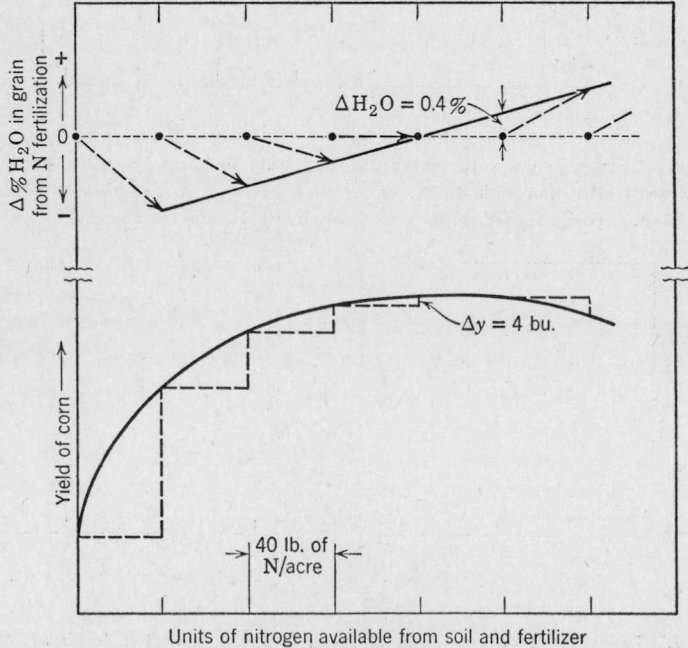

Fig. 19. Schematic representation of change in maturity of corn with application of 40-lb. increments of nitrogen to soils differing in nitrogen supply.

nificance of the regression equation obtained in the experiments with corn. Where the corn was deficient in nitrogen and the application of 40 lb. of nitrogen per acre produced a relatively large increase in yield, a relatively large decrease in the water content of the grain occurred. As the nitrogen supply in the unfertilized soil approached the amount conducive to the maximum yield, the increase in yield and the decrease in water content of the grain from fertilization became smaller. Where the soil nitrogen supply was such that a 4-bushel increase in yield resulted from fertilization, there was no effect of fertilization on the water content of the grain. Where there was no increase in yield from fertilization, the water content of the grain was increased 0.4 per cent. Thus the application of 40 lb. of nitrogen per acre resulted in earlier maturity where the corn was markedly deficient in nitrogen. It had no effect where the soil supply of nitrogen was slightly deficient, and resulted in later maturity where the soil supply was ample.

The effect of the third factor, the time of application, is indicated by data in Table 17. The application of nitrogen to oats at planting

Table 17.   Yield and Water Content of Oats Fertilized with Nitrogenous Fertilizer at Different Times

(Unpublished data, Iowa Agricultural Experiment Station, 1947)

Quantity of Nitrogen Applied per Acre and Time of Application	Yield of Oats per Acre, bu.	Water Content of Oat Plants 1 Week before Harvest, %
None	39	60
80 lb. at planting	81	59
80 lb. 1 week after emergence	86	61
80 lb. 3 weeks after emergence	79	63
80 lb. 5 weeks after emergence	72	65
80 lb. 7 weeks after emergence	43	62

time had essentially no effect on maturity. As the time of application was delayed more and more in the growing season, the maturity was delayed until an application 7 weeks after emergence reversed the trend.

The physiological explanation for the various effects of nitrogen is not known. Observations indicate that the earlier maturation connected with nitrogen fertilization of plants initially deficient in nitrogen is associated with more rapid elaboration of plant parts. Thus nitrogen-fertilized oats may head earlier than unfertilized, nitrogen-deficient oats. Silks and tassels may appear earlier on corn plants well supplied with nitrogen than on those deficient in nitrogen (Glover, 1953). Excessive nitrogen may delay maturity by diverting carbohydrate into vegetative growth and by increasing the total amount of other nutrient elements present in the vegetative tissue. The latter may induce a deficiency of one or more nutrients that results in a decrease in the rate of fruit development and maturation.

The situation described above for such crops as corn and oats does not hold for certain other crops. Crops such as cotton and snap beans do not have distinct periods of fruit formation and fruit development; rather, these periods overlap. The supply of nitrogen determines in part how long the plant continues to produce new flowers. If the nitrogen supply is relatively high, additional flowers are produced after the nitrogen-deficient plants have ceased flowering. While these flowers are being produced, development of the existing fruits is retarded, apparently because of diversion of part of the carbohydrate

Table 18.   Number of Flowers and Bolls Present at Different Dates on Cotton
Plants Receiving Different Applications of Nitrogen Fertilizer
(Crowther, 1934)

Ammonium Sulfate Applied per Acre, lb.	Flowers per Plant		Bolls per Plant	
	133 days	253 days	133 days	253 days
0	10	13	0.8	8
572	17	23	0.5	15

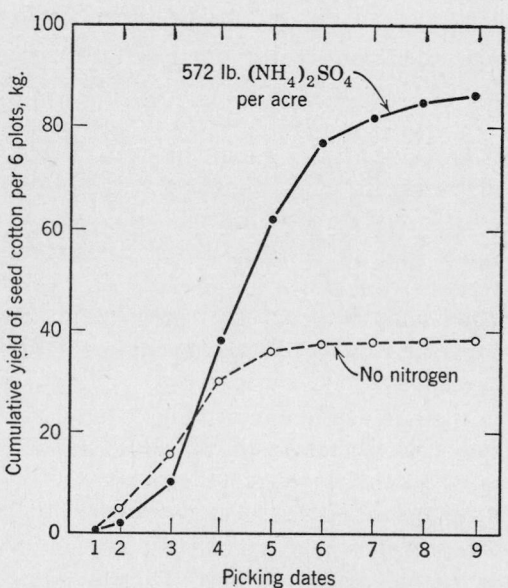

Fig. 20.   Cumulative yield of seed cotton at successive picking dates with different applications of ammonium sulfate.   (Crowther, 1934.)

to the production of the new growth. Nitrogen fertilization thus delays the maturation of the crop. These relationships are illustrated by the data of Crowther (1934) on nitrogen fertilization of cotton. Table 18 shows the effect of nitrogen fertilization on the numbers of flowers and bolls per plant on two different dates, and Fig. 20 shows the cumulative yield of seed cotton at different picking dates. It is evident from Fig. 20 that a given percentage of the total yield was obtained on an earlier date for the unfertilized plots than for the nitrogen-fertilized plots; that is, nitrogen fertilization delayed the maturation.

Low-temperature injury

Injury to plants by exposure to temperatures below freezing usually becomes intensified with an increase in the supply of nitrogen (Levitt, 1941). This behavior is explained by the fact that nitrogen promotes vegetative growth, which results in a reduction in content of sugar and other carbohydrates in plants. Low-carbohydrate plants usually are more susceptible to damage than high-carbohydrate plants, irrespective of the manner in which the carbohydrate condition is produced. Such an explanation is hardly enlightening, however, since the manner in which the carbohydrate condition is associated with low-temperature injury is not understood.

There are some exceptions to the usual pattern that have not been explained. Higgins, Walton, and Skinner (1943), for example, found that injury to the trunks of peach trees in Georgia at temperatures below freezing diminished with an increase in nitrogen fertilization. Injury at the highest rate of application was only one-thirtieth as great as that without nitrogen fertilization. On the same trees, injury to flower buds was essentially independent of the level of nitrogen applied in the fertilizer. Analyses showed that in these trees fertilization with nitrogen had increased the nitrogen percentage and had decreased the sugar percentage, in agreement with the usual response of plants to nitrogen.

Despite the unsatisfactory understanding of the subject, practical experience dictates the limitation of fall applications of nitrogen in those cases where injury by freezing may occur, even though fall-applied nitrogen might otherwise be utilized effectively. Carroll and Welton (1939) found that heavy fertilization of Kentucky bluegrass with nitrogen in the fall greatly reduced the survival of the grass after exposure to subzero temperatures. A similar effect is not produced by an equal application made early in the spring since most of the effect of the added nitrogen has been dissipated before the next fall. Boynton (1948) reported that orchardists in New York avoid fall applications of nitrogen to apple trees because nitrogen applied at that time may result in considerable low-temperature injury to the trunk. In the absence of such injury the time of nitrogen application to trees during the frost-free season does not seem to be of major importance. The roots absorb nitrogen as long as the soil remains unfrozen.

Disease incidence

Development of plant diseases often varies with the nitrogen supply. The response is not uniform, however, because of the variation in nature of plants and diseases and the environmental conditions that affect both. In some cases the severity of the attack increases with nitrogen supply, and in others the reverse is true. This subject has been reviewed by Wingard (1941), J. C. Walker (1946), and McNew (1953).

Nitrogen supply may alter the development of diseases in several different ways. First, it may alter the external environmental conditions in such a way as to change the initial infection. For example, infection by airborne diseases usually is greater at high than at low atmospheric relative humidity. By encouraging a more rank vegetative growth, nitrogen may raise the relative humidity around the plants and thereby increase infection by such diseases as mildews or rusts. The effect of nitrogen in this respect may be particularly important where nitrogen has induced lodging since air circulation around lodged plants is much reduced (Stakman and Aamodt, 1924). Another example is the effect of urea sprays in reducing bean rust (Cosper and Schuster, 1953). This effect appears to be direct since urea has an inhibitory action on the germination of the spores on agar plates.

Second, nitrogen supply may alter the resistance of plants to the entry of the disease. Third, it may alter the suitability of plant tissues as a medium for growth of the disease organism, once entry has been accomplished. Nightingale (1936) demonstrated the independent existence of the third. She noted that when apple twigs were inoculated by introducing the fire-blight bacterium into the tissue, lesions developed on succulent twigs but not on hardened twigs. The same was true in succulent and hardened portions of the same twig. Twigs and leaves of high-nitrogen trees were more susceptible than those of low-nitrogen trees, the susceptibility being associated with the succulence. Tests of the growth of the organism on juice expressed from twigs showed that juice from succulent, high-nitrogen twigs provided a relatively good culture medium, whereas that from hardened, low-nitrogen twigs was relatively poor. Growth of the organism was increased by adding asparagine (a nitrogen source) to the juice of hardened twigs. It was decreased by adding sugar to the juice of succulent twigs. Thus in this work the greater development of fire-blight lesions on high-nitrogen tissue was associated with the internal suitability of the tissue as a medium for development of the organism. Penetration was not involved. Spontaneous development of fire-blight lesions in practice is related to succulence in the same manner as it was experimentally. Variation in the resistance of the plants to the entry of the disease organism thus appears to be either unimportant or important but correlated with the internal conditions. The latter is the more probable. Critical work is needed to separate the possible effects of nitrogen supply on initial infection of the tissue from development within the plant.

Another instance in which nitrogen affects the internal suitability of plant tissue as a medium for development of a parasitic organism is that of wheat infected by the rust, *Puccinia glumarum*. According to McNew (1953), Parker-Rhodes found that the wheat plant produces a toxin for the organism, and that high-nitrogen plants produce more of the toxin than do low-nitrogen plants.

A fourth facet of the nitrogen-supply, plant-disease problem is disease-escape, which results from the effect of nitrogen in promoting growth. Disease-escape may or may not be associated with the effects of nitrogen on disease development. The effect of nitrogen supply on disease-escape is important with the so-called "take-all" of cereals. Take-all is a fungal disease that is carried over in the soil from one crop to the next in the diseased crop residues. Roots of the new crop are infected when they come into contact with this scattered inoculum. Garrett (1948) found that the application of nitrogen fertilizer to the new crop increased the susceptibility of the host to the disease, as indicated by the extent of damage to infected roots. At the same time, however, the total number of crown roots and the proportion remaining uninfected were increased by fertilization. The plants thus were enabled partially to escape the disease by virtue of the greater number of uninfected crown roots produced.

Plant competition

The competition between grasses and legumes in associated growth has received considerable attention since these plants often are grown together in practice and since the relative competitive abilities of the different species vary with environmental conditions. The competitive position of the grasses improves with increasing nitrogen supply. Apparently there are two reasons for this, namely, differential response of grasses and legumes to (*a*) levels of nitrogen availability in the soil and to (*b*) changes induced directly or indirectly in the supply of other growth factors by the changes in nitrogen supply.

The effect of soil nitrogen availability on the competitive ability of grasses and legumes results primarily from the fact that nitrogen deficiency limits the yield of grasses, although not of legumes, at low-nitrogen levels but limits the yield of neither at high-nitrogen levels. The connection between nitrogen supply and competitive ability is exceedingly intimate for the reason that in addition to the nitrogen supplied by mineralization of soil nitrogen, by rainfall, or fertilization, the grass may derive some nitrogen from the associated legume. The legume nitrogen may be transferred directly, by excretion in forms which the grass can absorb, or indirectly, by decay of legume roots and nodules. The amount of nitrogen derived from the legume decreases with increasing nitrogen availability in the soil. Walker, Orchiston, and Adams (1954) reasoned that the amount of nitrogen transferred from the legume to the grass must be nil in a pure stand of grass, and that if transference occurs in the presence of a legume, it should increase with the proportion of legume in the mixture. Since the yield of nitrogen in grass increases approximately linearly with the quantity added in the fertilizer over a considerable range, these investigators hypothesized that up to a point the yield of nitrogen in the grass component of the vegetation (G) is proportional to the nitrogen mineralized in the soil (S), to the yield of nitrogen in the legume (L), and to the nitrogen added in the fertilizer (F), leading to the equation

$$G = aS + bL + cF$$

where a, b, and c are parameters. If the legume absorbs nitrogen from the supply of mineral nitrogen in the soil, the values of the parameters a and c would be expected to vary with the proportion of legume in the mixture. Experiments with tracer nitrogen (T. W. Walker, 1955) indicate that the legume component of grass-legume mixtures absorbs essentially none of the mineral nitrogen in the soil. Therefore the product aS should represent a constant, which may be represented by k:

$$G = k + bL + cF$$

Walker, Orchiston, and Adams (1954) fitted the foregoing equation to the data from an experiment conducted at Lincoln, New Zealand, on a ryegrass-white clover meadow in which the variables were fertilizer nitrogen and frequency of cutting. Yields of nitrogen in the grass and in the clover were affected by both these variables. The parameters were found to have the values, $k = 36$, $b = 0.65$, and $c = 0.69$. The values of b and c were so nearly the same that the experimenters averaged the two and expressed the results by the simplified equation

$$G = 36 + 0.67(L + F)$$

The agreement between the calculated and observed values, which are plotted in Fig. 21, provides support for the validity of the equation. The slope constant 0.67 indicates that the ratio of the portion of the yield of nitrogen in the grass derived from the legume to the yield of nitrogen in the legume is 0.67. This value was found to be applicable to several different experiments.

The work of Walker and co-workers is of interest not only because of the light it sheds on the quantitative importance of the transfer of nitrogen from legume to grass, but also because it yields further expression of the competitive relationships involved. For example, in the experiment of Walker and co-workers, cutting the meadow four times instead of twice reduced the dominance of the grass and increased the yield of nitrogen in the legume from 105 to 155 lb. per acre. At the same time the yield of nitrogen in the grass increased

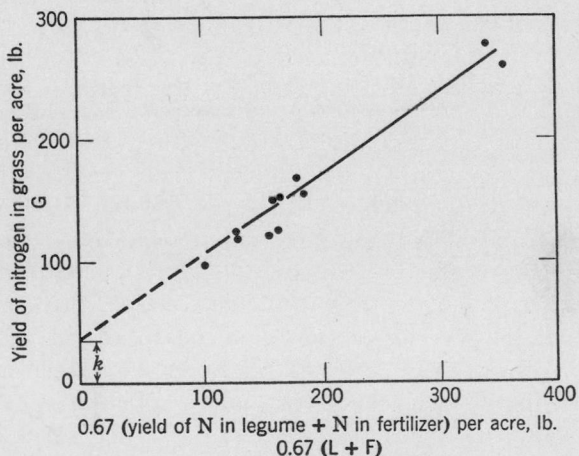

Fig. 21. Yield of nitrogen in grass versus yield of nitrogen in clover plus fertilizer nitrogen in an experiment on a ryegrass—white clover meadow. (Walker, Orchiston, and Adams, 1954.)

from 99 to 122 lb. per acre. Since the values of k and cF remain
constant in this comparison, the equation evidently predicts an increase in G with an increase in L. As a second example from the
same experiment, increasing F by 67 lb. per acre caused G to increase
47 lb. per acre and caused L to decrease by 45 lb. per acre, so that the
net increase in yield of nitrogen was only 2 lb. per acre. If L is
added to both sides of the equation to obtain the total yield of
nitrogen, the equation may be shown to predict this effect also. Thus
if an increase in F on the right-hand side of the equation brings about
a decrease in L, the value of $(G + L)$ on the left-hand side will increase less than if L remained constant or increased with F. Because
of the decrease in L with an increase in F, nitrogen fertilization resulted in trading some legume nitrogen for some grass nitrogen.

As pointed out above, a second reason for variation in the competitive ability of grasses and legumes with the supply of nitrogen is the
differential response that may occur to changes in the supply of
growth factors other than nitrogen. That such changes exist is indicated by the fact that the response of the individual species to
nitrogen fertilization may be rather different when the species are
grown together than when they are grown singly. For example,
Stewart and Bear (1951) in New Jersey found that nitrogen fertilization increased the yield of ladino clover grown alone and decreased
the yield of ladino clover grown in a mixture with orchard grass.

Little clear evidence exists regarding the cause of the differential
responses. In some instances light probably is an important factor.
Pritchett[3] investigated this factor in relation to mixed plantings of oats
and legumes. Here the legumes employed develop more slowly than
the oats; hence the increased density of canopy that may result from
nitrogen fertilization has an unfavorable effect on legume growth.
The increase in competitive ability of the oats associated with nitrogen
fertilization thus can be attributed in part to an induced deficiency of
light for the legumes. In New York, potassium has been suspected
to be an important factor. Blaser and Brady (1950) found that
nitrogen fertilization of an established mixture of ladino clover and
grass increased the severity of potassium deficiency symtoms on the
ladino clover plants. The existence in this instance of an unfavorable
effect of potassium deficiency specific to the ladino clover is indicated
by the fact that potassium fertilization markedly increased the relative
yield of clover but not of grass.

[3] Pritchett, William Lawrence. (1950) **Nitrogen fertilization of small grain and its
effect on competition with the legume-grass companion crop.** Ph.D. Thesis, Iowa State
College, Ames, Iowa.

LITERATURE CITED

Achromeiko, A. (1928) Der Einfluss des Pulverisierens und Trocknens des Boden auf desen Fruchtbarkeit. **Zeitschr. Pflanzenernähr. Düng. Bodenk.** 11A:65–89.

Adel, Arthur. (1951) Atmospheric nitrous oxide and the nitrogen cycle. **Science** 113:624–625.

Albrecht, W. A. (1937) The nitrate nitrogen in the soil as influenced by the crop and the soil treatments. **Missouri Agr. Exp. Sta. Res. Bul. 250.**

Allen, O. N., and I. L. Baldwin. (1954) Rhizobia-legume relationships. **Soil Sci.** 78:415–427.

Allison, F. E. (1947) **Azotobacter** inoculation of crops: I. Historical. **Soil Sci.** 64:413–429.

Allison, F. E. (1955) The enigma of soil nitrogen balance sheets. **Adv. Agron.** 7:213–250.

Allison, F. E., Margaret Kefauver, and E. M. Roller. (1953) Ammonium fixation in soils. **Soil Sci. Soc. America Proc.** 17:107–110.

Allison, Franklin E., Mildred S. Sherman, and Louis A. Pinck. (1949) Maintenance of soil organic matter: I. Inorganic soil colloid as a factor in retention of carbon during formation of humus. **Soil Sci.** 68:463–478.

Allison, F. E., and Luann D. Sterling. (1949) Nitrate formation from soil organic matter in relation to total nitrogen and cropping practices. **Soil Sci.** 67:239–252.

Avery, George S., Jr., P. R. Burkholder, and Harriet B. Creighton. (1936) Plant hormones and mineral nutrition. **Proc. Nat. Acad. Sci.** 22:673–678.

Batham, H. N., and L. S. Nigam. (1930) Periodicity of the nitrate content of soils. **Soil Sci.** 29:181–190.

Beijerinck, M. W. (1888) Die Bakterien der Papilionaceenknöllchen. **Bot. Zeitschr.** 46:726–735, 742–750, 758–771, 782–790, 798–804.

Beijerinck, M. W. (1901) Ueber oligonitrophile Mikroben. **Centbl. Bakt.** (Abt. 2) 7:561–582.

Blackman, G. E. (1936) The influence of temperature and available nitrogen supply on the growth of pasture in the spring. **Jour. Agr. Sci.** 26:620–647.

Blaser, R. E., and N. C. Brady. (1950) Nutrient competition in plant associations. **Agron. Jour.** 42:128–135.

Bonner, James. (1950) **Plant Biochemistry.** Academic Press, New York.

Bosemark, Nils Olof. (1954) The influence of nitrogen on root development. **Physiologia Plantarum** 7:497–502.

Bower, C. A. (1951) Availability of ammonium fixed in difficultly exchangeable form by soils of semiarid regions. **Soil Sci. Soc. America Proc.** (1950) 15:119–122.

Boynton, Damon. (1948) Your fruit trees will tell you about their nitrogen needs. **Amer. Fert.** 109, No. 6:7–8.

Bremner, J. M. (1949) Studies on soil organic matter. Part I. The chemical nature of soil organic nitrogen. **Jour. Agr. Sci.** 39:183–193.

Bremner, J. M. (1950) The amino acid composition of the protein material in soil. **Biochem. Jour.** 47:538–542.

Bremner, J. M. (1952) The nature of soil-nitrogen complexes. **Jour. Sci. Food Agr.** 3:497–500.

Broadbent, F. E., and A. G. Norman. (1947) Some factors affecting the availability of the organic nitrogen in soil—a preliminary report. **Soil Sci. Soc. America Proc.** (1946) 11:264–267.

Burris, R. H.   (1953)   Studies of biological nitrogen fixation with N^{15}.   **Kansas Agr. Exp. Sta. Rept.** 4:68–80.

Carroll, J. C., and F. A. Welton.   (1939)   Effect of heavy and late applications of nitrogenous fertilizer on the cold resistance of Kentucky bluegrass.   **Plant Physiol.** 14:297–308.

Chaminade, Raymond, and Gustave Drouineau.   (1936)   Recherches sur la mécanique chimique des cations échangeables.   **Ann. agron.** (N.S.) 6:677–690.

Chapman, H. D., and George F. Liebig, Jr.   (1947)   Nitrogen gains and losses in the growth of legume and nonlegume cover crops at various levels of nitrogen fertilization.   **Soil Sci. Soc. America Proc.** (1946) 11:388.

Clark, Francis E.   (1949)   Soil microorganisms and plant roots.   **Adv. Agron.** 1:241–288.

Collison, R. C., and Mensching, J. E.   (1930)   Lysimeter investigations: I. Nitrogen and water relations of crops in legume and non-legume rotations.   New York (Geneva) **State Agr. Exp. Sta. Tech. Bul.** 166.   1930.

Corbet, Alexander Steven, and Walter Reginald Wooldridge.   (1940)   The nitrogen cycle in biological systems.   3. Aerobic denitrification in soils.   **Biochem. Jour.** 34:1036–1040.

Cosper, Harold, and M. L. Schuster.   (1953)   Effect of urea on the incidence of bean rust.   **Agron. Jour.** 45:74–75.

Crowther, Frank.   (1934)   Studies in growth analysis of the cotton plant under irrigation in the Sudan: I. The effect of different combinations of nitrogen applications and water-supply.   **Ann. Bot.** 48:877–913.

Crowther, Frank, Adolf Tomforde, and Ahmed Mahmoud.   (1937)   Experiments in Egypt on the interaction of factors in crop growth.   5. Manuring of wheat, barley, maize and rice.   **Royal Agr. Soc. Egypt Bul.** 28.

Dawson, J. E.   (1950)   Soil organic matter.   In Frear, Donald E. H. (Editor) **Agricultural Chemistry**, Vol. 1, 778–797.   D. Van Nostrand Co., New York.

Delwiche, C. C.   (1956)   Nitrification.   In McElroy, William D., and Bentley Glass, (Editors) **Inorganic Nitrogen Metabolism**, pp. 218–232.   Johns Hopkins Press, Baltimore.

Demolon, A., and G. Barbier.   (1929)   Conditions de formation et constitution du complexe argilo-humique des sols.   **Compt. rend. acad. sci.** 188:654–656.

Drouineau, Gustave, Guy Lefèvre, and Denise Blanc-Aicard.   (1953)   Minéralisation de l'azote organique des sols au cours de la saison sèche sous le climat méditerranéen.   **Compt. rend. acad. sci.** 236:524–526.

Ellis, J. H.   (1938)   **The Soils of Manitoba.**   Manitoba Econ. Survey Board, Winnipeg.

Ensminger, L. E., and J. E. Gieseking.   (1939)   The adsorption of proteins by montmorillonitic clays.   **Soil Sci.** 48:467–473.

Ensminger, L. E., and J. E. Gieseking.   (1941)   The absorption of proteins by montmorillonitic clays and its effect on base-exchange capacity.   **Soil Sci.** 51:125–132.

Ensminger, L. E., and J. E. Gieseking.   (1942)   Resistance of clay-adsorbed proteins to proteolytic hydrolysis.   **Soil Sci.** 53:205–209.

Eriksson, Erik.   (1952)   Composition of atmospheric precipitation.   I. Nitrogen compounds.   **Tellus** 4:215–232.

Finn, R. F.   (1942)   Mycorrhizal inoculation of soil of low fertility.   **Black Rock Forest Papers** 1:116–117.

Fred, Edwin Broun, Ira Lawrence Baldwin, and Elizabeth McCoy.   (1932)   Root nodule bacteria and leguminous plants.   **Wisconsin Univ. Studies in Sci.** 5.

Gardner, Robert, and D. W. Robertson.   (1942)   The nitrogen requirement of sugar beets. **Colorado Agr. Exp. Sta. Tech. Bul. 28.**

Garrett, S. D.   (1948)   Soil conditions and the take-all disease of wheat. IX. Interaction between host plant nutrition, disease escape, and disease resistance. **Ann. Appl. Biol. 35:14—17.**

Gilbert, C. S., H. F. Eppson, W. B. Bradley, and O. A. Beath.   (1946)   Nitrate accumulation in cultivated plants and weeds. **Wyoming Agr. Exp. Sta. Bul. 277.**

Giöbel, Gunnar.   (1926)   The relation of the soil nitrogen to nodule development and fixation of nitrogen by certain legumes. **New Jersey Agr. Exp. Sta. Bul. 436.**

Glover, J.   (1953)   The nutrition of maize in sand culture. I. The balance of nutrition with particular reference to the level of supply of nitrogen and phosphorus. **Jour. Agr. Sci. 43:154—159.**

Goring, C. A. I., and Francis E. Clark.   (1949)   Influence of crop growth on mineralization of nitrogen in the soil. **Soil Sci. Soc. America Proc.**   (1948)   13:261—266.

Greaves, J. E., and E. G. Carter.   (1920)   Influence of moisture on bacterial activities of the soil. **Soil Sci. 10:361—387.**

Greaves, J. E., and E. G. Carter.   (1924)   The influence of irrigation water on the composition of grains and the relationship to nutrition. **Jour. Biol. Chem. 58:531—541.**

Gulati, A. N., and N. Ahmad.   (1947)   Effect of fertilizers on fineness of cotton. **Proc. Conf. Cott. Grow. Prob. India 1946:245—251.**   (Soils and Fertilizers 11:1293. 1948)

Haddock, Jay L.   (1952)   The nitrogen requirement of sugar beets. **Proc. Amer. Soc. Sugar Beet Technol. 7:159—165.**

Halliday, D. J.   (1948)   Nitrogen for cereals. **Jealott's Hill Res. Sta. Bul. 6.**

Hambidge, Gove (Editor)   (1941)   **Hunger Signs in Crops.** American Society of Agronomy and National Fertilizer Association, Washington, D. C.

Hardy, F.   (1945)   The significance of carbon-nitrogen ratio in soils growing cotton. **Tropical Agr. 22:119—127.**

Harmsen, G. W., and D. A. Van Schreven.   (1955)   Mineralization of organic nitrogen in soil. **Adv. Agron. 7:299—398.**

Hellriegel, H., and H. Wilfarth.   (1891)   Recherches sur l'alimentation azotée des graminées et des légumineuses. **Ann. sci. agron.**   (1890)   7:84—175, 189—352.

Hellriegel, H., H. Wilfarth, H. Römer, and G. Wimmer.   (1898)   Vegetationsversuche über den Kalibedarf einiger Pflanzen. **Arb. deut. Landw. Gesell. Heft 34.**

Higgins, B. B., G. P. Walton, and J. J. Skinner.   (1943)   The effect of nitrogen fertilization on cold injury of peach trees. **Georgia Agr. Exp. Sta. Bul. 226.**

Hill, Roscoe E., Ephriam Hixson, and Martin H. Muma.   (1948)   Corn rootworm control tests with benzene hexachloride, DDT, nitrogen fertilizers and crop rotations. **Jour. Econ. Entomol. 41:392—401.**

Jenny, Hans.   (1930)   A study on the influence of climate upon the nitrogen and organic matter content of the soil. **Missouri Agr. Exp. Sta. Res. Bul. 152.**

Jenny, Hans.   (1933)   Soil fertility losses under Missouri conditions. **Missouri Agr. Exp. Sta. Bul. 324.**

Jenny, Hans.   (1941)   **Factors of Soil Formation.** McGraw-Hill Book Co., Inc., New York.

Jensen, H. L.   (1929)   On the influence of the carbon: nitrogen ratios of organic material on the mineralisation of nitrogen. **Jour. Agr. Sci. 19:71—82.**

Jensen, H. L.   (1940)   Contributions to the nitrogen economy of Australian wheat soils, with particular reference to New South Wales. **Proc. Linnean Soc. New South Wales** 65:1—122.

Jewitt, T. N. (1942) Loss of ammonia from ammonium sulfate applied to alkaline soils. **Soil Sci.** 54:401—409.

Johnstone-Wallace, D. B. (1937) The influence of grazing management and plant associations on the chemical composition of pasture plants. **Jour. Amer. Soc. Agron.** 29:441—455.

Jones, Randall J. (1939) Nitrogen economy in different systems of soil and crop management. **Alabama Agr. Exp. Sta. Ann. Rpt.** 50:13—15.

Kelley, Arthur P. (1950) **Mycotrophy in Plants.** Chronica Botanica Co., Waltham, Massachusetts.

Khalil, Fahmy. (1929) The effect of drying on the microbiological processes in soils. **Zentbl. Bakt., Parasitenk. Infektionskr.** (II) 79:93—107.

Kitchen, Herminie Broedel (Editor). (1948) **Diagnostic Techniques for Soils and Crops.** The American Potash Institute, Washington, D. C.

Koch, Alfred. (1909) Weitere Untersuchungen über die Stickstoffanreicherung des Bodens durch freilebende Bakterien. **Jour. f. Landw.** 57:269—286.

Koch, Alfred, J. Litzendorff, F. Krull, and A. Alves. (1907) Die Stickstoffanreicherung des Bodens durch freilebende Bakterien und ihre Bedeutung für die Pflanzenernährung. **Jour. f. Landw.** 55:355—416.

Krantz, B. A. (1949) Fertilize corn for higher yields. **North Carolina Agr. Exp. Sta. Bul.** 366.

Kraus, E. J., and H. R. Kraybill. (1918) Vegetation and reproduction with special reference to the tomato. **Oregon Agr. Exp. Sta. Bul.** 149.

Landrau, Pablo, Jr. (1953) Influence of cropping and cultural practices on the seasonal trends in nitrification rates of soils used for growing corn in Nebraska. **Puerto Rico Univ. Agr. Exp. Sta. Tech. Paper** 10.

Lehr, J. J., and B. Veen. (1952) Nitrogen economy of the soil in relation to seasonal and periodical climatic variations. **Internat. Soc. Soil Sci. Trans.** 2:61—67.

Levitt, J. (1941) **Frost Killing and Hardiness of Plants.** Burgess Publishing Co., Minneapolis.

Lipman, Jacob G., and Adrienne B. Conybeare. (1936) Preliminary note on the inventory and balance sheet of plant nutrients in the United States. **New Jersey Agr. Exp. Sta. Bul.** 607.

Lyon, T. Lyttleton, and James A. Bizzell. (1913) Some relations of certain higher plants to the formation of nitrates in soils. **New York (Cornell Univ.) Agr. Exp. Sta. Mem.** 1.

Lyon, T. L., J. A. Bizzell, B. D. Wilson, and E. W. Leland. (1930) Lysimeter experiments: III. Records for tanks 3 to 12 during the years 1910 to 1924 inclusive. **New York (Cornell Univ.) Agr. Exp. Sta. Mem.** 134.

Magee, Wayne E., and R. H. Burris. (1954) Fixation of $N_2{}^{15}$ by excised nodules. **Plant Physiol.** 29:199—200.

Mann, Harold H. (1951) The effect of manures on the bolting of the beet plant. **Ann. Appl. Biol.** 38:435—443.

Massey, H. F., and M. L. Jackson. (1952) Selective erosion of soil fertility constituents. **Soil Sci. Soc. America Proc.** 16:353—356.

Mattson, Sante, and Elisaveta Koutler-Anderssen. (1943) The acid-base condition in vegetation, litter and humus: VI. Ammonia fixation and humus nitrogen. **Lantbrukshögskolans Annaler** 11:107—134.

McNew, George L. (1953) The effects of soil fertility. In **Plant Diseases.** United States Dept. Agr. Yearbook 1953, pp. 100—114.

Meiklejohn, Jane. (1940) Aerobic denitrification. **Ann. Appl. Biol.** 27:558—573.

Meiklejohn, Jane. (1953) The nitrifying bacteria: a review. **Jour. Soil Sci.** 4:59—68.

Melin, Elias, and Harald Nilsson. (1952) Transport of labelled nitrogen from an ammonium source to pine seedlings through mycorrhizal mycelium. **Svensk Bot. Tidskr.** 46:281—285.

Meyer, Rudolf, and Alfred Storck. (1927) Ueber den Pflanzenertrag als Funktion der Stickstoffgabe und der Wachstumszeit bei Hafer. **Zeitschr. Pflanzenernähr. Düng. Bodenk.** 10A:329—347.

Meyerhof, Otto. (1916) Untersuchungen über den Atmungsvorgang nitrifizierender Bakterien. III. Die Atmung des Nitritbildners und ihre Beeinflussung durch chemische Substanzen. **Pflüger's Arch. ges. Physiol.** 166:240—280.

Morgan, M. F., and O. E. Street. (1939) Seasonal water and nitrate leachings in relation to soil and source of fertilizer nitrogen. (A second report on Windsor lysimeter series "A".) **Connecticut (New Haven) Agr. Exp. Sta. Bul.** 429.

Mulder, E. G. (1954) Effect of mineral nutrition on lodging of cereals. **Plant and Soil** 5:246—306.

Munson, Robert D., and George Stanford. (1955) Predicting nitrogen fertilizer needs of Iowa soils: IV. Evaluation of nitrate production as a criterion of nitrogen availability. **Soil Sci. Soc. America Proc.** 19:464—468.

Nightingale, Alice Allen. (1936) Some chemical constituents of apple associated with susceptibility to fire-blight. **New Jersey Agr. Exp. Sta. Bul.** 613.

Nye, P. H. (1951) Studies on the fertility of Gold Coast soil. II. The nitrogen status of the soils. **Empire Jour. Exptl. Agr.** 19:275—282.

Pearson, R. W., and Roy W. Simonson. (1939) Organic phosphorus in seven Iowa soil profiles: distribution and amounts as compared to organic carbon and nitrogen. **Soil Sci. Soc. America Proc.** 4:162—167.

Peevy, W. J., and A. G. Norman. (1948) Influence of composition of plant materials on properties of the decomposed residues. **Soil Sci.** 65:209—226.

Pinck, L. A., F. E. Allison, and V. L. Gaddy. (1948) The effect of green manure crops of varying carbon-nitrogen ratios upon nitrogen availability and soil organic matter content. **Jour. Amer. Soc. Agron.** 40:237—248.

Pinck, L. A., R. S. Dyal, and F. E. Allison. (1954) Protein-montmorillonite complexes, their preparation and the effects of soil microorganisms on their decomposition. **Soil Sci.** 78:109—118.

Richardson, H. L. (1938) The nitrogen cycle in grassland soils: with especial reference to the Rothamsted Park grass experiment. **Jour. Agr. Sci.** 28:73—121.

Richer, A. C., and J. W. White. (1946) Response of Stayman apple trees in metal cylinders to varying amounts of inorganic nitrogenous fertilizers and green manures. VI. Fate of applied green manure and inorganic nitrogen fertilizers and their residual effect upon the soil. **Pennsylvania Agr. Exp. Sta. Bul.** 483:101—120.

Rodrigues, G. (1954) Fixed ammonia in tropical soils. **Jour. Soil Sci.** 5:264—274.

Russel, J. C., E. G. Jones, and G. M. Bahrt. (1925) The temperature and moisture factors in nitrate production. **Soil Sci.** 19:381—398.

Russell, M. B. (1952) Soil aeration and plant growth. **Agronomy** 2:253—301.

Scarseth, George D., Harry L. Cook, Bert A. Krantz, and Alvin J. Ohlrogge. (1943) How to fertilize corn effectively in Indiana. **Indiana Agr. Exp. Sta. Bul.** 482.

Scheel, Rudolf. (1936) Einfluss der Düngung auf Ertrag und Faserausbildung des Hanfes. **Ernährung der Pflanze** 32:322—327.

Schloesing, Th., fils, and Em. Laurent. (1892) Recherches sur la fixation de l'azote libre par les plantes. **Ann. inst. Pasteur** 6:65—115.

Shaw, W. N. (1906) An apparent periodicity in the yield of wheat for eastern England, 1885—1905. **Proc. Royal Soc. London** 78A:69—76.

Shields, Lora Mangum. (1953) Nitrogen sources of seed plants and environmental influences affecting the nitrogen supply. **Bot. Rev.** 19:321—376.

Siebert, Hermann. (1939) Der Einfluss von steigenden Stickstoffgaben auf Ertrag und Güte einiger Zwischenfrüchte. **Landw. Jahrb.** 87:112—158.

Simonart, P., and F. Peeters. (1954) Acides aminés libres dans l'humus. **Fifth Int. Congr. Soil Sci. Trans.** 3:132—135.

Slobod, R. L., and M. E. Krogh. (1950) Nitrous oxide as a constituent of the atmosphere. **Jour. Amer. Chem. Soc.** 72:1175—1177.

Soubies, L., R. Gadet, and P. Maury. (1952) Migration hivernale de l'azote nitrique dans un sol limoneaux de la région Toulousaine. **Ann. agron.** 3:365—383.

Stakman, E. C., and O. S. Aamodt. (1924) The effect of fertilizers on the development of stem rust of wheat. **Jour. Agr. Res.** 27:341—380.

Stanford, George, and W. H. Pierre. (1947) The relation of potassium fixation to ammonium fixation. **Soil Sci. Soc. America Proc.** (1946) 11:155—160.

Starkey, Robert L. (1939) The influence of reaction upon the development of an acid-tolerant **Azotobacter. Proc. Third Comm. Internat. Soc. Soil Sci.**, pp. 142—150.

Stewart, Ivan, and Firman E. Bear. (1951) Ladino clover—its mineral requirements and chemical composition. **New Jersey Agr. Exp. Sta. Bul. 759.**

Thompson, L. M., C. A. Black, and J. A. Zoellner. (1954) Occurrence and mineralization of organic phosphorus in soils, with particular reference to associations with nitrogen, carbon, and pH. **Soil Sci.** 77:185—196.

Umbreit, Wayne W., and E. B. Fred. (1936) The comparative efficiency of free and combined nitrogen for the nutrition of the soybean. **Jour. Amer. Soc. Agron.** 28:548—555.

Virtanen, Artturi Ilmari, Synnöve von Hausen, and Tauno Laine. (1937) Investigations on the root nodule bacteria of leguminous plants: XX. Excretion of nitrogen in associated cultures of legumes and non-legumes. **Jour. Agr. Sci.** 27:584—610.

Waksman, Selman A., and K. R. N. Iyer. (1932) Contribution to our knowledge of the chemical nature and origin of humus: I. On the synthesis of the "humus nucleus." **Soil Sci.** 34:43—69.

Walker, Albert C., Lucile R. Hac, Albert Ulrich, and F. J. Hills. (1950) Nitrogen fertilization of sugar beets in the Woodland Area of California. I. Effects upon glutamic acid content, sucrose concentration and yield. **Proc. Amer. Soc. Sugar Beet Tech.** 6:362—371.

Walker, J. C. (1946) Soil management and plant nutrition in relation to disease development. **Soil Sci.** 61:47—54.

Walker, R. H., and P. E. Brown. (1936) The phosphorus, nitrogen and carbon content of Iowa soils. In Brown, P. E. (1936) Soils of Iowa. **Iowa Agr. Exp. Sta. Spec. Report 3.**

Walker, T. W. (1955) Sulphur responses on pastures in Australia and New Zealand. **Soils and Fertilizers** 18:185—187.

Walker, T. W., H. D. Orchiston, and A. F. R. Adams. (1954) The nitrogen economy of grass legume associations. **Jour. British Grassland Soc.** 9:249—274.

Wallace, T. (1951) **The Diagnosis of Mineral Deficiencies in Plants by Visual Symptoms.** His Majesty's Stationery Office, London.

Wijler, J., and C. C. Delwiche.   (1954)   Investigations on the denitrifying process in soil. **Plant and Soil** 5:155–169.

Wilson, J. K.   (1943)   Nitrous acid and the loss of nitrogen. **New York** (Cornell Univ.) **Agr. Exp. Sta. Mem.** 253.

Wilson, P. W., and E. B. Fred.   (1939)   The carbohydrate-nitrogen relation in legume symbiosis. **Jour. Amer. Soc. Agron.** 31:497–502.

Wilson, P. W., and Orville Wyss.   (1937)   Mixed cropping and the excretion of nitrogen by leguminous plants. **Soil Sci. Soc. America Proc.** 2:289–297.

Wingard, S. A.   (1941)   The nature of disease resistance in plants. I. **Bot. Rev.** 7:59–109.

Winogradsky, S.   (1893)   Sur l'assimilation de l'azote gazeux de l'atmosphére par les microbes. **Compt. rend. acad. sci.** 116:1385–1388.

Woodman, R. M., and H. Paver.   (1944)   The effect of time of application of inorganic nitrogen on the turnip. **Jour. Agr. Sci.** 34:49–56.

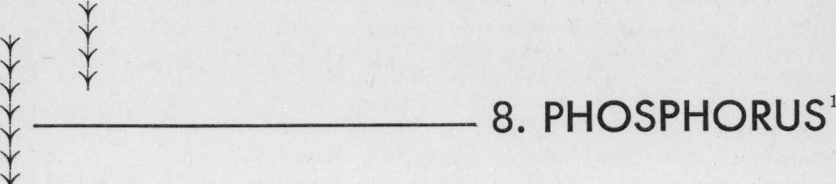

8. PHOSPHORUS[1]

Phosphorus is essential to plant growth. Phosphorus performs functions in plant metabolism, structure, and reproduction that cannot be performed by any other element. Arsenic, the element most similar to phosphorus with regard to chemical properties in aqueous systems, is toxic to plants. The concentration of phosphorus in plants usually is considerably lower than that of nitrogen, potassium, or calcium. As a limiting factor, however, phosphorus is more important than calcium, and probably is second in importance only to nitrogen.

CONTENT IN SOILS

The total content of phosphorus in soils is relatively small. Lipman and Conybeare (1936) obtained the average value of 1240 lb. per acre for the content of phosphorus in the surface 6 2/3 inches of the crop land of the United States. The figure is equal to 0.064 per cent phosphorus (assuming 2,000,000 lb. of surface soil per acre), a value considerably smaller than the corresponding figures of 0.14 per cent for nitrogen and 0.83 per cent for potassium. A generalized map of the phosphorus content of soils of the United States published by Parker et al. (1946) shows that soils of the Atlantic and Gulf Coastal Plain contain less than 0.017 per cent phosphorus. This is the most extensive low-phosphorus area. Most soils contain between 0.022 and 0.083 per cent phosphorus, but soils of a large area in the Northwest contain 0.087 to 0.13 per cent.

The phosphorus released in soluble form in soils from weathering of primary phosphorus-bearing minerals and additions of plant residues

[1] For a more detailed coverage of the subject the reader is referred to a symposium edited by Pierre and Norman (1953).

and fertilizers recombines primarily with the clay fraction. As a result, the phosphorus percentage of the clay fraction usually exceeds that of the coarser fractions (Failyer, Smith, and Wade [1908]). Moreover, the phosphorus percentage of the soil as a whole usually increases as the texture becomes finer, if other conditions are similar; this tendency is illustrated in Table 1.

Table 1.   Phosphorus Percentage of the Surface 6⅔ Inches of Soils
Derived from Glacial Deposits in Northeastern Iowa
(Walker and Brown, 1936)

Soil texture	Sand	Fine Sand	Sandy Loam	Fine Sandy Loam	Loam	Silt Loam
Phosphorus percentage	0.040	0.037	0.043	0.045	0.057	0.064

In soil profiles developed on uniform parent materials, the minimum phosphorus percentage usually occurs in the lower A or upper B horizon (Winters and Simonson, 1951). An example is shown in Fig. 1. The minimum phosphorus percentage apparently results from the combined action of absorption of phosphorus by plants and leaching. The higher content in the surface soil can be attributed to the return of some of the phosphorus absorbed by plants and to the retention of this phosphorus by the surface soil against rapid downward movement by leaching. As a whole, however, the upper part of the profile in Fig. 1 apparently has lost a part of its original content of phosphorus.

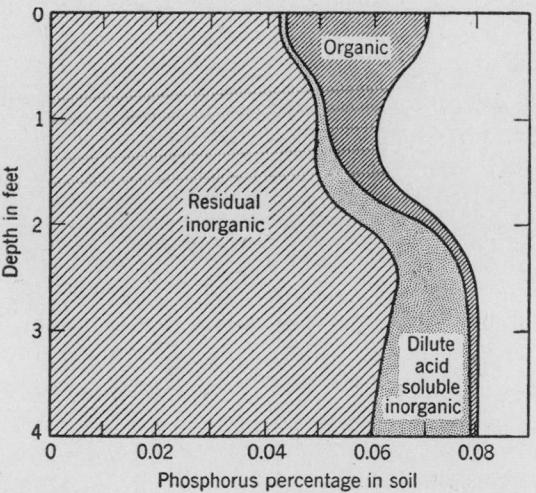

Fig. 1.   Vertical distribution of phosphorus in a prairie soil developed from loess.
(Pearson, Spry, and Pierre, 1940; Pearson and Simonson, 1939.)

Crop removal

Lipman and Conybeare (1936) estimated that for the United States as a whole the average amount of phosphorus removed in the harvested portion of crops in 1930 was approximately 4 lb. per acre. The corresponding figure for the total amount of phosphorus removed is, perhaps, 5 to 6 lb. per acre. The quantity 6 lb. of phosphorus per acre is equal to about 0.5 per cent of the average content of phosphorus in the plowed layer of soil. It will be recalled from the preceding chapter that the total removal of nitrogen in harvested crops in 1930 averaged about 40 lb. per acre, a quantity equal to 1.4 per cent of the total nitrogen in the plowed layer of soil. The removal of phosphorus in crops thus is lower than the removal of nitrogen, both in absolute terms and in relation to the amounts present in soils.

Leaching

Soluble phosphate fertilizers react rapidly with soils, so that most of the added phosphorus remains near the point of addition. This generalization is illustrated by Table 2 which shows the vertical distribu-

Table 2.   Dilute-Acid-Soluble Phosphorus at Different Depths In Unfertilized and Superphosphate-fertilized Silt Loam Soil

(Midgley, 1931)

	Dilute-Acid-Soluble Phosphorus in Soil, p.p.m.	
Depth of sample, in.	Unfertilized	Surface Application of Superphosphate
0–0.5	10	100
0.5–1	4	38
1–2	4	8
2–3	4	4

tion of dilute-acid-soluble phosphorus in a silt loam soil under permanent pasture in Wisconsin. The soil received a surface application of 600 lb. of superphosphate per acre on April 25 and was sampled for analysis on October 15 of the same year.

In consequence of the low solubility and limited movement of phosphorus in soils, loss of phosphorus by leaching is negligible in most soils. In fact the loss is so slow that the deposition of phosphorus in the soils in areas of man's early habitation is now of some value as an indicator of archaeological sites (Dauncey, 1952). Specific measurements of leaching losses have been made in lysimeter experiments. In an experiment in Connecticut with a sandy loam soil, Morgan and

Jacobson (1942) added as fertilizer the equivalent of 3005 lb. of phosphorus per acre in an 11-year period. During this time, an average of only 0.1 lb. of phosphorus per acre annually was lost by leaching through the 18-inch depth of soil used. In sixteen other sets of lysimeters receiving phosphorus in amounts ranging from 481 to 973 lb. per acre for the 11-year period, only one set lost a measurable amount of phosphorus. Hendrick and Welsh (1928) reported the loss of only a trace of phosphorus in the drainage water from a sandy loam soil in Scotland.

Probably the only soils from which leaching loss of phosphorus is significant are sands and peats that have little tendency to react with phosphorus and are fertilized heavily. Neller (1947) reported results of an experiment on a fine sandy soil from Florida in which 91 per cent of the citrate-soluble phosphorus of an application of 625 lb. of superphosphate per acre was leached through an 8-inch layer of soil by a rainfall of 28 inches that fell within the period from May 10 to September 4 of the same year.

Erosion

Lipman and Conybeare (1936) estimated that the loss of phosphorus by erosion from the crop land of the United States averages 10.6 lb. per acre annually. This figure is substantially higher than the figure for the removal of phosphorus in the harvested portions of crops. These figures, however, are not directly comparable, for two reasons.

First, the crop-producing potentiality of the phosphorus in the two forms is not the same. If the two sources were evaluated on the basis of their effectiveness in supplying plants with phosphorus, the phosphorus removed by plants would be found to be much more valuable, pound for pound, than the phosphorus removed by erosion.

Second, the loss of phosphorus by both plant removal and erosion is compensated to some extent. Loss by plant removal is compensated in part by the return to the soil of some of the phosphorus in forms of greater availability than the phosphorus in the soil initially. This point is discussed at length in the section on availability of organic phosphorus. Loss by erosion is compensated to some extent by the phosphorus in the new material brought into the profile from beneath. If the new phosphorus added from beneath has an availability equal to that of the phosphorus lost by erosion, there is no net change in phosphorus availability. Such, in fact, may be the case in some soils. More commonly, however, the availability of phosphorus is much higher in the surface portion of soil, from which erosion losses occur, than in the parent material that becomes a part of the root zone as a result of erosion. Under these circumstances, loss of surface soil by erosion will decrease phosphorus availability. Table 3 illustrates the

Table 3.   Yield of Sweet Clover with and without Heavy Phosphate Fertilization on Samples Taken from Different Horizons of Two Soils from Minnesota
(Rost, 1939)

Relative Yield per Culture

Soil Horizon Sampled	Fayette Silt Loam		Lindley Silt Loam	
	No Phosphorus Added	42 lb. P as Superphosphate per Acre	No Phosphorus Added	42 lb. P as Superphosphate per Acre
Upper A	100	108	100	105
Lower A	68	101	80	124
Upper B	54	88	36	129
Lower B	94	88	21	118
C_1	83	78	55	109
C_2	84	83	28	111

contrast in behavior that exists between two soils. Except for the lower A and upper B horizons, the supply of phosphorus was adequate for the growth of sweet clover throughout the Fayette silt loam profile. In the Lindley silt loam profile, only the upper A horizon had an adequate phosphorus supply. All other horizons were deficient.

FORMS IN SOILS

The phosphorus in soils may be divided into two broad categories, organic and inorganic. The proportionate amounts of phosphorus in these two categories vary widely. The extreme values reported in the literature for surface samples of soils (Basu and Kibe, 1945; Ghani and Aleem, 1943) range from 3 per cent organic and 97 per cent inorganic on the one hand to 75 per cent organic and 25 per cent inorganic on the other. The content of organic phosphorus in soils increases as the content of nitrogen increases and as the pH decreases. L. M. Thompson et al. (1954) found that the average relationship in a group of fifty soil samples could be expressed by the equation $p = 0.078n - 82\ pH + 552$, where $p =$ p.p.m. of organic phosphorus and $n =$ p.p.m. of total nitrogen.

Inorganic

Examination of soils by classical methods for identification of solids has not yielded much information regarding the inorganic phosphorus compounds present. Most of the inorganic phosphorus occurs characteristically in the clay fraction from which it cannot be separated by physical methods. The great preponderance of nonphosphatic material serves to mask any measurable properties of the phosphatic compounds that might otherwise be found by X-ray diffraction, electron microscope, or differential thermal methods.

The most direct evidence regarding the nature of inorganic compounds of phosphorus in soils has been obtained by microscopic examination of individual grains of the sand and silt fractions. Apatite, the original mineral source of perhaps 95 per cent or more of the soil phosphorus (Rankama and Sahama, 1950, p. 585), has been identified in a number of soils. McCaughey and Fry (1913) identified apatite in eleven of twenty-five soils from different parts of the United States. Plummer (1915–1916) found apatite in four of nine soils investigated in North Carolina. Leahey (1934–1935) found fresh-appearing grains of apatite in the leached layer of a podzol soil. Fluorapatite, the most common and most stable form of apatite, is a calcium phosphate having the composition $Ca_{10}F_2(PO_4)_6$. The ferrous phosphate, vivianite $[Fe_3(PO_4)_2 \cdot 8H_2O]$, has been found on occasion under conditions of poor drainage. Dudley (1890) reported an occurrence of vivianite in old root channels in buried alluvium. Bushinskiĭ (1946) found vivianite in peat deposits. A notable occurrence of vivianite is a layer up to 3 inches in thickness at a depth of 28 to 30 inches in a peat bog at Labish Center, Oregon (J. E. Dawson, private communication). According to Dyal (1953), the aluminum phosphate known as wavellite $[Al_3(OH)_3(PO_4)_2 \cdot 5H_2O]$ was found by J. G. Cady in the sand and silt fractions of a soil from Florida. Dyal found evidence that the same mineral is present in the clay fraction of the same soil. Discovery of wavellite in this soil is not unexpected, since the parent material contains 35 to 45 per cent wavellite. It is safe to say that apatite, vivianite, and wavellite in the silt and sand fractions usually constitute only a small part of the total inorganic phosphorus of soils. The remaining phosphorus is unidentified as yet.

Various indirect means have been employed in investigating the nature of inorganic phosphorus in soils. The approach used most commonly has been extraction with different acid and alkaline solutions. Calcium phosphates are more soluble in dilute hydrochloric acid than in dilute sodium hydroxide. Ferric and aluminum phosphates are more soluble in dilute sodium hydroxide than in dilute hydrochloric acid. Stelly and Pierre (1943) and others have compared the phosphorus solubility versus pH curves of various soils with those of known phosphorus-bearing minerals, and have noted suggestive sim-

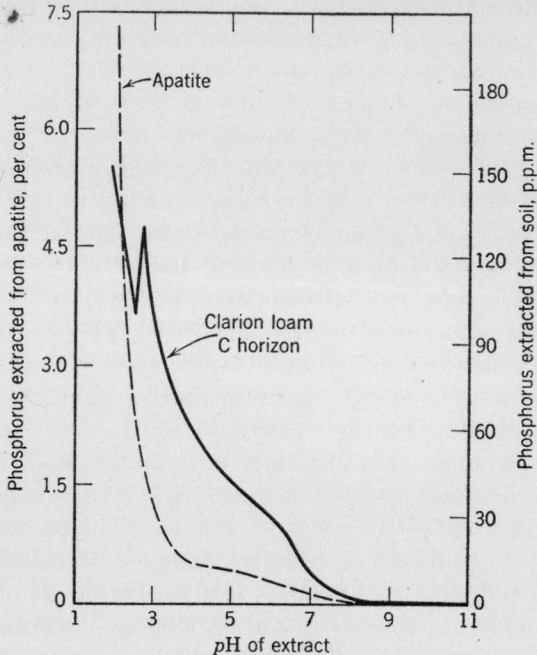

Fig. 2. Phosphorus extracted at various pH values from apatite and the C horizon of Clarion loam soil. (Stelly and Pierre, 1943.)

ilarities, as indicated in Fig. 2. The behavior of the phosphates in soils is correlated with the pH of the original soil. Alkaline soils usually display a solubility-pH curve similar to that of apatite. Acid soils usually display a solubility-pH curve similar to that of iron or aluminum phosphates. The initial reaction of the soil in Fig. 2 was pH 7.9.

Another indirect means that has been used in an attempt to identify the inorganic phosphorus compounds of soils is the solubility-product concept. The product of the activities of ions in solution is controlled by the nature of the solid-phase crystalline compound of sparing solubility with which these ions are in equilibrium. For example, the product of the activities of Ca^{++} and HPO_4^{--} ions in solution in equilibrium with crystals of dibasic calcium phosphate ($CaHPO_4$) remains constant despite the presence of other sources of these ions (if a correction is made for the ionic strength of the solution). This behavior can be used as a means of identifying crystalline compounds by finding whether the product of the activities of ions in solution corresponds with the solubility product that applies to a particular crystalline compound. Perhaps the principal experimental difficulty connected with the use of the solubility-product method is that although a constant and characteristic solubility-product figure is obtained if the solid-phase substances in question are well crystallized and if true equilibrium has been attained, it is by no means certain that these conditions exist in work done with soils.

Aslyng (1954) has employed the solubility-product concept as a means of finding whether dibasic calcium phosphate ($CaHPO_4 \cdot 2H_2O$) or hydroxyapatite [$Ca_5OH(PO_4)_3 \cdot H_2O$] is present in soils. Taking into account the concentrations of calcium, phosphate, and hydrogen in solutions that were in approximate equilibrium with various soils, he found that the phosphate concentration usually was somewhat greater than that which would be in equilibrium with hydroxyapatite, but never as high as that which would be in equilibrium with dibasic calcium phosphate. One thus may infer that dibasic calcium phosphate would be unstable in all the soils examined and that probably it was absent from them. In the soils having a phosphate concentration in excess of that which would be in equilibrium with hydroxyapatite, hydroxyapatite would be stable and it might be present. In soils having a phosphate concentration below that which would be in equilibrium with hydroxyapatite, hydroxyapatite would be unstable, and probably was absent. The soils examined by Aslyng were from England and Denmark. Clark and Peech (1955) used the same approach on soils from New York and found that the phosphate concentration was less than that required for equilibrium with hydroxyapatite in all instances examined, even when the soils had been treated with soluble phosphate. This work demonstrates that the inorganic soil phosphorus cannot be categorized neatly as either dibasic calcium phosphate or hydroxyapatite.

Geochemical evidence indicates that at least some of the phosphate is present in crystalline form as a minor constituent of crystalline silicate minerals, where it substitutes for silicon. Work on this subject was reviewed by Mason and Berggren (1941), who reported original data on phosphorus-bearing garnet and cited work of Hata, Kimura, and Kimura and Koyama on specimens of phosphorus-bearing zircon ($ZrSiO_4$) in which PO_4 groups were found substituting for as much as 25 per cent of the normal complement of SiO_4 groups. Such phosphate groups presumably are incorporated into the lattice framework during the process of crystallization and occur scattered throughout the structure. Experiments with the aluminosilicate clay mineral, kaolinite, indicate that some replacement of surface silicate groups by phosphate may occur subsequent to formation of the clay if the phosphate concentration is high in the external medium (Low and Black,

1950). Whether or not the inorganic soil phosphates as a whole are predominantly crystalline or amorphous, however, is a question that remains unanswered.

Organic

The technical problem of identifying the organic phosphorus compounds of soils is facilitated by the fact that with care the organic phosphorus can be extracted from soil as organic phosphorus and not simply as inorganic orthophosphate. By suitable fractionation methods, the bulk of the organic phosphorus can be separated from the bulk of the nonphosphatic organic matter that has been extracted therewith. Despite this substantial purification, however, the nature of the major part of the soil organic phosphorus still remains unknown.

For many years, the organic phosphorus was thought to consist principally or entirely of three types of compounds, namely, nucleic acids, inositol hexaphosphate (phytin), and phospholipids. Recent work indicates that this view is incorrect.

Adams, Bartholomew, and Clark (1954) attempted to identify nucleic acids in two soils high in organic phosphorus. After a complex fractionation procedure, which was shown to yield components of nucleic acids added to soils, they were unable to obtain any definite evidence for the existence of nucleic acids in soils. They tested for the presence of nucleic acids in the soil extracts by measuring the absorption of ultraviolet light in the wave-length range from 255 to 275 mμ. Nucleic acids absorb light in this wave band because of the nitrogen bases they contain.

Caldwell[2] developed a quantitative method for determining inositol hexaphosphate in soils on the basis of earlier work of Smith and Clark (1952). He found that phosphorus present as the meso isomer of inositol hexaphosphate constituted an average of 12 per cent of the total organic phosphorus in the samples of forty-nine soils he analyzed. Another 5 per cent of the organic phosphorus apparently was a different isomer of the same substance. Judging from the work of Smith and Clark (1951), the total inositol phosphate phosphorus is at least twice the quantity of inositol hexaphosphate phosphorus. The inositol phosphates are the most abundant of the soil organic phosphorus compounds that have been identified.

As pointed out by Black and Goring (1953), the existence of phospholipids in soils has been inferred from the presence of organic phosphorus in alcohol and ether extracts of soils and from the identification

[2] Caldwell, A. George. (1955) Inositol hexaphosphate in soils. Ph.D. Thesis, Iowa State College, Ames, Iowa.

of choline in soil extracts. Choline is a product of the hydrolysis of lecithin, one of the phospholipids. Work of various investigators indicates that the organic phosphorus in alcohol and ether extracts seldom exceeds 3 p.p.m., a negligible proportion of the total. In contrast to the recent findings on nucleic acids and inositol hexaphosphate, however, present evidence suggests that the phospholipids may occur in soils in quantities greater than those envisaged earlier. Goring and Bartholomew (1950) found that phospholipids are not extracted completely by the standard method when clay is present. The magnitude of the error remains to be determined, but the likelihood is small that phospholipids will emerge as a quantitatively important fraction of the soil organic phosphorus.

AVAILABILITY TO PLANTS

The state of knowledge of the mineralogical and chemical forms of phosphorus in soils has not advanced to the point where it can be applied directly in statements about phosphorus availability. The fact is that the forms that can be measured with some degree of precision appear to be of no special importance as a source of supply of phosphorus for plants. A more fruitful approach to the problem of understanding and predicting phosphorus availability in soils has been to view the matter from the standpoint of phosphorus behavior. The idea behind this approach is that as far as absorption by the plant is concerned, the behavior of phosphorus in the soil is of primary significance. The forms are of importance only as they affect the behavior.

Source used by plants

The prevailing view is that most, if not all, of the phosphorus absorbed by plants from the soil pre-exists in the soil solution as inorganic orthophosphate. Several lines of evidence support this view:

1. No indigenous form of phosphorus other than orthophosphate is known to be present in soils in more than trace quantities.
2. Much of the phosphorus is present as inorganic orthophosphate.
3. Plants are not known to absorb phosphorus directly from the solid phase, nor are they known to absorb the soil organic phosphorus present in the solution phase (Pierre and Parker, 1927).
4. The soil solution contains inorganic orthophosphate, and plants can absorb it almost quantitatively. Pierre and Parker (1927) found that corn would reduce the inorganic orthophosphate content of displaced soil solution to less than 0.007 p.p.m. of phosphorus, and Olsen

(1950) found that rye would decrease the concentration of inorganic orthophosphate in culture solution to 0.003 p.p.m. of phosphorus.

Concentration and renewal

Up to a limit, the phosphorus absorption and growth of plants in culture solutions increase with the concentration of phosphorus maintained in the solution. If the phosphorus absorbed by plants growing in soils comes from the soil solution, as argued above, it is reasonable to infer that, up to a limit, the phosphorus absorption and growth of plants in soils increase with the concentration of phosphorus maintained in the soil solution.

The importance of renewal of the phosphorus in the soil solution can be made evident from some simple calculations. If a soil has a bulk density of 1.2, contains 25 per cent water on the dry-weight basis, and contains 0.03 p.p.m. of phosphorus as inorganic orthophosphate dissolved in the water (this is the average concentration found by Pierre and Parker [1927] from analysis of the displaced solution from samples of twenty-one soils from southeastern and midwestern United States), the total quantity of phosphorus in solution in this soil is 0.04 lb. per acre to a depth of 2 feet. If a crop absorbs 10 lb. of phosphorus per acre from the surface 2 feet of soil, the soil solution contains at one time only 4/1000 of the total. If the absorption and renewal of phosphorus in the soil solution were to take place alternately, with complete removal and complete renewal in each cycle, the solid phase would be required to replenish the soil solution with phosphorus 249 times during growth of the crop. If the crop grows for 120 days, the phosphorus in the soil solution will be replaced an average of twice a day.

The rate of renewal of phosphorus in the portion of the soil solution from which absorption is occurring no doubt is much greater than is indicated by the foregoing example, since plants do not absorb phosphorus uniformly throughout the entire soil mass. Because of the properties of phosphorus in the soil system, appreciable movement of soil phosphorus to plant roots probably does not occur beyond a shell extending more than a few millimeters from the root into the soil. Although absorption of phosphorus from the soil probably takes place slowly over much of the root system, the most active absorption takes place near the root tip. The actively absorbing surface of the root system thus moves through the soil, continually exploiting new areas from which phosphorus absorption could not occur previously. At a given instant, therefore, replenishment of the solution-phase phosphorus probably is taking place rapidly in the small areas near the root tips, slowly in the larger areas surrounding the older portion of the root system, and not at all in the areas of soil yet to be explored by the roots.

Unpublished data of M. Fried and co-workers of the United States Department of Agriculture indicate that the rate of renewal of phosphorus in the soil solution by dissolution of solid-phase phosphorus is rapid in comparison with the rate of absorption by plants. Thus although renewal of the phosphorus in the soil solution may be virtually essential, the rate at which this process occurs appears to be rapid enough to maintain the concentration at substantially its equilibrium level despite absorption by plants. Since in most soils the concentration of phosphorus in the soil solution is in the range in which concentration limits uptake, concentration appears to be more important than rate of renewal in controlling the rate of absorption of phosphorus by plants.

Inorganic phosphorus behavior

Experimental work with radioactive phosphorus (McAuliffe et al., 1948; Olsen, 1953a, 1953b) has established the principle that the inorganic phosphate ions in the soil solution are exchanging continuously with inorganic phosphate ions held by the solid phase of the soil. That such an exchange occurs is indicated by Fig. 3. To obtain the data in this figure, McAuliffe et al. (1948) suspended a sample of soil in water for four days to allow the phosphorus in the solid phase to come to equilibrium with the solution phase. Then they added a trace of P^{32}-tagged inorganic orthophosphate in a small volume of

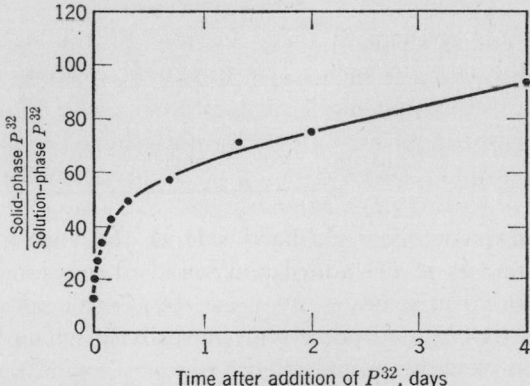

Fig. 3. Ratio of solid-phase P^{32} to solution-phase P^{32} versus time after addition of a trace of P^{32}-tagged inorganic orthophosphate to a suspension of Caribou soil. (McAuliffe, Hall, Dean, and Hendricks, 1948.)

water, thereby avoiding any substantial net movement of phosphorus either to or from the solid phase during the subsequent period of equilibration. Under these conditions all the P^{32} would have remained in the solution phase if there had been no solid-phase P^{31} with which the phosphate ions in solution were exchanging. The fact that most of the P^{32} was soon in the solid phase demonstrates the existence of a relatively large amount of solid-phase phosphorus with which the solution-phase phosphorus was in equilibrium.

With respect to the continuous exchange between solution and solid phase, the behavior of phosphate is analogous to that of exchangeable bases. Soil cannot be said, however, to have an anion exchange capacity that is analogous to the cation-exchange capacity. The solid-phase constituents of the soil retain phosphate by virtue of their property of forming relatively insoluble phosphates. The capacity of soil to react with phosphate is limited essentially by the total content of elements that will react with phosphate to produce compounds of low solubility. This is proved by occurrences of various rocks that have been altered to phosphates on contact with phosphate-bearing solutions (Clarke, 1920, pp. 516–519).

The exchange that takes place between solution-phase P^{32} and solid-phase P^{31} may be represented by the equation

$$P^{32}_{solution} + P^{31}_{solid} = P^{32}_{solid} + P^{31}_{solution}$$

The equilibrium constant of this reaction is given by

$$\frac{P^{32}_{solid} \times P^{31}_{solution}}{P^{32}_{solution} \times P^{31}_{solid}} = K = 1$$

The equilibrium constant is unity because of the near identity of behavior of the two isotopes. The foregoing expression may be rearranged to

$$P^{31}_{solid} = \frac{P^{32}_{solid} \times P^{31}_{solution}}{P^{32}_{solution}}$$

Since all variates on the right-hand side of the equality are known from the quantities of P^{32} added and found in solution, and the total phosphorus found in solution, P^{31}_{solid} can be calculated. P^{31}_{solid} represents the quantity of solid-phase phosphorus with which the P^{32} added to the solution phase has equilibrated.

Values of P^{31}_{solid} calculated in this way are not exact, because the assumed condition of equilibrium does not obtain. Nevertheless, they provide a valuable means for gaining a conception of soil phosphorus behavior. The work of McAuliffe et al. (1948) in Table 4 may be cited in this connection. To obtain the data, samples of soil were equilibrated with water for several days before adding a trace of P^{32}-tagged inorganic orthophosphate. The equilibration then was continued until the most rapid phase of the exchange with the soil was completed (this would be after about 1 day for the soil in Fig. 3), at which time the solution was analyzed for its content of inorganic P^{31} and P^{32}. The calculations indicated in Table 4 show that the

Table 4. Estimated Quantity of Solid-Phase Orthophosphate of Different Soils Involved in Exchange with Inorganic Orthophosphate in the Solution Phase

(McAuliffe, Hall, Dean, and Hendricks, 1948)

	P on Dry Soil Basis, p.p.m.		
Soil Series and Sample Number	Solid-Phase P^{32} / Solution-Phase P^{32} (A)	Inorganic P in Solution Phase (B)	Solid-Phase P^{31} Involved in Exchange with Solution-Phase P^{32}, as Estimated from (A) × (B)
Caribou No. 1	220.0	0.145	32
Caribou No. 2	71.0	1.35	96
Sagemoor No. 1	20.0	0.145	3
Sagemoor No. 2	3.3	9.5	31

reservoir of solid-phase phosphorus in these soils was much greater in size than the reservoir of solution-phase inorganic phosphorus with which it was in equilibrium. The contrast in relative magnitudes would be much greater under natural conditions, in which the content of water in the soil would be perhaps one twenty-fifth as great as that employed experimentally. The solid-phase phosphorus with which the P^{32} exchanges over a period of a few days is almost all inorganic. Direct exchange with organic phosphorus apparently is negligible, and the quantity of P^{32} incorporated into organic forms by microbial synthesis is small in relation to that which exchanges with the inorganic phosphorus (Goring, 1955).

Table 4 shows also that the quantity of phosphorus in the solid-phase reservoir may differ greatly among soils. Moreover, the quantities of phosphorus in the solid phase do not necessarily increase in a regular manner with the quantities in the solution. Evidently, the quantity of phosphorus in the solution-phase reservoir is not an accurate indication of the quantity in the solid-phase reservoir, even though the two coexist in direct contact and continuous phosphate exchange occurs between them. The absence of a simple and direct relationship may be attributed in part to differences in the ionic composition of the solutions, and in part to differences in the sites to which phosphate is attached in the solid phase. Little is known about the latter, but it is clear that in a given soil, the phosphate ions in the solid-phase sites do not all exchange equally readily with the phosphate ions in solution; this may be inferred from Fig. 3. If the phosphate ions in all sites exchanged as readily as those with which exchange occurred first, the curve would be flat after perhaps a day. That is to say, equilibrium would be established. The fact that the ratio of P^{32}_{solid} to $P^{32}_{solutoin}$ continued to increase after this time demonstrates the existence of phosphate ions of lower exchangeability in the solid phase. Some of these ions may have been located in surface positions and exchanged slowly because of a low degree of ionization. With others the exchange may have been slow because of the time required for the diffusion of phosphate along narrow channels or through solid material to and from relatively inaccessible positions. In view of such differences within a given soil, the existence of differences in exchangeability among soils is not unlikely.

The foregoing concepts may be incorporated into a hypothesis about the sequence of events in the presence of plants. When plants absorb phosphate ions from the soil solution, they do not return an equal number of phosphate ions by exchange. This disturbs the equilibrium that existed previously between the solid-phase and solution-phase phosphorus. Until equilibrium is re-established, phosphate ions leave the solid phase more rapidly than they return, being replaced by other anions, such as silicate, hydroxyl, or carbonate. The net consequence of this disturbance is that the solution phase is depleted somewhat of phosphorus, but not to an extent commensurate with the quantity of phosphorus removed because of the outflow of phosphorus from the solid phase into the solution. In the process, of course, the concentration of phosphorus in the solution adjacent to the roots may drop substantially below the final equilibrium value. With continued removal of phosphorus from the soil, the rate at which removal can occur will decline gradually because of the diminishing concentration of phosphorus in the solution phase, and the diminishing rate at which phosphate ions enter the solution from the solid phase. The decrease in the rate of solution can be attributed to the decrease in the number of ions in the solid-phase reservoir and to the decrease in the mobility of these ions, the latter resulting from the attachment of the remaining ions to sites at which exchange does not occur readily.

Inorganic phosphorus evaluation

Various laboratory techniques have been used to estimate soil phosphorus availability. The voluminous literature on the subject has been reviewed in several papers (Behrens, 1937, 1940; Anonymous, 1950; Nelson, Mehlich, and Winters, 1953). These techniques have in common the objective of separating the soil inorganic phosphorus into two or more fractions on the basis of reactivity under specified conditions. Only the "reactive" fraction (or fractions) is measured.

Research has shown that the quantities of the reactive fraction of phosphorus found in a group of soils may correlate fairly well with the plant response on the various soils provided the range in soil properties is restricted sufficiently. When the range of soil properties is not restricted, however, the significance of a given figure for phosphorus obtained in the laboratory usually depends on the nature of the soil. The situation is illustrated by Figs. 4 and 5, in which the phosphorus absorbed by alfalfa from two groups of soils in greenhouse cultures is plotted against the phosphorus extracted from the soils by two different reagents.

From the standpoint of laboratory techniques, the failure of a given measurement to have the same significance in different soils may be attributed to two causes. The first of these is that the proportionate quantities of phosphorus extracted from different sources in the soil are not the same with the laboratory techniques as with plants. For example, in the two figures just cited, the divergence between the two groups of soils was much greater with the 0.1 N acid extractant (Fig. 4) than with the 0.025 N acid extractant (Fig. 5), presumably because

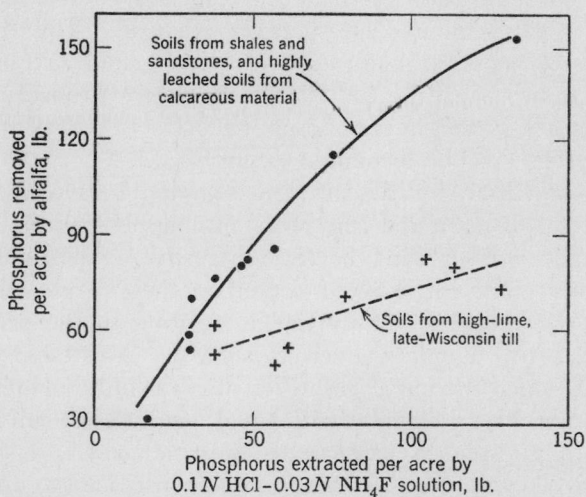

Fig. 4. Phosphorus removed from two groups of soils by alfalfa versus phosphorus extracted by 0.1N HCl-0.03N NH$_4$F solution. (Thompson and Pratt, 1954.)

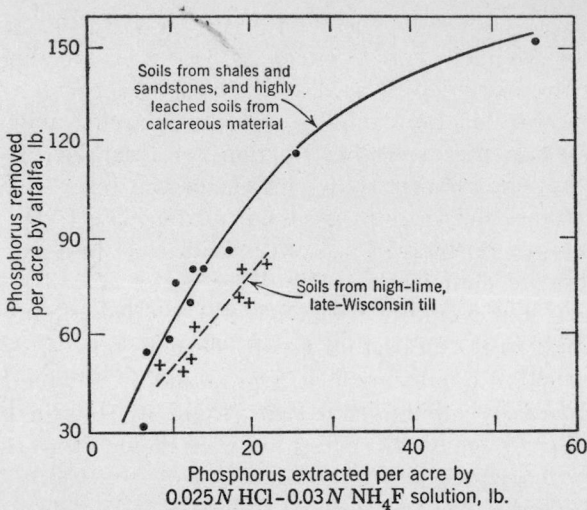

Fig. 5.   Phosphorus removed from two groups of soils by alfalfa versus phosphorus extracted by 0.025N HCl-0.03N NH₄F solution.   (Thompson and Pratt, 1954.)

the soils from high-lime, late-Wisconsin till contained much more acid-soluble phosphorus of low availability than did the soils from shales and sandstones.   The strong acid extracted considerable of this acid-soluble phosphorus, and the weak acid did not.   In some instances part of the phosphorus dissolved by the reagent is reprecipitated in the soil before the phosphorus measurement is made.   This difficulty is thought to be most pronounced with strong-acid extractants that remain in contact with the soil for a long time.   Probably the sharp dip between pH 2 and 3 in the phosphorus extraction curve for Clarion loam soil in Fig. 2 can be accounted for in this way.

The second reason for the difference among soils with respect to significance to plants of the laboratory findings is that the laboratory technique may not act with the same intensity on the phosphorus of different soils.   The intensity of action on the soil phosphorus may depend on the properties of the soil in relation to the properties of the reagent.   An example is given in Table 5.   This table shows that two soils, in which the initial pH difference was only 0.1 unit, differed by 0.7 pH unit after treatment with equal quantities of sulfuric acid, a common soil phosphorus extractant.   Sulfuric acid is a strong acid and is relatively unbuffered.   Hence, in this instance the difference in intensity of action of the reagent on the two soils may be attributed to the difference in buffer properties of the soil.   The soil with the

Table 5.   Reaction of Two Soils before and after Addition of Acid
(Runk, 1925)

Soil Type	Initial Soil Reaction, pH	Soil Reaction after Addition of 1.4 m.e. of H_2SO_4 per 100 g., pH
Norfolk loamy sand	5.6	3.3
Sassafras silt loam	5.7	4.0

higher cation-exchange capacity was the one less affected by the acid. Extractants having a high buffer capacity, on the other hand, bring all soils to about the initial pH of the extractant, irrespective of the initial pH of the soil. With such reagents, the difference in intensity of action on the soil phosphorus may be attributed to differences in initial soil pH, and not to differences in buffer properties.

Of the laboratory methods now in use for estimating soil inorganic phosphorus availability, perhaps the closest approach to a valid estimate over a wide variety of soils is obtained by determining the amount of phosphorus extracted with 0.025 N hydrochloric acid and 0.03 N ammonium fluoride (Bray and Kurtz, 1945), 0.5 M sodium bicarbonate (Olsen et al., 1954), or an anion-exchange resin (Amer et al., 1955), or by estimating the amount of soil phosphorus that exchanges with tagged inorganic orthophosphate (McAuliffe et al., 1948). The first two of these methods are more subject to question than the last two on the basis of acting with different intensities on the phosphorus of different soils. All four methods are subject to question on the basis that the proportions of the various sources of soil phosphorus they measure may be rather different from the proportions actually used from those sources by plants.

Organic phosphorus

Since plants do not appear to absorb organic phosphorus compounds from the soil, the accumulation of organic phosphorus in the soil profile depicted in Fig. 1 may seem to be an undesirable consequence of organic matter accumulation. In this soil, the organic phosphorus apparently has been produced primarily at the expense of the dilute-acid-soluble phosphorus, since the sum of the two fractions is about the same throughout the profile.

Despite the locking up of phosphorus in organic forms, however, the availability of the phosphorus in the profile described in Fig. 1 is greater near the surface, where part of the inorganic phosphorus has been changed to the organic form, than in the subsoil, where the phosphorus remains in inorganic form. That such is the case was demonstrated by Stelly,[3] who grew plants on samples of soil taken from different depths in the profile. The increase in yield from phosphorus fertilization was relatively small in the surface samples and large in the subsoil samples. Part of the availability effects observed by Stelly probably resulted from the inorganic phosphorus in the plant residues returned to the soil. But part of the effects probably are attributable more directly to the organic phosphorus.

The organic phosphorus is a part of the organic matter and, along with nitrogen, tends to follow the pattern of accumulation and loss set by the organic matter as a whole (Thompson, Black, and Zoellner, 1954). A small amount of inorganic phosphorus thus is released continually in the soil by the same decomposition processes that release nitrogen in mineral form. Since this phosphorus is present in water solution at the time of release, its availability to plants should be equivalent to that of phosphate fertilizer introduced into the soil solution at the same rate and distributed throughout the soil in the same manner. Although the value of a phosphate fertilizer applied in this way cannot be determined, some concept of the possible effect of the phosphorus fertilization resulting from organic phosphorus mineralization may be derived from data on the quantities of organic phosphorus mineralized. Table 6 records estimates of organic phosphorus min-

Table 6. Estimated Quantities of Organic Phosphorus Mineralized in Samples of Four Soils during 30 Days' Incubation in the Laboratory at Two Temperatures
(Bower, 1949)

Soil Type and Treatment	Organic Phosphorus Mineralized at Indicated Temperature, p.p.m.	
	25° C	35° C
Grundy silt loam (cropped)	3	14
Grundy silt loam (virgin)	37	69
Marshall silt loam (cropped)	2	13
Marshall silt loam (virgin)	6	25

eralized in different soils during incubation in the laboratory for a period of 30 days. The experimental values represent the increase in acid-soluble inorganic phosphorus in the samples resulting from incubation. Other work has shown that these values approximate the decrease in content of organic phosphorus and, hence, that they can be used as estimates of organic phosphorus mineralization. The lowest figure, 2 p.p.m., is equivalent to about 4 lb. of phosphorus per acre to plow depth, or 46 lb. of ordinary superphosphate containing 20 per

[3] Stelly, Matthias. (1942) Forms of inorganic phosphorus in the lower horizons of some Iowa soils as indicated by plant availability and chemical methods. Ph.D. Thesis, Iowa State College, Ames, Iowa.

Phosphorus = organic P × 2

cent P_2O_5 or 8.73 per cent phosphorus.   The highest figure, 69 p.p.m., is equivalent to about 138 lb. of phosphorus per acre to plow depth, or 1580 lb. of ordinary superphosphate.   The fertilization thus may be substantial.

When superphosphate is mixed thoroughly with the soil, the recovery of the added phosphorus in the crop seldom exceeds 20 per cent. There is no reason to believe that the recovery by the crop of the inorganic phosphorus that has been added throughout the soil by mineralization of organic phosphorus is any greater.   Undoubtedly, most of the mineralized phosphorus remains in the soil from year to year, in consequence of which the inorganic phosphorus that plants absorb from the soil is derived in part from organic phosphorus that was mineralized in earlier years.

Thus, instead of a sink into which some of the soil phosphorus has been lost beyond recall, the organic phosphorus fraction may be visualized as a reservoir, itself beyond the reach of plants, but from which phosphorus slowly drains through the soil solution into a second reservoir, the inorganic phosphorus in the solid phase that exchanges readily with the phosphorus in solution.   The self-fertilization resulting from organic phosphorus mineralization and the return of inorganic phosphorus in plant residues constitute the primary means, under natural conditions, by which the phosphorus availability is increased from the low level usually found in the parent materials to the relatively high level usually found in the soils.

The contribution of the previously mineralized phosphorus to the phosphorus availability in the soil is included automatically in the estimate of phosphorus availability obtained by all the usual techniques; however, the availability of the inorganic phosphorus derived from mineralization subsequent to analysis is not accounted for.   One may therefore inquire whether the estimate of the importance of organic phosphorus that is included in the inorganic phosphorus measurement is adequate or whether the significance of the phosphorus mineralized currently is sufficient to warrant independent estimation.   This problem was investigated by Eid et al. (1951, 1954) and Semb and Uhlen (1954), who found that the organic phosphorus was of significant value in predicting the phosphorus availability to plants independently of the inorganic phosphorus supply which was measured separately. Eid et al. found that organic phosphorus was important in warm soils (35° C) but not in cool soils (20° C), presumably because of the effect of temperature on mineralization (Table 6).   Semb and Uhlen found that organic phosphorus was important in soils having pH values above 5.5, but not below 5.5, presumably because of the effect of pH

on mineralization (described in the following section). These results indicate that an estimate of the quantity of organic phosphorus that will be mineralized while the crop is growing may be of value in increasing the precision of estimates of soil phosphorus availability if conditions are favorable for organic phosphorus mineralization.

Effect of soil reaction

Phosphorus availability in soils varies with the reaction or pH of the soil, as has been mentioned already in the chapters on soil acidity and on soil salinity and alkalinity. A general picture of the situation is given in Table 7 which summarizes the results of measurements on a

Table 7. Percentage of Soil Samples Having Low Phosphorus Availability in Groups Classified According to pH Value

(Jenny, Vlamis, and Martin, 1950)

Soil Reaction Group, pH	Number of Samples Tested	Percentage of Samples Having Low Phosphorus Availability
Below 5.9	105	79
6.0–6.3	91	65
6.4–6.7	89	37
6.8–7.9	116	26
8.0–8.3	27	44
Above 8.3	20	80

large number of samples of soils from California. The criterion of phosphorus availability in this work was the ratio of the yield of lettuce grown on the soil without phosphate fertilization (p_0) to the yield with heavy phosphate fertilization (p), where soil in both the p_0 and p treatments received an application of nitrogen and potassium. Samples having a value of p_0/p less than 0.2 are said to have low phosphorus availability. Clearly, the frequency of occurrence of samples having low phosphorus availability was least in the approximately neutral group and greatest in the most acid and most alkaline groups.

From the data in Table 7 one would expect the phosphorus availability to be increased when soils that are strongly acid or strongly alkaline are treated to adjust the pH value toward neutrality. A variety of experimental evidence indicates that soil behavior usually follows this pattern. Table 8 gives an example for acid soil, showing results of measurements on samples from limed and unlimed plots in a field experiment. The contention that liming had increased phosphorus availability in this soil is strengthened by the evidence that the increase in absorption of phosphorus by the plants was parallelled by an increase in concentration of phosphorus in the soil solution.

Table 8. Concentration of Phosphorus in Soil Solution, and Removal of Phosphorus by Wheat Seedlings from Samples of Limed and Unlimed Acid Soil from Field Plots

(Fudge, 1928)

	Phosphorus in Displaced Soil Solution, P.P.M.	Phosphorus Removed from Soil by Wheat Seedlings, mg.
Unlimed soil (pH 4.6)	0.03	1.2
Limed soil (pH 6.3)	0.33	3.4

When acid soils are limed, there are apparently two processes that bring about release of inorganic phosphorus in soluble form. The first of these is the hydrolysis of iron and aluminum phosphates. Hydroxyl ions compete with phosphate ions for attachment to the iron and aluminum present as hydrous oxides in the soil. Application of calcium carbonate increases the OH^- ion concentration, which shifts the balance toward retention of hydroxyl, and increases the equilibrium concentration of phosphate in solution.

Organic phosphorus provides an additional source of soluble phosphorus when acid soils are limed. Several investigators have found that the content of organic phosphorus in acid soils decreases as a result of liming. Laboratory experiments on samples of various unlimed soils have shown that, per unit of organic phosphorus present, the rate of mineralization increases with soil pH. Work on this subject was reviewed by Black and Goring (1953). The explanation for the effect of liming on organic phosphorus mineralization probably is similar to that for inorganic phosphorus solubility, that is, raising the pH reduces the sorption capacity of the hydrous oxides for the organic phosphorus compounds, thus increasing their solubility and susceptibility to mineralization.

The effect of liming, however, is not entirely one of increasing the solubility of soil phosphorus. Solid-phase calcium phosphates may be formed. The solubility of the phosphorus in these phosphates decreases with the increase in activities of calcium and hydroxyl ions, both of which are increased by liming. Thus, liming activates two processes that release phosphorus and one that locks it up. Examination of samples of soil collected from field experiments on liming usually discloses a higher concentration of phosphorus in the soil solution of limed than of unlimed soils, but the reverse is not impossible and, in fact, has been observed repeatedly in laboratory experiments (Aslyng, 1954).

With some acid soils, liming may decrease the availability of phosphorus temporarily. Pierre and Browning (1935) found that with eight of nine strongly acid soils investigated in West Virginia the yield of alfalfa the first year after liming was less when the soil was limed to about pH 7.2 than to pH 6.5. The depression in yield was less marked the second year after liming. In that year, five of the soils produced a higher yield at about pH 7.2 than at pH 6.5. Corn likewise was affected adversely, yielding less on soil limed to pH 7 than to pH 5.8. That an induced phosphorus deficiency was at least partly responsible for the unfavorable effect of the higher pH value is indicated by the fact that the phosphorus percentage in the plants was lower and the increase in yield from phosphate fertilization was greater at pH 7 than at pH 5.8. In this experiment, the content of water-soluble inorganic phosphorus in the soil was virtually the same at the two pH values. Evidently, therefore, neither the water-solubility nor the availability of soil phosphorus is increased invariably when acid soils are limed.

Failure of the availability to follow the water solubility, although disturbing, may mean merely that water-solubility is not always a suitable criterion for inferring the relative availability of phosphorus in limed versus unlimed soils. That is to say, although there is no doubt that phosphorus availability increases with the concentration of phosphorus in solution in either an unlimed soil or a limed soil when the change in concentration is brought about by the addition of a phosphate fertilizer, it is not known whether a given concentration is associated with the same availability in the limed soil as in the unlimed soil.

As would be expected from Table 7, treatments that have a moderate acidifying effect usually increase the phosphorus availability in alkaline soils. An example is shown in Fig. 6. The inference from this figure is that the interaction of the soil phosphorus with the nitric acid increased the phosphorus availability to an extent as great as did the application of about 175 lb. of fertilizer phosphorus per acre. The interaction of soil phosphorus with the sulfuric acid produced from sulfur oxidation increased the phosphorus availability to an extent as great as did the application of about 350 lb. of fertilizer phosphorus per acre. The original data from which Fig. 6 was constructed provided no check on the validity of the assumption that the yield was a unique function of phosphorus availability, but the extremely large effect of the phosphate fertilizer serves to verify that the increase in yield produced by the acid treatments was caused at least in part by an increase in phosphorus availability. The increase in phosphorus solubility accompanying the acidification of alkaline soils has been demonstrated by Gardner and Kelley (1940) and others.

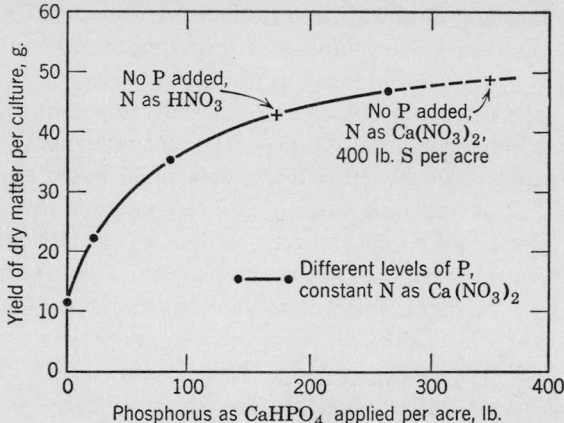

Fig. 6. Yield of sudan grass on a slightly calcareous clay loam soil with different applications of dibasic calcium phosphate and constant application of nitrogen. (Chapman, 1936.)

The cause of the observations in the foregoing paragraph is thought to be that the inorganic phosphorus in alkaline soils is predominantly in combination with calcium as some sort of calcium phosphate. Calcium phosphates are dissolved by acids because the tendency of the phosphate ion to associate with hydrogen instead of calcium increases rapidly as the acidity increases. If the calcium phosphate contains hydroxyl, as is the case with hydroxyapatite, an additional cause of solution of the phosphate with increasing acidity is the decrease in hydroxyl-ion activity in the solution.

To complete the picture, the effect of pH on absorption of phosphorus by plants must be considered independently of the changes that go on in the soil. In experiments with plants growing in solution cultures, Van den Honert (1933) and others have found that plants absorb the $H_2PO_4^-$ ion preferentially over the HPO_4^{--} and PO_4^{---} ions. As the pH increases through the range suitable for the growth of plants, the proportion of the total orthophosphate present as $H_2PO_4^-$ decreases. Hence the ratio of the effective concentration to the total concentration decreases as the pH increases. Presumably these same principles apply in soils, where plants are thought to absorb phosphorus as inorganic orthophosphate from the soil solution.

FUNCTION IN PLANTS

Although phosphorus occurs in the inorganic form in plants, it occurs also in a host of organic forms. For convenience in discussion the organic forms may be classified into two groups, namely, the storage and structural compounds, and the compounds of intermediate metabolism.

The first group of compounds includes phytin, phospholipids, and nucleoproteins. Phosphorus in seeds is stored principally as phytin, the calcium-magnesium salt of inositol hexaphosphoric acid. During germination the compound is hydrolyzed enzymatically, which changes the phosphate to the inorganic form, from which it may be used for other purposes by the developing seedling. Phospholipids are esters of glycerol or inositol with phosphoric acid, fatty acids, and sometimes other substances. The phosphoric acid may be present as a salt, or it may be esterified further with a nitrogenous base. Phospholipids apparently act as storage material in seeds, and in growing plants they probably have other functions that have not been discovered. Nucleoproteins are conjugated phosphorus-bearing compounds containing a protein and a nucleic acid. The phosphorus is contained in the nucleic acid portion. Nucleic acids are high-molecular-weight compounds, the building units of which are called nucleotides. Nucleotides contain one molecule each of a purine or pyrimidine base, ribose or desoxyribose sugar, and phosphoric acid and are linked together by the phosphoric acid groups. Nucleoproteins occur in chromosomes and have been observed to undergo changes during the mitotic cycle, from which it is inferred that the nucleoproteins are important in reproduction. Corroborative evidence has been obtained from a study of viruses, which are nucleoproteins that have the property of reproduction.

Compounds in the second group will not be named individually because of the large number. Instead, the metabolic processes in which these compounds are involved will be described briefly with reference to the role of phosphorus. Phosphorus occurs not only in certain enzymes that catalyze metabolic reactions but also in certain of the metabolites. The phosphorus in the enzymes is present in the coenzyme portion, but it does not appear to be involved directly in the catalysis.

In the metabolites, phosphorus plays a direct rôle as a carrier of energy. This rôle is made possible by the fact that the phosphate in several organic linkages may be split off by hydrolysis with a relatively high yield of energy. Phosphate groups that have this property are called high-energy phosphate. The most important carrier of high-energy phosphate is adenosine triphosphate, in which the high-energy bonds are indicated by the symbol $\sim$. The ester

$$
\begin{array}{c}
NH_2 \\
| \\
C \qquad N \\
N \diagdown \quad C \diagup \quad CH \qquad O \\
HC \qquad C———N—C \qquad C—C—O—P—O\sim P—O\sim P—OH \\
N \qquad\qquad H\diagdown H\ H\diagup H\ \ H \qquad OH\ \ OH\ \ OH \\
C—C \\
|\ \ | \\
OH\ OH
\end{array}
$$

Adenosine triphosphate

linkages of phosphate groups in phytin, phospholipids, and nucleo-proteins are not high-energy bonds and yield less energy on hydrolysis. Although there are various kinds of high-energy bonds besides that of phosphorus, the phosphorus high-energy bond has the unique property of being relatively stable in water. By means of enzymes, the high-energy phosphate can be transferred from a source such as adenosine triphosphate to another compound, like glucose, without dissipation of the energy in transit. Once the high-energy phosphate is in combination with the phosphate acceptor, however, the energy is transferred largely to the remainder of the molecule, and the phosphate becomes the low-energy type. The extra energy that has been trans-ferred to the accepting compound makes that compound more reactive. For example, the activation energy needed to cause glucose to form starch is supplied by the transfer of a high-energy phosphate group to each molecule of glucose. The phosphate is eliminated as inorganic phosphate when the glucose molecules are linked.

Adenosine triphosphate is the principal source of high-energy phos-phate used in reactions of the type described above. Regeneration of adenosine triphosphate from the diphosphate is brought about by carbohydrate oxidation. With glucose, for example, the molecule is activated by addition of two high-energy phosphate groups. The degradation process takes place through various rearrangements and side reactions that result in the production of a net total of 38 new high-energy phosphate groups per molecule of glucose oxidized to carbon dioxide and water. Much of the energy released in the oxidation is stored in the phosphate groups.

In addition to these rôles, phosphorus is involved in the initial reac-tions of photosynthesis. Carbon dioxide is thought to react with a five-carbon sugar containing two phosphate groups, with the forma-tion of two molecules of a three-carbon compound (phosphoglyceric acid). The latter is upgraded by energy supplied from high-energy phosphate.

The synthesis of plant tissue thus represents a process by which energy of the sun is captured in simple organic compounds, and the simple compounds are elaborated into complex compounds of higher energy content at the expense of part of the energy derived from the initial photosynthetic reaction. Phosphorus plays an essential rôle in all three phases of the process.

Although the rôle of organic forms of phosphorus has been emphasized in the preceding discussion, the auxiliary rôle played by the inorganic phosphorus in the plant must not be overlooked. The inorganic phosphorus represents both the source of phosphate ions that enter the organic part of the metabolic cycle and the repository of these ions as they leave. A given phosphate ion probably does not remain for an extended period in either organic or inorganic form but changes frequently from one to the other. If the concentration of inorganic phosphorus is too low, the rate of the metabolic processes will be limited by the rate at which phosphate ions arrive at the sites where they are bound in organic form. This obligate relationship between organic metabolism and phosphorus in the inorganic form probably is responsible for the tendency of the inorganic phosphorus concentration to be relatively high in tissues that are metabolizing rapidly.

The role of phosphorus in plants has been discussed here in only the barest outline, omitting details concerning specific compounds, reactions, and enzymes. For more detailed coverage and references to the literature, the works of Arnon (1953), Bonner (1950), and Vishniac (1955) should be consulted.

PHOSPHORUS SUPPLY AND PLANT BEHAVIOR

Deficiency symptoms

Although extreme phosphorus deficiency may result in some leaf yellowing, the more common appearance is a dull or dark bluish-green color, which may be coupled with tints of bronze or purple. The purple coloration is the most striking and most frequently mentioned symptom of phosphorus deficiency. As a diagnostic criterion, however, the purple coloration unfortunately is of little value for plants in general because of its low degree of specificity. Similar tints sometimes are produced by a deficiency of nitrogen or by other conditions. Moreover, some kinds of plants produce the color whether phosphorus is deficient or not. Others do not produce it even when phosphorus is deficient. The complete range of behavior is found in different varieties of corn.

Phosphorus deficiency produces certain effects that are similar to effects of nitrogen deficiency. With deficiencies of both elements, the stalks are thin, the leaves are small, and lateral growth is limited; defoliation is premature, beginning first with the lower leaves; blossoming is reduced, and the opening of buds in the spring is delayed. The similarity of phosphorus and nitrogen in these respects perhaps can be attributed to two causes. First, under conditions of deficiency, both phosphorus and nitrogen characteristically are withdrawn from older tissue and translocated to meristematic tissue where metabolism is more rapid (Williams, 1955). Second, of all the mineral nutrients, phosphorus and nitrogen play the most fundamental and all-pervading rôles in metabolism. A deficiency of either element slows down the metabolism in general, with a minimum of unbalance.

In general, phosphorus deficiency symptoms are not particularly striking or characteristic. Phosphorus deficiency thus may be difficult to diagnose from visual examination of plants. Chemical analysis or trials with phosphate fertilizer may be required.

Further discussion of phosphorus deficiency symptoms and references to the literature will be found in the works of McMurtrey (1948), Hambidge (1949), and Wallace (1951). The last two contain colored pictures showing the appearance of various kinds of plants under conditions of phosphorus deficiency.

Root growth

Phosphorus sometimes is said to stimulate root growth, the implication being that phosphorus has some special effect on the growth of roots that it does not have on the above-ground portion of the plant. The answer to this question depends on what is meant by "root."

If "root" designates the subterranean storage tissue of root crops, the phosphorus supply does have a special effect. If such a crop is deficient in phosphorus, phosphorus fertilization usually increases the yield of roots more than that of the above-ground parts. This is true whether the increases in yield are expressed on the absolute or relative basis. Table 9 gives an example from a field experiment with mangolds. A reasonable explanation for this behavior seems to be that the maximum leaf weight is attained at a later date by the phosphorus-deficient plants than by the phosphorus-fertilized plants, with the result that carbohydrate translocation to the storage tissue proceeds for a longer period of time in the phosphate-fertilized plants than in the phosphorus-deficient plants.

Table 9.   Average Yield of Leaves and Storage Roots of Mangolds with and
without Application of Phosphate Fertilizer over the Period from 1904
to 1940 at the Rothamsted Experimental Station

(Watson and Russell, 1943)

	Yield per Acre	
Plant Part	No Phosphate Added, ton	Phosphate Fertilized, ton
Leaves	3.4	3.4
Storage roots	10.5	16.0

On the other hand, if "root" refers to the absorbing roots, phosphorus does not seem to have any special "stimulating" effect.   In fact,
treatment of phosphorus-deficient plants with phosphate fertilizer
ordinarily increases the yield of the above-ground parts to a greater
extent than the absorbing roots.   This effect is illustrated in Table 10,

Table 10.   Yield of Shoots and Roots of Wheat with Different Applications
of Phosphorus as Dibasic Calcium Phosphate

(Goedewaagen, 1937)

Plant Part	Grams of Dry Matter per Culture with Indicated Addition of Phosphorus per Kilogram of Soil			
	None	44 mg.	175 mg.	306 mg.
Shoots	3	76	124	135
Roots		23	37	26

which shows the response of the shoots and roots of wheat to phosphorus fertilization on a sandy soil that was extremely deficient in
phosphorus.   An analogous response to nitrogen is described in Fig.
14 of the chapter on nitrogen.   The first explanation given for the
response to nitrogen serves to account for the response to phosphorus.
Plants deficient in phosphorus tend to be high in carbohydrate.   When
conditions are made more favorable for utilization of the carbohydrate
in growth, as when the supply of phosphorus is increased, the proportion of the carbohydrate translocated to the root decreases.

The difference in the manner in which the two types of crops respond to phosphate fertilization does not necessarily mean that there
is some fundamental difference between them.   The below-ground
storage tissue of the mangold is developed late in the season, and is
not analogous to the root system of wheat.   The development of the
absorbing roots of the mangold parallels that of the above-ground parts
and probably is affected by phosphorus supply in the same manner
as the root system of wheat.   This conclusion may be inferred from
the behavior of potatoes.   Work of Houghland (1947) indicates that
the effect of phosphorus supply on the relative growth of the absorb-

ing roots (tubers not included) and above-ground parts of potatoes follows the pattern indicated above for wheat; that is, phosphate fertilization increases the growth of the above-ground parts more than the growth of roots.

Time of maturity

If soil phosphorus availability is high, young plants absorb phosphorus rapidly. By the time they have accumulated 25 per cent of the seasonal total of dry matter they may have absorbed as much as 75 per cent of the seasonal total of phosphorus.

Rapid absorption of phosphorus early in the life of the plant is conducive to rapid development. Williams (1948), for example, found that the time required for plants to attain the maximum rate of phosphorus absorption decreased as the concentration of phosphorus in the growth medium increased. Glover (1953) found that corn reached the stages of tasseling and silking at an earlier date when the supply of phosphorus was ample than when it was deficient.

In consequence of the difference in rates of development, plants that are deficient in phosphorus mature late in comparison with plants that are amply supplied with phosphorus. This principle is illustrated in Table 11 by the increase in percentage of the total yield of snap beans

Table 11. Yield and Earliness of Maturity of Snap Beans with Different Rates of Phosphorus Fertilization of a Sandy Soil in Alabama

(Ware, 1938)

Phosphorus Applied per Acre in Fertilizer, lb.	Yield of Snap Beans per Acre, hampers	Yield of Early Beans as Percentage of Total, %
0	8	25
17	92	40
35	164	47
52	157	48

obtained in the early crop accompanying an increase in the phosphorus supply. As indicated by the work of Crider (1927) and Franck (1931) and the results of the highest two rates of phosphorus fertilization in Table 11, however, the maturity date is advanced little or none by phosphorus fertilization unless the yield is increased.

The effect of phosphorus fertilization on the time of maturity may be of practical importance with crops that utilize the full growing season, as with corn in the northern states. With cotton, much has been written about the importance of early maturity as a means of escaping boll weevil infestation. In some instances, earliness of maturity may make possible the harvesting of the crop under relatively favorable weather conditions. Robertson (1927) commented on this in connection with experiments on phosphate fertilization of oats in northern Ireland. He noted that oats on the control plots ripened 2 weeks later than oats on phosphate-fertilized plots.

Response throughout the season

The relative response of crops to phosphorus fertilization usually is greatest early in the season when the growth rate is high and decreases gradually as maturity is approached. Table 12 illustrates the usual

Table 12. Total Yield of Dry Matter and Yield of Phosphorus of Oats at Different Dates on Plots Differing with Respect to Fertilization with Superphosphate

(Unpublished data, Iowa Agricultural Experiment Station and United States Department of Agriculture, 1949)

Date of Sampling	Yield of Dry Matter per Acre			Yield of Phosphorus per Acre		
	No P Added, lb.	35 lb. P per Acre, lb.	Increase from P, %	No P Added, lb.	35 lb. P per Acre, lb.	Increase from P, %
June 2	500	670	34	1.4	2.3	64
June 22	2700	3100	15	5.5	7.2	31
July 8	3700	4200	13	6.5	8.0	23

behavior. It may be inferred from this table that of the total phosphorus absorbed by July 8, most of the fertilizer phosphorus was absorbed before June 2, but most of the soil phosphorus was absorbed after June 2. Probably this behavior is the result of a number of factors, including the inherent responsiveness of the crop, the fact that the fertilizer was mixed with the surface of the soil where it would be contacted immediately by the roots, the decrease in availability of the fertilizer phosphorus with increasing time of contact with the soil and with increasing soil dryness, and the eventual presence of roots in soil layers below the fertilizer zone and absorption of phosphorus from these layers.

Phosphorus fertilization thus may produce a relatively large increase in yield when the plant is young by providing a favorable phosphorus environment at that time. But if absorption can be prolonged over a great enough period of time, the unfertilized plant eventually may accumulate enough phosphorus to produce a yield almost as great as that obtained with phosphorus fertilization. The importance of high soil phosphorus availability therefore is greatest for crops having a short growth cycle. And since soil phosphorus availability is in part a matter of the susceptibility of the phosphorus to absorption in a unit of soil volume and in part a matter of the total volume of soil occupied by roots, the importance of high soil phosphorus availability is greater for crops having a restricted root volume than a large root volume. Conditions of poor drainage and low soil temperature restrict root growth and, hence, may be expected to be associated with a need for relatively high phosphorus availability per unit of soil volume. Low soil temperatures are associated with a need for high phosphorus availability for the additional reason that roots absorb phosphorus relatively slowly at low soil temperatures.

The response of crops to phosphate fertilizers differing in solubility follows the same general pattern described above for their response to differences in phosphorus availability in soils. A high degree of solubility in water is most important for crops having a short growing season and a restricted root volume. Long-season crops that grow rapidly (corn, for example) may indicate the same superiority of water-soluble phosphate fertilizers early in the season.

The pattern of response of plants to phosphorus fertilization indicated in Table 12 may be followed also where nitrogen is concerned. The pattern will be followed if the nitrogen deficiency develops when the plants are small and the soil continues to supply a moderate amount of nitrogen throughout the latter part of the season. On the other hand, one may find the greatest relative increase in yield from nitrogen fertilization occurring at a relatively late date, perhaps even at maturity, and little or no response when the plant is young. This difference in response of plants to phosphorus and nitrogen results from the fact that, because of the difference in behavior of these two nutrients in the soil, plants can absorb the available nitrogen more rapidly and more completely than the available phosphorus.

Disease incidence

The importance of phosphorus supply in relation to the incidence of plant diseases apparently is less than that of nitrogen and potassium. Probably the most important effect of phosphorus supply in this respect is on root rots. Susceptibility of plants to certain fungal root rots is greater under conditions of phosphorus deficiency than of phosphorus sufficiency. This effect is noted particularly with plants in the seedling stage. Little study has been made of the manner in which the phosphorus effect is brought about. In some instances the effect of phosphorus appears to be exerted not so much through a change in the inherent susceptibility of a particular root to infection as through an increase in the rate of growth and production of new roots. In such cases an adequate supply of phosphorus may be said to facilitate escape from the diseases rather than to increase resistance to them. The work of Vanterpool (1935) on pythium root rot of wheat may be mentioned in this connection.

The effect of phosphorus supply sometimes is just the opposite of that described above for fungal root rots; that is, the susceptibility to the disease is greater when the supply of phosphorus is ample than when it is deficient. Several such instances have been noted by McNew (1953), one of these being the virus diseases. Although it is doubtful that the observed effect is a direct consequence of the phosphorus content of the plant, it may be noted that phosphorus is a component of the self-propagating nucleoprotein molecules that constitute the virus diseases.

Species differences

Plant species grown individually on a particular soil may differ markedly in the degree to which their yield can be increased upon addition of phosphorus-bearing fertilizer. Table 13 gives an example.

Table 13. Ratio of Yield of Different Crops Obtained without Phosphate Fertilization to the Yield Obtained with 5 Tons of Concentrated Superphosphate per Acre on a Clay Loam Soil in California

(Lilleland, Brown, and Conrad, 1942)

Crop	$\dfrac{\text{Yield of Control}}{\text{Yield with Superphosphate Added}}$
Squash	0.03
Cucumber	0.07
Corn	0.21
Wheat	0.38
Oats	0.41
Alfalfa	0.57
Wax beans	0.63
Almond	1.00*

* Based on ratio of cross sectional areas of trunk.

The crops listed were grown individually in the same field experiment, with and without application of superphosphate.

Probably plant species differ more in their reaction to the supply of soil phosphorus than to soil potassium and nitrogen, if legumes are excepted where nitrogen is concerned. Marked differences in botanical composition of mixed plantings thus may accompany variations in the phosphorus supply. Illustrative data have been reported by Hartwell and Damon (1927), Rossiter (1947), and others. Usually the proportion of legumes in the total produce of mixed plantings of forage crops increases with increasing supply of phosphorus, which means that the competitive ability of the legumes is poorer under conditions of low than of high soil phosphorus availability.

Various hypotheses have been proposed to account for the differences among species. One of these is the carbon dioxide hypothesis. Some plants excrete more carbon dioxide in the soil than others; as a result of this, differences in acidity may exist in the soil around the roots. In consequence of the differences in acidity, the concentration of phosphorus in the soil solution around the roots may be greater with some plants than others. According to Gerretsen (1949), the microorganisms in the soil directly around the roots may play an important part in the solubilization of phosphate.

A second proposal may be termed the calcium-absorption hypothesis. Truog (1916) suggested that the difference in availability to various plants of the phosphorus of phosphate rock (an impure form of apatite) is caused by differences in calcium absorption. Some plants absorb more calcium than others. Since the phosphorus concentration in solution should increase as the calcium concentration decreases, the concentration of phosphorus in solution should be greatest with plants that absorb the most calcium. Sweet clover absorbs much calcium and grows relatively well with phosphate rock as a phosphorus source. Corn absorbs little calcium and grows relatively poorly with phosphate rock as a phosphorus source. Truog's hypothesis considers the plant as a whole. Drake and Steckel (1955) modified Truog's view by postulating that the calcium is inactivated by the cation-exchange properties of the roots. According to Drake and Steckel, availability of the phosphorus of phosphate rock should be greater for plants having high-exchange-capacity roots than low-exchange-capacity roots.

A third hypothesis is the root-extent hypothesis. The soil phosphorus availability should be greater for plants that have a large absorbing surface than for those that have a small absorbing surface in relation to the quantity of phosphorus required; corn and potatoes may be cited as examples of the first and second types, respectively.

Fourth, there is the mycorrhizal-fungi hypothesis. On soils relatively low in plant nutrients, the growth of coniferous trees has been found to be better when mycorrhizal fungi infect the roots than when the fungi are absent. One reason for the improved growth associated with the presence of the fungi appears to be that in some way they facilitate the absorption of phosphorus by the plant (McComb, 1938).

The level of other nutrients is a fifth factor that may be responsible for species differences. Probably this factor is most important when inoculated legumes are compared with other crops. If the inoculation is adequate, the response of legumes is characteristic of an ample nitrogen supply even though the external nitrogen supply is limited. The data of Trumble and Shapter (1937) in Table 14 may be cited as an example. This table shows that the increase in yield of rye

Table 14. Yield of Wimmera Rye Grass and Subterranean Clover with Different
Applications of Phosphorus and Nitrogen

(Trumble and Shapter, 1937)

| | | Yield of Dry Matter per Culture | |
Nitrogen Applied per Culture, mg.	Phosphorus Applied per Culture, mg.	Wimmera Rye Grass, g.	Subterranean Clover, g.
50	22	9	2
50	218	11	74
2000	22	48	2
2000	218	199	58

grass from phosphorus fertilization was large when the supply of nitrogen was ample, and small when it was deficient. Clover behaved
similarly at both levels of nitrogen.

Evidently a variety of causes may exist for the differences in degree
to which the yield of various plant species can be increased by phosphate fertilization. Research in this area is difficult technically, and
essentially no progress has been made in assessing the relative importance of the individual factors in particular cases.

LITERATURE CITED

Adams, A. P., W. V. Bartholomew, and Francis E. Clark. (1954) Measurement of
nucleic acid components in soil. Soil Sci. Soc. America Proc. 18:40—46.

Amer, F., D. R. Bouldin, C. A. Black, and F. R. Duke. (1955) Characterization of
soil phosphorus by anion exchange resin adsorption and P^{32}-equilibration. **Plant and
Soil** 6:391—408.

Anonymous (1950) Recent work on the chemical determination of readily soluble
phosphorus in soil. Part 1, Part 2. **Soils and Fertilizers** 13:235—239, 315—320.

Arnon, Daniel I. (1953) The physiology and biochemistry of phosphorus in green
plants. **Agronomy** 4:1—42.

Aslyng, H. C. (1954) The lime and phosphate potentials of soils; the solubility and
availability of phosphates. **Kong. Veterinaer- og Landbohøjskole Årsskrift** 1954:1—50.

Basu, J. K., and M. M. Kibe. (1945) The fertility of a typical black cotton soil as
related to its different phosphorus fractions, after ten years of manuring. **Jour. Univ.
Bombay** 14, Part 3A:29—34.

Behrens, W. U. (1937) Die Fortschritte in der Bestimmung des Kali- und Phosphor-
säurebedarfs der Böden. **Forschungsdienst** 4:463—477.

Behrens, W. U. (1940) Die Fortschritte in der Bestimmung des Kali- und Phosphor-
säurebedarfs der Böden (II). **Forschungsdienst** 9:237—253.

Black, C. A., and C. A. I. Goring. (1953) Organic phosphorus in soils. **Agronomy**
4:123—152.

Bonner, James (1950) **Plant Biochemistry.** Academic Press, New York.

Bower, C. A. (1949) Studies on the forms and availability of soil organic phosphorus. **Iowa Agr. Exp. Sta. Res. Bul. 362.**

Bray, Roger H., and L. T. Kurtz. (1945) Determination of total, organic, and available forms of phosphorus in soils. **Soil Sci.** 59:39—45.

Bushinskiĭ, G. I. (1946) The conditions in the formation of siderites, vivianites, and brown iron ores in the peat bogs of White Russia. **Byull. Moskov. Obshchestva Ispytat. Prirody, Otdel Geol.** 21, No. 3:65—82. (Chem. Abstr. 48:6330).

Chapman, H. D. (1936) Effect of nitrogenous fertilizers, organic matter, sulfur, and colloidal silica on the availability of phosphorus in calcareous soils. **Jour. Amer. Soc. Agron.** 28:135—145.

Clark, J. S., and Michael Peech. (1955) Solubility criteria for the existence of calcium and aluminum phosphates in soils. **Soil Sci. Soc. America Proc.** 19:171—174.

Clarke, Frank Wigglesworth. (1920) The data of geochemistry. **United States Geol. Survey Bul.** 695 (fourth ed.)

Crider, F. J. (1927) Effect of phosphorus in the form of acid phosphate upon maturity and yield of lettuce. **Arizona Agr. Exp. Sta. Bul.** 121.

Dauncey, K. D. M. (1952) Phosphate content of soils on archeological sites. **Advanc. Sci.** 9:33—36.

Drake, Mack, and J. E. Steckel. (1955) Solubilization of soil and rock phosphate as related to root cation exchange capacity. **Soil Sci. Soc. America Proc.** 19:449—450.

Dudley, Wm. L. (1890) A curious occurrence of vivianite. **Amer. Jour. Sci., Ser. 3,** 40:120—121.

Dyal, R. S. (1953) Mica leptyls and wavellite content of clay fraction from Gainesville loamy fine sand of Florida. **Soil Sci. Soc. America Proc.** (1953) 17:55—58.

Eid, M. T., C. A. Black, and O. Kempthorne. (1951) Importance of soil organic and inorganic phosphorus to plant growth at low and high soil temperatures. **Soil Sci.** 71:361—370.

Eid, M. T., C. A. Black, O. Kempthorne, and J. A. Zoellner. (1954) Significance of soil organic phosphorus to plant growth. **Iowa Agr. Exp. Sta. Res. Bul.** 406.

Failyer, G. H., J. G. Smith, and H. R. Wade. (1908) The mineral composition of soil particles. **U. S. Dept. Agr. Bur. Soils Bul.** 54.

Franck, Olle. (1931) Gödsling, mognadstid och kärnkvalitet. **Nordisk Jordbrugsforskning** 13:282—290.

Fudge, J. Franklin. (1928) The influence of various nitrogenous fertilizers on the availability of phosphate and potassium. **Alabama Agr. Exp. Sta. Bul.** 227.

Gardner, Robert, and O. J. Kelley. (1940) Relation of pH to phosphate solubility in Colorado soils. **Soil Sci.** 50:91—102.

Gerretsen, F. C. (1949) The influence of microorganisms on the phosphate intake by the plant. **Plant and Soil** 1:51—81.

Ghani, M. O., and S. A. Aleem. (1943) Studies on the distribution of different forms of phosphorus in some Indian soils. I. Surface distribution. **Indian Jour. Agr. Sci.** 13:283—288.

Glover, J. (1953) The nutrition of maize in sand culture. I. The balance of nutrition with particular reference to the level of supply of nitrogen and phosphorus. **Jour. Agr. Sci.** 43:154—159.

Goedewaagen, M. A. J. (1937) The relative weight of shoot and root of different crops and its agricultural significance in relation to the amount of phosphate added to the soil. **Soil Sci.** 44:185—202.

Goring, C. A. I. (1955) Biological transformations of phosphorus in soil. I. Theory and methods. **Plant and Soil** 6:17—25.

Goring, C. A. I., and W. V. Bartholomew. (1950) Microbial products and soil organic matter: II. The effect of clay on the decomposition and separation of the phosphorus compounds in microorganisms. **Soil Sci. Soc. America Proc.** (1949) 14:152—156.

Hambidge, Gove (Editor). (1949) **Hunger Signs in Crops: a symposium.** American Society of Agronomy and National Fertilizer Association, Washington, D. C.

Hartwell, Burt L., and S. C. Damon. (1927) The degree of response of different crops to various phosphorus carriers. **Rhode Island Agr. Exp. Sta. Bul. 209.**

Hendrick, J., and H. D. Welsh. (1928) The substances removed by the drainage from a Scottish soil. **Proc. and Papers, First Internat. Congr. Soil Sci.,** Commission II:358—366.

Houghland, G. V. C. (1947) Minimum phosphate requirement of potato plants grown in solution cultures. **Jour. Agr. Res. 75:1—18.**

Jenny, H., J. Vlamis, and W. E. Martin. (1950) Greenhouse assay of fertility of California soils. **Hilgardia 20:1—8.**

Leahey, Alfred. (1934—1935) Mineralogical and chemical studies on some of the inorganic phosphorus compounds in the soil. **Scientific Agr. 15:704—712.**

Lilleland, Omund, J. G. Brown, and John P. Conrad. (1942) The phosphate nutrition of fruit trees III. Comparison of fruit tree and field crop responses on a phosphate deficient soil. **Proc. Amer. Soc. Hort. Sci. 40:1—7.**

Lipman, Jacob G., and Adrienne B. Conybeare. (1936) Preliminary note on the inventory and balance sheet of plant nutrients in the United States. **New Jersey Agr. Exp. Sta. Bul. 607.**

Low, Philip F., and C. A. Black. (1950) Reactions of phosphate with kaolinite. **Soil Sci. 70:273—290.**

Mason, Brian, and Thelma Berggren. (1941) A phosphate-bearing spessartite garnet from Wodgina, Western Australia. **Geologiska Föreningens, Stockholm, Förhandlingar 63:413—418.**

McAuliffe, C. D., N. S. Hall, L. A. Dean, and S. B. Hendricks. (1948) Exchange reactions between phosphates and soils: hydroxylic surfaces of soil minerals. **Soil Sci. Soc. America Proc.** (1947) 12:119—123.

McCaughey, W. J., and William H. Fry. (1913) The microscopic determination of soil-forming minerals. **U. S. Dept. Agr. Bur. Soils Bul. 91.**

McComb, A. L. (1938) The relation between mycorrhizae and the development and nutrient absorption of pine seedlings in a prairie nursery. **Jour. Forestry 36:1148—1154.**

McMurtrey, J. E., Jr. (1948) Visual symptoms of malnutrition in plants. In Kitchen, Herminie Broedel (Editor). **Diagnostic Techniques for Soils and Crops.** The American Potash Institute, Washington, pp. 231—289.

McNew, George L. (1953) The effects of soil fertility. In **Plant Diseases,** the yearbook of agriculture, 1953, pp. 100—114. United States Department of Agriculture, Washington, D. C.

Midgley, A. R. (1931) The movement and fixation of phosphates in relation to permanent pasture fertilization. **Jour. Amer. Soc. Agron. 23:788—799.**

Morgan, M. F., and H. G. M. Jacobson. (1942) Soil and crop interrelations of various nitrogenous fertilizers. Windsor lysimeter series B. **Connecticut (New Haven) Agr. Exp. Sta. Bul. 458.**

Neller, J. R. (1947) Mobility of phosphates in sandy soils. **Soil Sci. Soc. America Proc.** (1946) 11:227—230.

Nelson, W. L., A. Mehlich, and Eric Winters. (1953) The development, evaluation, and use of soil tests for phosphorus availability. **Agronomy 4:153—188.**

Olsen, Carsten.   (1950)   The significance of concentration for the rate of ion absorption by higher plants in water culture.   **Physiol. Plant.** 3:152—164.

Olsen, Sterling R.   (1953a)   Inorganic phosphorus in alkaline and calcareous soils. **Agronomy** 4:89—122.

Olsen, Sterling R.   (1953b)   The measurement of phosphorus on the surface of soil particles and its relationship to plant available phosphorus.   **Kansas Agr. Exp. Sta. Rpt.** 4:59—67.

Olsen, Sterling R., C. V. Cole, Frank S. Watanabe, and L. A. Dean.   (1954)   Estimation of available phosphorus in soils by extraction with sodium bicarbonate.   **U. S. Dept. Agr. Cir.** 939.

Parker, Frank W., J. Richard Adams, K. G. Clark, K. D. Jacob, and A. L. Mehring. (1946)   Fertilizers and lime in the United States: resources, production, marketing, and use.   **U. S. Dept. Agr. Misc. Publ.** 586.

Pearson, R. W., and Roy W. Simonson.   (1939)   Organic phosphorus in seven Iowa soil profiles: distribution and amounts as compared to organic carbon and nitrogen. **Soil Sci. Soc. America Proc.**   (1939)   4:162—167.

Pearson, R. W., Robert Spry, and W. H. Pierre.   (1940)   The vertical distribution of total and dilute acid-soluble phosphorus in twelve Iowa soil profiles.   **Jour. Amer. Soc. Agron.** 32:683—696.

Pierre, W. H., and G. M. Browning.   (1935)   The temporary injurious effect of excessive liming of acid soils and its relation to the phosphate nutrition of plants. **Jour. Amer. Soc. Agron.** 27:742—759.

Pierre, W. H., and A. G. Norman.   (Editors)   (1953)   Soil and fertilizer phosphorus in crop nutrition.   **Agronomy** 4.

Pierre, W. H., and F. W. Parker.   (1927)   Soil phosphorus studies: II. The concentration of organic and inorganic phosphorus in the soil solution and soil extracts and the availability of the organic phosphorus to plants.   **Soil Sci.** 24:119—128.

Plummer, J. K.   (1915—1916)   Petrography of some North Carolina soils and its relation to their fertilizer requirements.   **Jour. Agr. Res.** 5:569—582.

Rankama, Kalervo, and Th. G. Sahama.   (1950)   **Geochemistry.**   University of Chicago Press, Chicago.

Robertson, George Scott.   (1927)   Experiments in northern Ireland with various types of phosphatic fertilisers.   **Northern Ireland Min. Agr. Jour.** 1:7—36.

Rossiter, R. C.   (1947)   The effect of potassium on the growth of subterranean clover and other pasture plants on Crawley sand.   **Australian Jour. Council Sci. Indust. Res.** 20:389—401.

Rost, C. O.   (1939)   The relative productivity of some humid subsoils.   **Soil Sci. Soc. America Proc.** 4:281—287.

Runk, C. R.   (1925)   Hydrogen-ion concentration, buffer action, and soil type as a guide to the use of lime.   **Jour. Amer. Soc. Agron.** 17:345—353.

Semb, Gunnar, and Gotfred Uhlen.   (1954)   A comparison of different analytical methods for the determination of potassium and phosphorus in soil based on field experiments.   **Acta Agriculturae Scandinavica** 5:44—68.

Smith, Donald H., and Francis E. Clark.   (1952)   Chromatographic separations of inositol phosphorus compounds.   **Soil Sci. Soc. America Proc.** 16:170—172.

Smith, Donald H., and Francis E. Clark.   (1951)   Anion-exchange chromatography of inositol phosphates from soil.   **Soil Sci.** 72:353—360.

Stelly, M., and W. H. Pierre.   (1943)   Forms of inorganic phosphorus in the C horizons of some Iowa soils.   **Soil Sci. Soc. America Proc.**   (1942)   7:139—147.

Thompson, L. F., and P. F. Pratt.   (1954)   Solubility of phosphorus in chemical extractants as indexes to available phosphorus in Ohio soils. **Soil Sci. Soc. America Proc.** 18:467–470.

Thompson, L. M., C. A. Black, and J. A. Zoellner. (1954) Occurrence and mineralization of organic phosphorus in soils, with particular reference to associations with nitrogen, carbon, and pH. **Soil Sci.** 77:185–196.

Trumble, H. C., and R. E. Shapter. (1937) Investigations on the associated growth of herbage plants. 2. The influence of nitrogen and phosphorus treatment on the yield and chemical composition of Wimmera rye-grass and subterranean clover, grown separately and in association. **Australia Council Sci. Indust. Res. Bul.** 105:25–36.

Truog, E. (1916) The utilization of phosphates by agricultural crops, including a new theory regarding the feeding power of plants. **Wisconsin Agr. Exp. Sta. Res. Bul.** 41.

Van den Honert, T. H. (1933) Physiology of nutrition of the sugar cane. II. Experiments on phosphate absorption. Arch. Suikerind. 41, III, Mededeel. Proefsta. Java-Suikerind. 1119–1156. (**Chem. Abstr.** 28:2832. 1934)

Vanterpool, T. C. (1935) Studies on browning root rot of cereals. III. Phosphorus-nitrogen relations of infested fields. IV. Effects of fertilizer amendments. V. Preliminary plant analyses. **Canadian Jour. Res.** 13C:220–250.

Vishniac, Wolf. (1955) Biochemical aspects of photosynthesis. **Ann. Rev. Plant Physiol.** 6:115–134.

Walker, R. H., and Brown, P. E. (1936) The phosphorus, nitrogen and carbon content of Iowa soils. In Brown, P. E. Soils of Iowa. **Iowa Agr. Exp. Sta. Spec. Rpt.** 3.

Wallace, T. (1951) **The Diagnosis of Mineral Deficiencies in Plants by Visual Symptoms: a colour atlas and guide.** His Majesty's Stationery Office, London.

Ware, L. M. (1938) Influence of the major fertilizer elements on the earliness and yield of snap beans. **Proc. Amer. Soc. Hort. Sci.** (1937) 35:699–703.

Watson, D. J., and E. J. Russell. (1943) The Rothamsted experiments on mangolds, 1872–1940. Part II. Effect of manures on the growth of the plant. **Empire Jour. Exptl. Agr.** 11:65–77.

Williams, R. F. (1948) The effects of phosphorus supply on the rates of intake of phosphorus and nitrogen and upon certain aspects of phosphorus metabolism in gramineous plants. **Australian Jour. Sci. Res.** B1: 333–361.

Williams, R. F. (1955) Redistribution of mineral elements during development. **Ann. Rev. Plant Physiol.** 6:25–42.

Winters, Eric, and Roy W. Simonson. (1951) The subsoil. **Adv. Agron.,** 3:1–92.

9. POTASSIUM[1]

Potassium is an essential element for plant growth and reproduction. Potassium is one of the macronutrients; usually it is present in plants in quantities larger than any of the other nutrients except nitrogen. Some plants and plant tissues accumulate relatively large concentrations of potassium. Tobacco leaves, for example, may contain as much as 8 per cent potassium on the dry weight basis and may show symptoms of potassium deficiency if the content falls much below 3 per cent.

Despite the absorption of relatively large quantities of potassium by plants, however, deficiency of potassium in soils is not as widespread as deficiency of nitrogen. Experience in the midwestern United States has shown that nitrogen may be deficient for a number of years before potassium becomes deficient. Then, within a period of a few years, definite potassium deficiency may develop. The explanation for this behavior appears to be that many soils originally have a large reserve of potassium, from which potassium may be withdrawn at a rate determined to a considerable extent by the plant. The behavior of potassium in this respect is quite in contrast to that of nitrogen, the maximum rate of withdrawal of which is largely beyond the control of the plant.

CONTENT IN SOILS

The content of potassium in mineral soils usually is much greater than that of nitrogen or phosphorus. A generalized map of the po-

[1] For a more detailed coverage of various aspects of the subject, the reader is referred to a review paper and bibliography by Reitemeier (1951 and 1952, respectively), a review paper by Lawton and Cook (1954), a symposium of the International Potash Institute (1954), and the List of references to literature on potash as a plant nutrient, published serially by the American Potash Institute, Inc., Washington 6, D. C.

tassium content of the surface soils of the United States (Parker et al., 1946) shows that soils of the Coastal Plain from southern Virginia to the Mississippi Delta usually contain less than 0.3 per cent potassium. In the south central part of the United States is a large area of soils containing from 0.3 to 1 per cent potassium. The northeast quarter of the United States has a few soils with as little potassium as the southeast quarter, but most contain 1 to 2.5 per cent potassium. Soils of the western half of the United States usually contain 1.7 to 2.5 per cent potassium, except for a strip along the northern part of the west coast, where the content is 1 to 1.7 per cent.

The potassium content of soils of the various regions is related to parent material and the degree of weathering. Soils of the coastal plain area, for example, have been developed from transported parent materials that were low in potassium at the time of deposition as a result of previous strong weathering. The low potassium content of soils of the Pacific Northwest, on the other hand, can be attributed primarily to weathering in place and not to an initial dearth of potassium in the parent material.

With increasing depth, the potassium percentage usually remains about the same or increases in soils of initially uniform parent material. The deficit in the upper part of the profile may be attributed primarily to a combination of chemical weathering and leaching. Where strong weathering has reduced the potassium content of the entire profile to a low level, however, the surface soil sometimes has a higher potassium percentage than the subsoil. The action of plants in transporting potassium to the surface probably is responsible.

LOSSES FROM SOILS

Crop removal

Lipman and Conybeare (1936) estimated that in the year 1930 the average removal of potassium from the soils of the harvested crop land of the United States amounted to 17 lb. per acre. This figure refers only to the potassium in the harvested portion of the crops. The total removal of potassium probably was of the order of 30 to 40 lb. per acre. Forty pounds of potassium per acre is equal to about 0.24 per cent of the average content of potassium in the plowed layer of soil. The total removal of potassium is much higher than removal of phosphorus and about equal to the removal of nitrogen. In relation to the total amount present in the soil, however, potassium is removed less rapidly than either phosphorus or nitrogen.

Leaching

Substantial loss of potassium by leaching may occur under certain conditions. Kime (1943) filled a 5-gallon jar with fine sandy soil from Florida, added a mixed fertilizer containing potassium, and then added the equivalent of 16 inches of rain. Of the 69 lb. of exchangeable and soluble potassium present initially and the added 66 lb. (a total of 135 lb. on an acre basis), 126 lb. appeared in the leachate.

Contrasting results were obtained by Stauffer (1942) who determined the loss of potassium from six fallow soils from Illinois. Undisturbed samples of soil were placed in lysimeters of 40-inch depth, and losses were measured for a period of three years and eight months. In this time, the most permeable of these soils, Muscatine silt loam, lost 23 inches of percolate containing the equivalent of 5 lb. of potassium per acre. On an annual basis the potassium loss was only 1.4 lb. per acre, a negligible amount; the other soils lost even less. The amount of water passing through the soil thus was greater with the silt loam soil of Stauffer than the sandy soil of Kime, but the potassium loss was less.

The difference in the tendency of potassium to leach from the soil in the two experiments probably results largely from two factors: (*a*) the difference in the degree of potassium saturation and (*b*) the ratio of soluble salts to cation-exchange capacity. The sandy soil had a low cation-exchange capacity, so that the exchangeable and added potassium together produced a relatively high degree of potassium saturation. The silt loam soil undoubtedly contained more exchangeable-plus-soluble potassium than the sandy soil. In consequence of a much higher exchange capacity, however, the silt loam soil had a lower degree of potassium saturation than did the sandy soil. The probability that ions present in solution would replace exchangeable potassium rather than some other exchangeable cation thus was greater in the fine sand than in the silt loam. In addition, the fine sand received a heavy application of mixed fertilizer, so that the ratio of replacing ions to exchangeable ions was high. The silt loam received no fertilizer.

Three other factors have received some attention in relation to the loss of potassium by leaching. The first of these is the subsoil. Sandy soils, in which potassium leaching may be serious, sometimes have fine-textured subsoils that will retain some of the potassium lost from the surface (Volk, 1940). The second is the presence of a crop, which will decrease the loss by absorbing both water and potassium.

The combination of upward and downward components of potassium movement in soils bearing vegetation probably is responsible for the fact that in many unfertilized soils the minimum content of exchangeable potassium is not in the surface but in the subsoil. The third is the degree of saturation of the exchange positions with bases other than potassium. Retention of potassium in exchangeable form usually increases with the replacement of exchangeable hydrogen by calcium because the latter subsequently is the more readily removed by replacing ions. Work on this subject has been reported by Mehlich and Reed (1946) and others.

Erosion

Selective removal of the finer fractions during erosion serves to deplete the more valuable portion of the potassium in soils. Losses in this way seldom are taken as seriously as those of nitrogen, however, because of the difference in distribution of these two elements in soil profiles. Nitrogen is concentrated near the surface, as a result of which the nitrogen availability decreases with increasing erosion. Potassium, on the other hand, is present throughout the profile. The loss of surface potassium by erosion, which may cause the plant to develop in a surface soil having lower potassium availability, is compensated in part by the addition of a new source of potassium in the deeper soil horizons that are brought nearer the surface.

FORMS IN SOILS

Mineralogical

In soils that are not strongly weathered, feldspars and micas ordinarily are the most abundant of the potassium-bearing minerals (Reitemeier, Brown, and Holmes, 1951). The most important of these are orthoclase and microcline feldspar, biotite and muscovite mica, and illite. The feldspars occur almost exclusively in the sand and silt fractions of soils but are found occasionally in the coarse clay. The feldspars may be of either primary or secondary origin. In soils they probably are mainly primary. The micas likewise may be of either primary or secondary origin. Biotite and muscovite occur mainly in the silt and sand fractions. The forms of these minerals found in soils have been altered somewhat from the original, having lost some interlayer potassium and gained some water of hydration (Denison, Fry, and Gile, 1929). Illite, the main potassium-bearing mineral of the clay fraction, is micaceous in nature, and is of secondary origin.

The occurrence of various potassium-bearing minerals in soils may be illustrated by Schachtschabel's (1937a, 1937b) detailed mineralogical studies of seven soils of Germany. The samples he analyzed contained an average of 2.3 per cent potassium. On the average, the samples consisted of 27 per cent by weight of potassium-bearing minerals (15.5 per cent potassium feldspar and 11.3 per cent micaceous minerals), 62 per cent of nonpotassium-bearing minerals and large stones, and 5 per cent of unidentified minerals. Of the feldspar, 14.5 per cent was in the sand and silt, and 1 per cent was in the clay. Of the micaceous material, 2.7 per cent was in the sand and silt, and 8.6 per cent was in the clay. The clay fraction of these soils averaged 40 per cent micaceous material, which probably would be classified now as illite.

Micas are altered more readily than feldspars, and may disappear from the sand and silt fractions while considerable feldspar remains. An example illustrating the preferential loss of mica in a soil profile from Sumatra was quoted by Mohr and Van Baren (1954, p. 244) from work of Kiel and Rachmad. During disappearance of the feldspar and mica from the sand and silt fractions some illite may be present in the clay fraction, even under conditions of strong weathering such as those in certain areas of Puerto Rico (Jeffries, Bonnet, and Abruña, 1953).

Chemical

From the chemical standpoint, soil potassium often is divided into three categories: nonexchangeable, exchangeable, and water soluble. In most soils the great bulk of the potassium is nonexchangeable. As noted in Table 1 of the chapter on exchangeable bases, an average of 99.6 per cent of the total potassium in samples of twenty soils of New Jersey was nonexchangeable. The remaining 0.4 per cent included both the exchangeable and water-soluble forms. The water-soluble potassium usually constitutes only a small part of the sum of the water-soluble and exchangeable forms. Anderson, Keyes, and Cromer (1942) found that the exchangeable potassium content of surface samples of six soils from the humid and subhumid region of the United States ranged from 0.17 to 0.87 m.e. per 100 g. of dry soil. When calculated on the same basis, the potassium content of the displaced soil solutions of the same soils ranged from 0.003 to 0.02 m.e per 100 g.

In most experimental work conducted at the present time, the soil-solution potassium is not measured independently but is included with the exchangeable potassium, since the two fractions are extracted simultaneously by salt solutions. In humid regions, the content of exchangeable-plus-soluble potassium in soils usually is less than 0.5 m.e. per 100 g., and rarely is more than 1.5 m.e. per 100 g. In arid regions the amount may be higher.

AVAILABILITY TO PLANTS

Absorption from exchangeable and nonexchangeable forms

The traditional laboratory methods for measuring exchangeable potassium in soils were not developed specifically for the purpose of estimating the content of potassium available to plants. Although measurements of exchangeable potassium often are made for this purpose, there is now ample evidence that in most soils exchangeable potassium and available potassium are by no means identical.

The first extensive work to determine the source of the potassium used from soils by plants was reported by Fraps (1929). He found that plants grown on samples of thirty-one different soils in the greenhouse removed potassium from those soils to the extent of 120 p.p.m., on the average. Analysis of the soils showed, however, that during the growth of the plants only 51 p.p.m. of exchangeable-plus-soluble potassium had disappeared from the soils. The balance of 69 p.p.m. thus must have come from nonexchangeable forms. This work has been repeated many times by other investigators, who used other soils, but obtained similar results. Clearly, plants in some way absorb potassium that was not present in exchangeable and water-soluble forms at the beginning of the growth period. Since plants absorb nonexchangeable potassium, at least the amount absorbed must be classified as available.

Availability coefficients of exchangeable and nonexchangeable forms

Although the experiment of Fraps demonstrates that both exchangeable and nonexchangeable potassium are available to plants, it does not yield any information on the relative availability coefficients (the availability coefficient of a nutrient is the ratio of the availability or effective quantity of the nutrient to the available quantity) of potassium in the respective forms. Data of Schachtschabel (1937a) in Table 1 supply a qualitative answer to this question. The fact that in successive crops on the same soil the potassium absorbed from the exchangeable form diminished rapidly in comparison with that absorbed from the nonexchangeable form indicates that the exchangeable potassium was being depleted more rapidly and, hence, that it had the higher availability coefficient.

A more quantitative answer was obtained by Pratt (1951), who

Table 1. Potassium Absorbed from Exchangeable and Nonexchangeable
Forms in Soil by Successive Crops of Rye Seedlings
(Schachtschabel, 1937a)

	Potassium Absorbed by Crop per 100 g. of Soil	
	Exchangeable, mg.	Nonexchangeable, mg.
First crop	16	18
Second crop	4	9
Third crop	1	9
Fourth crop	0	8

used statistical methods to investigate the value to plants of three
fractions of soil potassium, namely, (*a*) exchangeable-plus-water-
soluble, (*b*) potassium liberated from nonexchangeable form on incubating the soil with a cation-exchange resin, and (*c*) potassium not
liberated from nonexchangeable form on incubating the soil with a
cation-exchange resin. His calculations indicate that the ratio of the
availability coefficient of fraction *b* to that of fraction *a* was 0.28, and
that the ratio of the availability coefficient of fraction *c* to that of
fraction *a* was 0.003. These results illustrate not only that a given
quantity of exchangeable potassium is absorbed by plants much more
readily than the same quantity of nonexchangeable potassium, but also
that a certain fraction of the nonexchangeable potassium is absorbed
much more readily than another.

The availability coefficient of the exchangeable potassium may vary
with the proportions and quantities of the other exchangeable cations
and with the aeration of the soil. The former of these subjects was
discussed in the chapter on exchangeable bases and will not be considered here. The latter will be discussed later in a separate section.

The causes of the difference in the availability coefficient of the potassium found within the nonexchangeable form are to be sought in
the chemical and physical conditions in which the nonexchangeable
potassium occurs. These conditions will be given consideration in
following sections.

Exchangeable-nonexchangeable equilibrium

In 1939, Bray and DeTurk suggested that micaceous clay is an
important source of the nonexchangeable potassium used by plants.
In addition, they proposed what is now a generally accepted principle,
namely, that micaceous clay represents a reservoir of fixed size and
variable potassium content with which the exchangeable potassium
comes slowly to equilibrium.

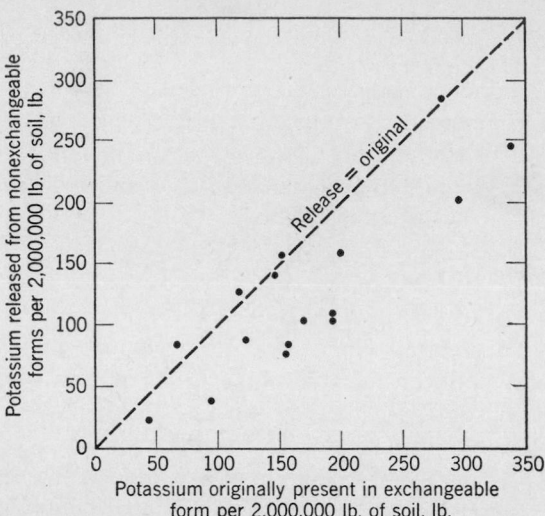

Fig. 1. Potassium released from nonexchangeable to exchangeable forms in various soils during six months' incubation versus the original quantity of exchangeable potassium present before removal and incubation. (Bray and DeTurk, 1939.)

They gave results of several experiments that supported their equilibrium concept. First, when they removed the exchangeable potassium from soils, potassium soon reappeared in the exchangeable form. The amount that reappeared during a 6-month incubation period usually was somewhat less than the original, but was well correlated with the original (Fig. 1). This result is the type one would expect if the exchangeable potassium were present in less than the equilibrium amount. Second, they took samples of soil from the field, and incubated them in a moist condition for 5 years without removing the exchangeable potassium. At the end of the incubation period they found that the exchangeable potassium had increased somewhat in certain samples and decreased somewhat in others, but on the average there had been no significant change one way or the other. This result is the type one would expect if the potassium equilibrium had already been approximately established before incubation. Third, they demonstrated that when they added a quantity of a soluble potassium salt to samples of various soils, and allowed the latter to stand for 8 weeks, some of the exchangeable-plus-soluble potassium was converted to nonexchangeable forms. This result is what would be expected if the exchangeable potassium were above the equilibrium value.

As has been shown in a preceding section, plants in some way absorb potassium that is present in nonexchangeable form at the beginning of the season. That plants actually absorb nonexchangeable potassium while it is nonexchangeable does not seem reasonable. The "equilibrium" concept supplies a more plausible explanation, namely, that removal of potassium from exchangeable and water-soluble forms by plants disturbs the equilibrium condition. In consequence, potassium is released from nonexchangeable to exchangeable and soluble forms that may be absorbed by plants.

Rôle of micaceous clay

The results of the experiments of Bray and DeTurk (1939) described above supported their idea of an equilibrium between exchangeable and nonexchangeable potassium, but they did not supply any information regarding the rôle of micaceous clay in that equilibrium. Considerable evidence now has been amassed to verify that micaceous clay does indeed play the rôle supposed by Bray and De-Turk. The most important lines of evidence are the following. First, in soils that can be presumed to contain micaceous clay the most active fraction in release and fixation of potassium has been found to be the clay. Merwin and Peech (1951) found that after removing the exchangeable potassium from samples of four soils of New York, most of the potassium released from nonexchangeable to exchangeable forms during a subsequent incubation period was derived from the clay fraction. Their results are summarized in Table 2. Volk (1934) found,

Table 2. Relative Quantities of Nonexchangeable Potassium Released to Exchangeable Form from Different Mechanical Fractions of Soils during Incubation Following Removal of Exchangeable Potassium

(Merwin and Peech, 1951)

Basis of Calculation	Relative Quantities of Nonexchangeable Potassium Released to Exchangeable Form from Indicated Fraction		
	Sand	Silt	Clay
Equal weights of all fractions	3	18	100
Relative weights found in the soils	8	61	100

conversely, that the clay fraction of samples of four different soils was much more active than the silt or sand fractions in changing added soluble potassium to nonexchangeable forms. Second, micaceous minerals are the only potassium-bearing minerals known to exist in quantity in the clay fraction. Third, micaceous minerals exhibit the postulated properties of release and fixation of potassium (Barshad, 1954). Fourth, a positive correlation has been found between the content of micaceous clay in soils and the amounts of potassium absorbed from nonexchangeable forms by plants (Schachtschabel, 1937a, 1937b; Rouse and Bertramson, 1950). Fifth, in the investigations of Schachtschabel and Rouse and Bertramson just cited, the potassium absorbed by plants from nonexchangeable forms was not found to be related to the content of micas in the coarser fractions or to the content of feldspar, the other major group of potassium-bearing minerals.

Since there is no doubt that some of the nonexchangeable potassium utilized by plants comes from sources other than micaceous clay, one may question why the tests of plant growth failed to disclose correlations with such minerals. One reason may be that in the experiments conducted thus far, either the number of soils employed has been small or potassium feldspars have not been distinguished from feldspars in general. A second reason may be that because of their reactivity toward potassium, the micaceous clays dominate the behavior of soil potassium in relation to plant growth. To be more specific, one may visualize that over a period of time, some of the potassium released from feldspars will be rendered nonexchangeable again by reaction with micaceous clay. For any given crop, this potassium will behave as "clay" potassium, even though it originated from feldspar. The quantity of such feldspar-derived potassium in the clay fraction will be correlated to some degree with the rate of potassium release from feldspar. The potassium released from feldspar during the current season likewise will undergo some reaction with the micaceous clay. Thus, the possibility for discovery of an effect of nonmicaceous-clay potassium that cannot be predicted from the micaceous clay component is limited in soils containing micaceous clay. In view of the success with which Pratt (1951) and Schmitz and Pratt (1953) have been able to predict potassium absorption from relatively simple chemical measurements, the problem of separating the possible independent effects of different potassium-bearing minerals appears to be mainly of academic interest.

The micaceous minerals currently dominate the thought and research on soil potassium, almost to the exclusion of other possible sources. Probably the cause for the limited consideration of other sources is partly geographical. Soils commonly contain micaceous clays in the areas where most of the research on soil potassium is being conducted. Micaceous clays apparently are absent from some soils, however, particularly those that are strongly weathered. Plants may not absorb much nonexchangeable potassium from such soils, but that which they do absorb must come from sources other than micaceous clay.

Potassium in micaceous clay

Various names have been applied to the micaceous clay in soils. "Illite" now is used rather generally to denote the potassium-bearing types. "Vermiculite" is the name used for a semi-expanding-lattice type of mica that has magnesium and calcium as interlayer cations. The structure of illite is considered briefly in the chapter on exchangeable bases. Grim (1953, pp. 65–69, and 72–77) has reviewed the properties of illite and vermiculite in detail.

Considerable experimental work has been done in an attempt to obtain an understanding of the release and fixation of potassium by micaceous clay. The status of this work was summarized briefly by Barshad (1954). The current view may be stated as follows. The interlayer potassium in micaceous clay is not exchanged readily by other cations because the lattice layers are close together. The closed condition of the lattice layers in turn is caused by the presence of potassium. An analogous condition of closure of lattice layers and difficulty of replacement is encountered with ammonium and other cations of similar size, but not with sodium or other cations of different size. The apparent importance of ionic size is accounted for on the basis of openings in the network of oxygen ions forming the surface of the lattice layers. The diameters of the openings and the potassium ions are such that the oxygen ions of adjacent lattice layers will essentially touch with the potassium fitting snugly in openings in both layers. Because of the good fit and the existence of opposite electrostatic charges on the ion and the clay, the potassium bonds the adjacent layers together. Physically, at least, the interlayer potassium ions belong as much to one layer as to the other. Ions larger than potassium do not sink far enough into the voids in the oxygen network to permit full closure of the lattice layers. Ions smaller than potassium presumably lie more within the sphere of one lattice layer than the other, so that they do not provide an interlayer bond sufficiently strong to prevent entry of water and expansion of the lattice.

A definite physical conception of the status of potassium in micaceous clays thus is being developed. The basic concept described above, however, is not sufficient to account for the exchange behavior observed in practice. At least four modifying factors must be considered.

First, the tendency of potassium to remain between the lattice layers increases with the total strength of charge per unit area of interlayer surface. Because of variations in chemical composition of the lattice layers (see the chapter on exchangeable bases), the number of electrostatic charges available for holding cations per unit area is not constant.   Moreover, the source within the lattice is not constant.   Some of the charges originate nearer the surface than others, and hence should provide a stronger attraction for cations.

Second, the tendency of potassium to be held between closed lattice layers varies with the nature of the other ions present in exchangeable form and in solution.   In consequence, the boundary between exchangeable and nonexchangeable potassium in micaceous minerals is somewhat arbitrary and not entirely consistent among different methods.   Ammonium, which behaves virtually like potassium, is a poor replacing agent for potassium held between closed lattice layers, and vice versa.   Sodium, magnesium, and calcium are much better.   The peculiar position of potassium in this respect may be explained in part on the basis that the reactivity of micaceous potassium covers a range contiguous with that of exchangeable potassium.

Third, the difficulty of removal of potassium from between closed lattice layers increases with the size of the particles.   The slow transportation of ions, particularly potassium, along the narrow interplanar spaces probably is the cause of the particle-size effect.

Fourth, the difficulty of removing the potassium increases with the degree of lattice closure.   Closure takes place spontaneously when potassium is introduced into interlayer exchange positions in minerals such as many vermiculites that have a sufficiently high interlayer charge.   It does not take place spontaneously with expanding lattice minerals like montmorillonite.   If lattice closure in such minerals is induced by drying, however, the presence of enough interlayer exchangeable potassium will cause some of the lattice layers to remain closed; the closed layers, in turn, will cause some of the potassium to become nonexchangeable.

The idea of micaceous clay in soil as a reservoir of fixed capacity and variable potassium content now can be correlated with the foregoing conception of the potassium status in such clays.   The potassium content of the reservoir is the number of potassium ions actually present in interlayer positions and not removed therefrom by treatment with a replacing agent.   The capacity of the reservoir is the number of interlayer exchange positions from which potassium would not be released if the clay were saturated with potassium ions and then treated with a replacing reagent to remove the exchangeable potassium.   The capacity of micaceous minerals for holding potassium is high, as indicated by the comparative values of about 0.5 m.e. of exchangeable potassium per 100 g. of soil, 208 m.e. of total potassium per 100 g. of muscovite mica (Pirsson and Knopf, 1947, p. 41), and as

much as 147 m.e. of total potassium per 100 g. of illite (Grim, Bray, and Bradley, 1937).

Fixation

In some instances, the availability of added potassium to plants decreases with increasing opportunity for reaction with or fixation by the soil. Figure 2 gives an example. The purpose of the work shown in this figure was to find the relative value to plants of potassium applied in the spring just before planting and in the fall several months before planting. The soil was kept moist during the winter to allow the reaction to proceed. The figure shows that 524 mg. of potassium applied in the fall produced the same yield of barley as about 160 mg. applied in the spring, which means that the availability coefficient of the added potassium as a whole was a little less than one-third as great when applied in the fall as when applied in the spring. The decrease in availability may be said to result from fixation by the soil, since no leaching was permitted.

The experiment described in Fig. 2 employed a soil that was known to cause a substantial part of the added potassium to change to nonexchangeable forms. In samples of eight soils from France investigated by Chaminade (1936), incubation did not cause a reduction in value of the added potassium to plants on soils where there was no change to nonexchangeable forms, and vice versa.

The fact that some of the added potassium becomes nonexchange-

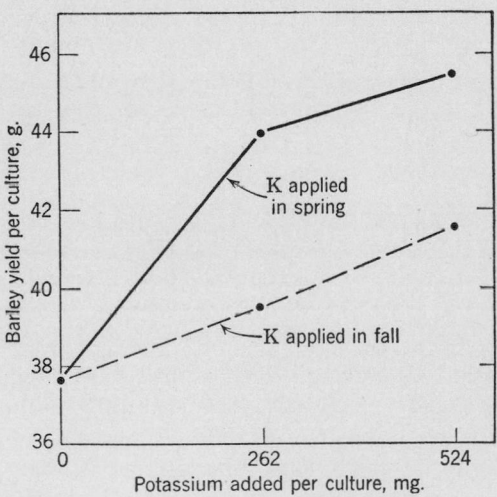

Fig. 2. Yield of barley on soil with different applications of potassium as potassium chloride in the spring just before planting or in the preceding fall. (Chaminade, 1936.)

able does not necessarily mean, however, that this potassium has become unavailable to plants. According to the exchangeable-nonexchangeable equilibrium concept, the added potassium that has become nonexchangeable should serve as a source of potassium for plants upon depletion of the exchangeable potassium and, hence, should have some degree of availability. That this is actually true is indicated by Table 3. This table gives results obtained in an experiment on sam-

Table 3. Potassium Absorbed by Ladino Clover in the Greenhouse from Exchangeable and Nonexchangeable Forms in Soils That Had Accumulated Different Amounts of Potassium as a Result of Previous Field Treatments

(Reitemeier, Brown, and Holmes, 1951)

Potassium Applied per Acre Annually, lb.	Potassium per Acre (2,000,000 lb. of Soil)			Absorbed by 15 Cuttings of Ladino Clover	
	Nonexchangeable Released by $N\,HNO_3$, lb.	Exchangeable before Cropping, lb.	Exchangeable after Cropping, lb.	Exchangeable, lb.	Nonexchangeable, lb.
0	291	71	61	10	98
66	402	183	65	118	132
66*	654	914	75	839	467

* Plus potassium added in 10 tons of manure.

ples of soil from three plots in a field experiment in Maine. The field treatments had caused a considerable increase of both exchangeable and acid-soluble, nonexchangeable potassium. Cropping with ladino clover in the greenhouse removed a substantial amount of potassium that had become fixed in nonexchangeable form.

Indications are, therefore, that the availability coefficient of potassium that has been added to soils is sometimes equal to and sometimes less than that of the exchangeable (and soluble) potassium. If it is less than that of the exchangeable potassium, the overall availability coefficient is a composite of the individual coefficients of the parts of the potassium occurring in the exchangeable and nonexchangeable forms.

The observation that the availability coefficient of added potassium may decrease with increasing time of contact with the soil is made possible by the fact that the transference of added potassium to the nonexchangeable form is a slow process that is not completed within the time required to grow a test crop. An indication of the rate at which the process occurs under continually moist soil conditions is found in Fig. 3 which represents results obtained with a silt loam soil from Illinois to which 500 p.p.m. of potassium were added as dibasic potassium phosphate. The initial content of exchangeable and soluble potassium was 64 p.p.m. Chaminade (1936) found, from an average of six samples of soils from France, that when he added 415 p.p.m.

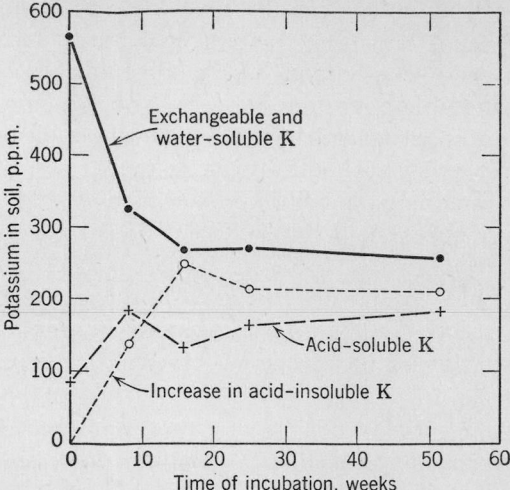

Fig. 3. Distribution of potassium among different fractions in a silt loam soil at different intervals after addition of 500 p.p.m. of potassium. (DeTurk, Wood, and Bray, 1943.)

of potassium he recovered 364 p.p.m. in exchangeable and soluble form after 2 days, 338 p.p.m. after 15 days, and 291 p.p.m. after 6 months of continuous moist incubation.

Effect of soil reaction

For purposes of discussion, the effect of soil reaction on the potassium status of soils may be divided into several phases: the exchangeable-soluble equilibrium, the exchangeable-nonexchangeable equilibrium, and the soil-plant relationships. Each will be considered briefly in turn.

Observations on the effect of soil reaction on the exchangeable-soluble equilibrium may be explained on the basis of the complementary-ion principle (see the chapter on exchangeable bases) and the concentration of replacing ions in solution (Peech and Bradfield, 1943). The concentration of potassium in solution is reduced and its retention in exchangeable form increased as the concentration of replacing ions in solution is reduced and also as the exchangeable hydrogen (and aluminum) of acid soils is replaced by calcium.

The rôle of soil reaction in the exchangeable-nonexchangeable equilibrium is obscure. Many experiments have shown that when acid soils are limed some release of potassium from nonexchangeable to exchangeable forms occurs. When soluble potassium is added, more is fixed in nonexchangeable forms in limed than in unlimed acid soils. On the other hand, unpublished work of Kirk Lawton at the Iowa Agricultural Experiment Station has demonstrated that in some soils more nonexchangeable potassium is released to the exchangeable form upon incubation under acid than under neutral conditions.

Experiments with solution cultures indicate that absorption of potassium by plants is affected but little by variations in pH over the range common in agricultural soils. Experiments that have been conducted with plants growing in soil, however, cannot be interpreted clearly in terms of potassium availability because of the complications of the various other effects that may be associated with pH changes. The importance to plants of the effects observed in the laboratory thus is not well established.

Results of field experiments indicate that liming an acid soil sometimes reduces potassium availability. There is no reason to think that the complementary-ion effect is not a cause, but it is by no means certain that it is the only cause. Moderate liming of acid soils usually increases crop yields, particularly those of leguminous crops, resulting in utilization of greater amounts of potassium. The heavier draft on potassium in the limed soil may in time induce a potassium deficiency. Table 4 shows the results of a long-time field experiment in Illinois,

Table 4. Yield of Corn over a Period of Years with Application of Different Management Practices on a Silt Loam Soil at the Ewing Experimental Field in Illinois

(Sears, 1933)

	Yield of Corn per Acre in Indicated Year					
Soil Treatment	1911, bu.	1915, bu.	1919, bu.	1923, bu.	1927, bu.	1931, bu.
None	13	18	9	16	20	18
Limestone, sweet clover	23	47	28	13	5	9
Limestone, phosphate rock, sweet clover	21	43	27	12	5	14
Limestone, phosphate rock, sweet clover, potassium	26	56	37	45	52	54

in which the effect of liming on potassium deficiency increased over a period of years. This type of behavior would be expected if the deficiency were induced through greater crop withdrawals on limed than on unlimed soil. (Other examples have been recorded by Thorne (1930, p. 152) from Ohio, Williams, Rankin, and Hendricks (1942) from North Carolina, and Baker and Mayton (1944) from Alabama.) The fact that the deficiency appeared gradually, however, is not sufficient evidence to discount the importance of the complementary-ion effects, since the reaction of limestone with soil is also a slow process.

Complementary-ion effects and greater crop withdrawal both seem to be of importance, judging from measurements of exchangeable potassium made on various experimental fields in Illinois (Illinois Agricultural Experiment Station, 1936). On fields where exchangeable potassium was low and the increase in yield from potassium fertilization on limed plots was high, there was a tendency for exchangeable potassium to be a little lower in limed than in unlimed soil. On fields where exchangeable potassium was high with little or no increase in the yield of corn from potassium fertilization, there was a tendency for exchangeable potassium to be a little higher in limed than in unlimed plots. These are the results one would expect to obtain if liming caused an increase in the rate of change of nonexchangeable potassium to the exchangeable form, a decrease in potassium availability as a result of the complementary-ion effect, and an increase in rate at which crops withdraw potassium from the soil.

Effect of drying

Allowing soil to become air-dry before analysis for exchangeable potassium often results in a value different from that obtained using a comparable sample that has been maintained in a moist condition. If a change occurs, the usual finding is that drying decreases the content of exchangeable potassium in soil treated with soluble potassium salts and increases it in soil not so treated (Attoe, 1947). The effect observed in the laboratory is paralleled by the absorption of potassium by plants. Table 5 gives the results of an experiment in which three

Table 5. Exchangeable Potassium in Dried and Undried Silt Loam Soil and in Oat Crops Grown on the Soil

(Attoe, 1947)

	Exchangeable Potassium in Soil per Acre, lb.				Potassium Removed by Crops per Acre, lb.	
	Before Crop		After Crop			
	Undried	Dried	Undried	Dried	Undried	Dried
First crop	153	280	99	94	182	206
Second crop	99	205	68	84	66	98
Third crop	68	130	71	74	68	106
Total					316	410

crops were grown consecutively on soil maintained continuously in a moist condition and on comparable soil that was allowed to become air-dry at room temperature before each crop.

The effects of drying are of current interest from the theoretical standpoint because the mechanism is still in doubt. The explanation of potassium entrapment between closed lattice layers accounts for the fixation of added potassium but not for the release of native potassium. This release must be brought about by a process still unknown.

The fact that drying causes the exchangeable potassium to increase in some soils and not in others evidently is of considerable practical concern, since estimates of potassium availability in soils usually are based on measurements of exchangeable potassium and since the measurements customarily are made on air-dry samples. Some doubt arises as to whether the present procedure is the best one, since there is seldom more than a thin surface layer of soil in the field that becomes dry enough to produce a substantial increase in exchangeable potassium. Most of the effect of drying on potassium release seems to take place when the soil approaches the air-dry condition.

Effect of aeration

Absorption of potassium from soils by certain plants is limited by conditions of poor aeration. The inhibitory effect of poor aeration apparently is more pronounced with potassium than with any of the other nutrients. Table 6 shows the results of an experiment of Law-

Table 6.   Relative Yield of Nutrients and Yield of Dry Matter in Corn Plants
Grown on Nonaerated and Aerated Cultures of a Silt Loam Soil
Containing 50 per cent Water
(Lawton, 1946)

	Relative Yield, Nonaerated/Aerated
Potassium	0.3
Nitrogen	0.7
Phosphorus	1.3
Calcium	0.9
Magnesium	0.8
Dry matter	0.6

ton (1946) on corn that illustrate the contrast in behavior between potassium and certain other nutrients.

The effect of aeration on potassium absorption by plants is exerted primarily on the plants and not on the status of potassium in the soil. The validity of this statement is indicated by the fact that the effect occurs not only in soils but also in solution cultures, where the potassium is present entirely in the solution phase (Chang and Loomis, 1945). Furthermore, measurements on soils have failed to disclose important differences in water-soluble or exchangeable potassium even where large differences in potassium availability were apparent from the plant responses (Bower, Browning, and Norton, 1945).

Hammond[2] found that absorption of potassium by corn plants is reduced by either a deficiency of oxygen or an excess of carbon dioxide. The manner in which the effect on potassium uptake is brought about is not understood as yet. Perhaps a deficiency of oxygen or an excess of carbon dioxide limits the rate of metabolism in the roots, with the result that the content of organic acids decreases. The uptake and retention of potassium then decrease as a result of the limited number of organic acid anions available as counter-ions.

FUNCTION IN PLANTS

Potassium is associated with the metabolism of plants; it does not appear to represent a permanent structural component, at least not in the full amount. Several lines of evidence substantiate the view that the function of potassium is not structural. First, no organic compounds bearing potassium as a nonionizable component have been isolated from plants. Second, Scott and Hayward (1953) found that within a period as short as an hour the potassium contained in cells of the marine alga, *Ulva lactuca*, had equilibrated completely with the K^{42}-tagged potassium of the sea water used as culture medium. This experiment demonstrates the absence from the cells of nonionic forms of potassium that failed to equilibrate with the external medium. The cell potassium presumably was all ionic. Third, Eddy and Hinshelwood (1951) found that resting cells of *Bacterium lactis aerogenes* could be depleted of potassium almost completely by washing with dilute acid. Removal of the potassium did not affect the viability of the cells, as would have been expected had potassium been functioning in a structural capacity. Fourth, the content of potassium in plants can be accounted for on the basis that the potassium is combined with inorganic and ether-soluble organic acid anions (Pierce and Appleman, 1943).

There are two lines of evidence that substantiate the view that the rôle of potassium is metabolic. First, the potassium content of plants is correlated positively with the rate of metabolism. The work of Hoagland and Broyer (1936) and Luttkus and Bötticher (1939) may be cited in this connection. Second, potassium is known to be required in two types of metabolic reactions. Potassium is essential in certain enzymatically-catalyzed transphosphorylation reactions in-

[2] Hammond, Luther Carlisle. (1949) The influence of oxygen and carbon dioxide levels in the substrate upon potassium absorption by plants. Ph.D. Thesis, Iowa State College, Ames, Iowa.

volving the adenylic acid system (Lardy, 1951). Far-reaching consequences may be envisioned for the action of potassium in trans-phosphorylation reactions. The adenylic acid system is the universal medium of energy exchange in both plants and animals. In carbohydrate metabolism, the reactions requiring potassium represent steps in the process by which energy is obtained from sugar for synthetic purposes. In addition to its rôle in obtaining the requisite energy, potassium has been found to be necessary in carrying out some of the syntheses. Webster and Varner (1954) found that potassium is required in the coupling of certain amino acids to form peptides, thus suggesting that potassium is essential in protein synthesis.

DISTRIBUTION IN PLANTS

Potassium is not distributed uniformly throughout the plant. Microchemical studies of Macallum (1905) and Penston (1931) indicate that within individual cells potassium occurs in the cytoplasm and vacuoles, but not in the nucleus. Dead cells may be almost free of potassium. Within a given organ the cells may differ considerably in potassium content.

Under conditions of deficiency, potassium is most concentrated in the newly-developed parts of the plant, as might be anticipated from its mobility and from its rôle in metabolism. The higher concentration in the younger tissue may be produced in part at the expense of potassium in older tissue. Withdrawal of potassium may hasten the senescence of the older leaves, as indicated by the finding of Alten, Goeze, and Fischer (1938) that under conditions of potassium deficiency the photosynthetic activity of the older leaves declines rapidly. When the supply is ample, however, the potassium concentration may be greater in the older than in the younger tissues (Bowling and Brown, 1947), and the photosynthetic rate is maintained for a longer period of time. Table 7 illustrates the distribution of potassium in

Table 7. Deficiency Symptoms and Potassium Content of Leaves of Tobacco with Different Applications of Potassium as Potassium Sulfate
(Bowling and Brown, 1947)

Potassium Applied in Fertilizer per Acre, lb.	Potassium Deficiency Symptoms	Potassium Percentage in Dry Matter of Leaves		
		Lower, %	Middle, %	Upper, %
0	Very severe	0.6	0.6	1.3
20	Severe	1.0	1.6	2.2
40	Moderate	2.4	2.5	2.8
100	None	5.3	4.4	3.1
139	None	6.2	5.4	4.7

leaves from different positions on tobacco plants in relation to the supply of potassium in the soil.

RELATION TO OTHER CATIONS

Although plants have an absolute requirement for potassium, the rôle of potassium in some instances can be played in part by other cations.   Potassium-sparing action has been observed with ammonium and rubidium in certain lower plants and with sodium and rubidium in certain higher plants.   Most research has dealt with sodium since the sodium effects are of some practical importance.

The results of an experiment with cotton demonstrating partial substitution of sodium for potassium are shown in Fig. 4.   The low yield of the plants in the absence of added potassium shows that sodium was not a complete substitute for potassium, and the failure of sodium to increase the yield at high levels of potassium indicates that sodium had no independent effect of its own.   Appling and Giddens (1954) observed that when soil potassium was deficient for cotton, potassium accumulation was greatest in the upper, immature leaves, and sodium accumulation was greatest in the lower leaves.   This behavior suggests that sodium may act for potassium in its rôle in balancing organic and inorganic anions, but not in its essential rôle in metabolic reactions. Partial substitution of sodium for potassium probably is responsible in part for the favored position of sodium nitrate for topdressing cotton in the southeastern United States, where availability of soil potassium is low.

In some instances sodium has a favorable effect in its own right.

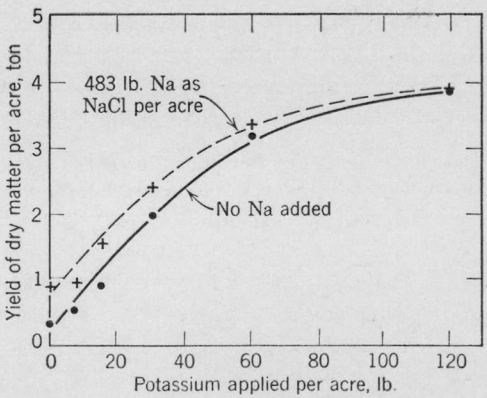

Fig. 4.   Yield of cotton in sand cultures with different applications of potassium in the presence and absence of a constant application of sodium.   (Holt and Volk, 1945.)

The existence of such an effect is indicated when the maximum yield attainable by adding increasing amounts of potassium is higher in the presence than in the absence of added sodium. Table 8 gives an ex-

Table 8. Increase in Yield of Fodder Beets with Different Applications of Potassium Chloride in the Presence of Sodium Nitrate and Calcium Nitrate

(Lehr, 1953)

Application of Potassium per hectare, kg.	Increase in Yield per hectare, ton*	
	Nitrogen Applied as Sodium Nitrate	Nitrogen Applied as Calcium Nitrate
0	8	0
133	8	−2
266	6	1

* Metric ton = 1000 kg.

ample. There is some uncertainty regarding the proper terminology for describing this effect of sodium. The effect may result from a requirement for sodium as an essential nutrient or from some favorable but nonessential function of sodium.

Plants differ considerably in their behavior toward sodium. Corn, for example, tends to exclude sodium and shows essentially no effect of amounts in the range of fertilizer applications even when potassium is deficient. Cotton absorbs sodium readily and exhibits partial substitution of sodium for potassium. Beets absorb sodium readily, and if the level of sodium in the soil is low, they respond to applications of sodium even with ample potassium. Classifications of crops into different categories with respect to response to sodium have been published by Harmer and Benne (1945) and Lehr (1953).

POTASSIUM SUPPLY AND PLANT BEHAVIOR

Deficiency symptoms

The most commonly observed symptom of potassium deficiency is a marginal browning and drying of the leaves, popularly termed "firing" or "scorching." In the course of its development, the leaf-scorch symptom may appear first as a browning of the leaf tips, moderate interveinal chlorosis, or as small, yellowish to brown spots that are most concentrated near the periphery and tip of the leaf. In some instances, the margin of the leaves affected by necrosis curls toward the upper or lower surface, and the body of the leaf has a crinkled appearance; leaves as yet unaffected by necrosis have an unusually dark green or bluish-green color.

Potassium deficiency symptoms usually appear first on the basal leaves and progress gradually up the plant toward the youngest leaves, but this is not the case invariably. Tomatoes and tobacco sometimes show the deficiency symptoms first on the middle leaves. In apples the symptoms usually occur first on leaves located near the middle of the current-season growth and spread in both directions. In the small-seeded legumes the symptoms appear almost simultaneously on all leaves.

The occurrence of potassium deficiency symptoms usually is not a sign of incipient deficiency but rather an indication that potassium is a severely limiting factor. Potassium fertilization thus may be of distinct benefit even though no foliar symptoms of deficiency appear.

For details on potassium deficiency symptoms on individual crops, the works of Eckstein, Bruno, and Turrentine (1937), Hambidge (1949), McMurtrey (1948), and Wallace (1951) should be consulted.

Water utilization

The literature records many observations and statements to the effect that potassium fertilization improves the water relations of plants. The action of potassium in this respect may be divided into four categories, according to the presumed cause.

The first category perhaps is the most intriguing, because it appears to be specific to potassium and because of the obscurities in the processes involved. Representative observations were recorded by Anderson et al. (1929, 1930), who noted that tobacco plants grown on field plots without potassium fertilization wilted sooner and more severely on hot days than did plants on comparable plots fertilized with potassium. Although the plants that did not receive potassium fertilizer were reduced in size, they showed no acute deficiency symptoms. Eckstein, Bruno, and Turrentine (1937, pp. 38–39) have reviewed similar observations of other investigators.

Mann (1924) and Alten and Goeze (1937) have made some measurements of transpiration of plants differing in supply of potassium. Mann determined the comparative loss of water from leaves detached from gooseberry plants grown in sand cultures supplied with a minus-potassium solution and with a complete nutrient solution. He found that the rate of loss was about the same if he took green leaves before the development of potassium deficiency symptoms. After the initial symptoms of potassium deficiency had appeared, the leaves from potassium-deficient plants lost water more rapidly than those from potassium-sufficient plants. Experiments on attached leaves of shoots cut from apple trees and placed in water indicated that the transpiration rate of leaves from potassium-deficient plants was above that of leaves from potassium-sufficient plants in the sunshine but below when the sun was covered by clouds. Alten and Goeze (1937) found that the first leaf of potassium-deficient wheat seedlings transpired less rapidly than the comparable leaf of potassium-sufficient plants at low light intensity. They made no observations at high light intensities. Their observations thus are in agreement with those of Mann (1924).

The only explanation that seems to have been advanced for these observations has to do with an effect of potassium supply on the development of cuticle. Lee and Priestley (1924) thought that the cuticle was thinner on leaves of potassium-deficient than of potassium-sufficient plants. Vogel (1933) reported that in certain crucifers his potassium-deficient plants lacked the characteristic waxy layer on the leaves. Both Vogel (1933) and Mann (1924) suggested poor cuticle development as a possible cause of rapid water loss from potassium-deficient plants. Although the existence of a thin cuticle on leaves of potassium-deficient plants might be directly responsible for more rapid water loss from these plants than from potassium-sufficient plants, it could hardly be directly responsible for the opposite effect observed experimentally in some of the work reported above. The problem apparently is more complex. Eckstein, Bruno, and Turrentine (1937, p. 39) attributed the flaccidity of potassium-deficient plants to poor development of mechanical tissue, thereby implying that water relationships are not involved. This explanation likewise does not seem entirely adequate, since the flaccidity does not always appear unless the plants are under conditions conducive to rapid water loss.

The second effect of potassium on the water relationships of plants may be termed a general "growth" effect. As noted in the chapter on soil water, the amount of water utilized in producing a gram of plant material has been observed frequently to decrease with an increase in the amount of plant material produced. This nonspecific effect apparently results simply from the fact that as the aerial growth of the plants fills the available space more and more completely, a limit of evaporation loss is reached beyond which greater plant density is without influence. In other words, this effect is attributable only indirectly to potassium.

The third effect of potassium on the water relationships of plants may be termed a general "salt" effect. The action of salts in reducing water uptake by plants was discussed in the chapter on soil salinity and alkalinity. A salt effect probably was involved, for example, in an experiment of Maercker and Tacke (1896), in which heavy applications of kainit and sodium chloride were used. Both substances caused a reduction in the total amount of water used and in the amount of water used per gram of dry matter produced. There was no appreciable increase in yield from the potassium or sodium treatments, and in some cases there was a substantial reduction.

The fourth effect may be described as the result of an interaction of water supply and potassium supply. The observations are of the type shown in Table 9 for field beans. The yield on the control plots

Table 9. Yield of Field Beans with and without Potassium Fertilization in Moist and Dry Years in Germany
(Bruns, 1935)
Average Yield per Hectare, *Dz*.

	Control (*A*)	Potassium Fertilized (*B*)	*A/B*
Five moist years	12	32	0.37
Six dry years	4	18	0.22

divided by that on the potassium-fertilized plots was lower in the dry years than in the moist years, whereas one would expect the reverse from the behavior of nitrogen, for example. The explanation perhaps is that dry weather causes leaves of potassium-deficient plants to become dry and inactive at an earlier date than they would in the presence of an ample water supply. The decrease in active leaf surface then limits the yield possibilities.

Carbohydrate and nitrogen metabolism

As noted above in the section on function, potassium is essential for the action of enzymes that catalyze certain transphosphorylation reactions and couplings of amino acids. The former may be classified as a rôle in carbohydrate metabolism, and the latter as a rôle in nitrogen metabolism. When plants become deficient in potassium, soluble forms of nitrogen usually accumulate in the plant tissues. According to Wall (1940), this accumulation begins before it would be expected on the basis of a stoppage of growth. The cause presumably is a reduced rate of formation of proteins from amino acids which in turn is affected by the supply of potassium.

The course of changes in carbohydrate metabolism under conditions of potassium deficiency usually leads to plants that are relatively low in carbohydrates (Wall, 1940), but sometimes to the reverse (Scheck, 1953). Current evidence admittedly does not throw much light on the manner in which such diverse effects are related to changes in the supply of potassium, and, indeed, the relationship may well be rather remote and indirect.

Total production of carbohydrates by potassium-deficient plants is limited in two ways. First, the rate of carbon dioxide assimilation per unit area of leaf surface is reduced (Alten and Goeze, 1937), probably as an indirect result of other metabolic disturbances. This effect, of course, is compounded with time so that less new leaf area is produced. Second, the leaves are dropped from the plant prematurely, thus actually reducing the total leaf area. In experiments on cotton grown on soils deficient in potassium (Turner, 1944), the loss of leaves by the time of the first picking amounted to 65, 53, and 31 per cent on plots receiving potassium at rates of 17, 33, and 66 lb. per acre, respectively. The ratio of the carbohydrate-producing capacity to the number of fruits thus may be relatively low in potassium-deficient plants.

A number of the effects of potassium deficiency on plant behavior seem to stem from a deficiency of carbohydrates. A low supply of potassium results in plant behavior that is similar in some respects to that obtained with a high supply of nitrogen (Russell, 1939, pp. 136–144).

Perhaps one of the most direct practical effects of the deranged metabolism associated with potassium deficiency is found in sugar cane. Potassium deficiency results in a reduction in sucrose percentage in the cane as well as a reduction in total yield of cane (Samuels and Landrau, 1954).

The two most frequently mentioned effects of potassium deficiency, namely, weak straw of cereals and poor fiber in fiber crops, likewise may be attributed to the low-carbohydrate condition of the plants. Anatomical changes associated with this condition may be visualized from the measurements on cross sections of barley straw recorded in Table 10. The stems of potassium-deficient plants evidently had

Table 10. Characteristics of the Straw of Barley Fertilized with Different Quantities of Potassium

(Acker, 1932)

Potassium Applied per hectare, kg.	Scleren- chyma Percent- age in Wall of Straw, %	Cell Wall Thickness			Lumen Diameter		
		Epi- dermis Outer Wall, μ	Paren- chyma, μ	Scleren- chyma, μ	Epi- dermis Outer Wall, μ	Paren- chyma, μ	Scleren- chyma, μ
0	8.7	2.9	2.0	3.2	14.4	18.2	11.4
41	10.1	5.4	2.3	5.5	14.3	21.9	11.7
162	12.7	6.6	4.2	6.8	12.2	23.5	10.7

a relatively low proportion of sclerenchyma (which is the woody, supporting tissue) and were composed of cells with relatively thin walls. Both these effects are conducive to a lower rigidity of the stems of potassium-deficient than of potassium-sufficient plants.

The type of effects noted in Table 10 carry over into the fiber of fiber plants. Fiber cells usually are sclerenchyma cells. Anatomical investigations (Alten and Goeze, 1936) have shown that the fiber cells have relatively thin walls under conditions of potassium deficiency. Although cotton fibers are not classified as sclerenchyma, they respond in the same manner to variations in supply of potassium to the plant. Moore and Rankin (1937) and various others have noted that if cotton is grown on soils deficient in potassium, application of potassium fertilizer results in a smaller proportion of thin-walled fibers and an increase in strength of individual fibers. The strength per unit weight of fibers cut to a standard length, however, is lower with fibers from plants well supplied with potassium than from plants deficient in potassium (Nelson, 1949).

Observations on grain crops indicate that the maximum yield of grain occurs at about the same level of potassium as does the maximum yield of straw. This behavior is in contrast to that observed with nitrogen. The level of nitrogen required to produce the maximum yield is greater for straw than for grain in crops like oats, and greater for grain than for straw in corn.

There is a distinction between potassium on the one hand and nitrogen and phosphorus on the other with respect to the effect on the size of individual cereal grains. Grain size usually is not much reduced by deficiencies of nitrogen or phosphorus; an individual grain either is produced or it is not. With a deficiency of potassium, however, more grains are initiated than are filled, so that the grain is light in weight. Thus, Hellriegel et al. (1898) found that in barley the average weight of one grain ranged from 5 mg., under conditions of extreme potassium deficiency, to 34 mg., with the heaviest application of potassium they employed. In corn, the size of individual grains becomes smaller and the filling becomes poorer in proceeding from the basal to the distal portion of the ear. The ears are said to be "chaffy," and they tend to taper to a point. This behavior perhaps is attributable to a combination of the tendency for potassium to migrate to meristematic regions and the deranged metabolism under conditions of potassium deficiency. The general problem was reviewed by Wiessmann (1923).

The effect of potassium on root development has received considerable attention because of the marked effect of potassium on root crops, as indicated by the data in Table 11 for potatoes. The explanation for this behavior presumably is that fully developed storage roots or

Table 11. Starch Percentage in Potato Tubers, and Yield of Different Parts
of Potato Plants Fertilized with Different Quantities of Potassium
(Wilfarth and Wimmer, 1902)

Potassium Applied per Culture, g.	Yield of Dry Matter per Culture, g.			Percentage of Total Dry Matter, %			Starch Percentage in Tuber Dry Matter, %
	Tubers	Roots	Tops	Tubers	Roots	Tops	
0	8	1	41	16	2	82	53
0.23	29	3	51	35	4	61	62
0.70	70	2	49	58	2	40	67
1.56	109	3	53	66	2	32	68
3.90	125	2	49	71	1	28	66

tubers contain a substantial portion of the total potassium in the plant
(a good crop of potato tubers contains about twice as much potassium
as the tops), and that during development some of this potassium is
translocated from the tops. In consequence, the tops initially must
contain more potassium than is needed for their development to avoid
the limitation of photosynthetic activity that otherwise would ensue
upon translocation of potassium to the developing tubers or storage
roots.

An additional consideration regarding root behavior is the degeneration of conducting tissues that may take place in potassium-deficient
plants. Hoffer and Carr (1923) and Hoffer and Trost (1923) found
that iron and aluminum compounds accumulate in nodes of corn plants
deficient in potassium. According to Hoffer and Carr (1923), large
numbers of the conducting vessels in the affected areas are clogged,
which hinders translocation. Porter (1927) found that the nodal tissue eventually disintegrates and becomes infected with different organisms.

Further references to the literature on the subject of potassium supply and root development will be found in the reviews by Wiessmann
(1923) and Rohde (1937).

Miscellaneous quality factors

Of all the plant nutrients, potassium is mentioned most often in relation to crop quality. The low starch content of potassium-deficient
potatoes was illustrated above in Table 11. Potassium-deficient potatoes also tend to become dark in color after cooking. Potassium-deficient apples do not color well. Potassium deficiency results in relatively poor keeping quality of various fruit and vegetable crops.
With tobacco, the fire-holding quality and aroma are impaired. With

barley, the brewing quality is impaired.   With peas, the seed coats are toughened.   With cabbage, the heads are not solid, and the color and flavor of sauerkraut are poor.   Potassium deficiency results in a decrease in acidity of citrus fruits, and in a decrease in oil content of oil seeds such as soybean and tung.   Literature on this subject was reviewed by Eckstein, Bruno, and Turrentine (1937) and Lawton and Cook (1954).

Disease incidence

Potassium deficiency usually increases the susceptibility of plants to various diseases (Arland, 1931; Eckstein, Bruno, and Turrentine, 1937, pp. 52–53).   The susceptibility is associated with the low-carbohydrate, high-nitrogen condition of the plants.   Except for the degeneration of conducting tissue (Hoffer and Carr, 1923; Porter, 1927), however, the factors involved have not been worked out beyond the stage indicated for high-nitrogen conditions in the chapter on nitrogen. The problem no doubt involves not only the physiology of the plant and the attacking organism, but also the environmental conditions. The complexity of the situation may be inferred from the observations of Eglits (1934) on the attack of rye plants by rust, mildew, and aphids under conditions of three different combinations of nitrogen and phosphorus in sand cultures.   Within these nine combinations of disease (or insect) and nutrition, there were four instances in which attack of the plants decreased regularly with increasing potassium supply, one in which the attack decreased regularly with increasing potassium supply except that no attack occurred where no potassium was added, one in which the attack was independent of potassium level, one in which there was no attack at any potassium level, and two in which there was no attack in the absence of potassium but a uniform attack where potassium was supplied.

Low-temperature injury

Plants deficient in potassium are more likely to be damaged by cold than are plants that are well supplied with potassium (Arland, 1931; Eckstein, Bruno, and Turrentine, 1937, pp. 53–54).   Observations of Boysen (1933) on frost damage to potatoes may be cited as an example. Plants that received no potassium fertilizer showed definite potassium deficiency symptoms.   Plants that received 33 and 66 kg. of potassium per hectare showed no deficiency symptoms, but the plants with the higher rate of application were somewhat the larger.   The first frost on August 31 killed practically all the foliage of the unfertilized plants, about one-third of that on plants with 33 kg. of potassium, and

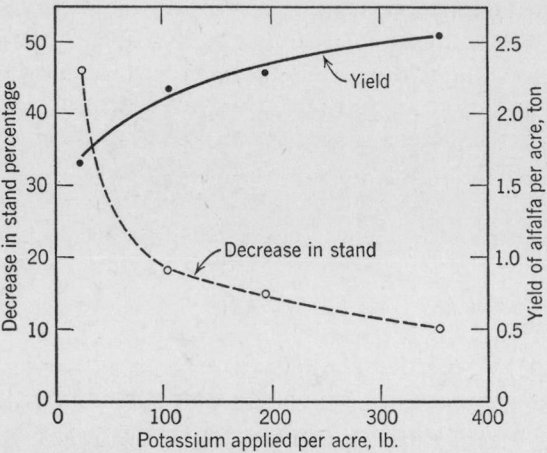

Fig. 5. Average yield (1947–1949) and decrease in stand percentage (1946–1949) of alfalfa planted on a potassium-deficient sandy soil in Indiana in the autumn of 1946. (Stivers and Ohlrogge, 1952.)

none on plants with 66 kg. of potassium. A somewhat more severe frost on September 4 killed over half the foliage on the plots receiving 33 kg. of potassium, and about one-third the foliage on the plots receiving 66 kg. of potassium. On September 13, the frost was so severe that all remaining foliage was killed. The heavy rate of potassium fertilization thus had lengthened the growing period by 13 days. Final tuber yields were 15,160, 21,680, and 26,510 kg. per hectare on the plots treated with 0, 33, and 66 kg. of potassium per hectare, respectively.

The foregoing example demonstrates the behavior of a crop that does not tolerate temperatures appreciably below the freezing point of water. The effect of the higher levels of potassium cannot be explained on the basis of osmotic depression of the freezing point, since the depression is too small. Thus, Bolhuis (1928) found that the freezing point of the sap from the foliage of potato plants was only 0.09° C. lower when the potassium supply was ample than when it was extremely deficient. Despite the small difference in the freezing point of the sap, however, the potassium-fertilized plants survived exposure to a temperature 0.5° C. lower than the temperature that killed the potassium-deficient plants. The action of the potassium presumably is connected in some way with the higher content of soluble carbohydrates in potassium-sufficient than in potassium-deficient plants. Although the explanation is not clear, plants relatively high in soluble carbohydrates tend to be cold resistant.

Potassium exerts an effect also on the cold resistance of plants that characteristically withstand freezing temperatures. Alfalfa is such a plant. Figure 5 shows the results of an experiment on potassium fertilization of alfalfa on a potassium-deficient sandy soil in Indiana. In this experiment the effect of potassium was to increase the hay yield and decrease the stand deterioration. Loss of alfalfa stands occurs mainly over the winter and among the plants having the lowest root reserves. Potassium deficiency limits the storage of reserves in the roots.

Time of maturity

Franck (1931) recorded the observations shown in Fig. 6 for oats grown on soils differing in supply of potassium. The maturity evidently was delayed when potassium was deficient. Alten and Gottwick (1939) found that the length of the growing period of soybeans was 181 days under conditions of potassium deficiency and 157 days when potassium fertilizer was supplied. Yields of soybeans were 562 and 967 kg. per hectare, respectively. Lagatu and Maume (1932) noted that grapes developed less rapidly and matured less completely when potassium was deficient than when the supply was ample. Unpublished data of L. C. Dumenil at the Iowa Agricultural Experiment Station indicate that potassium deficiency delays the maturity of corn.

In contrast to the foregoing observations, which represent the type reported most frequently, deficiency of potassium sometimes causes

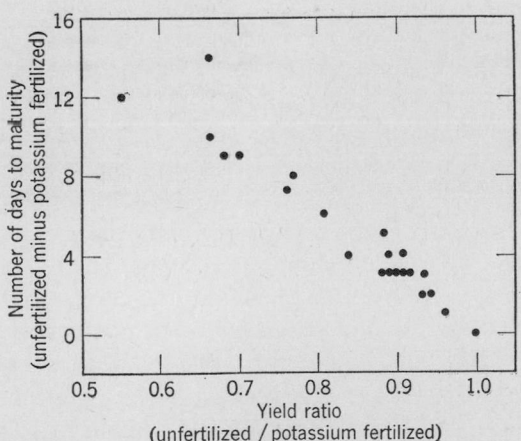

Fig. 6. Increase in number of days required for oats to reach maturity without potassium fertilization versus ratio of yield of unfertilized to yield of potassium-fertilized oats grown on different soils. (Franck, 1931.)

plants to mature earlier, and according to Williams, Jackson, and Mann (1926) and Volk (1942), this is true of cotton. The "early maturity" of potassium-deficient cotton plants perhaps can be attributed to a combination of two things. First, the flowering stage of these plants is cut short by potassium deficiency, so that the process of boll maturation begins while the potassium-sufficient plants continue to produce new flowers and bolls. Second, the leaves of the potassium-deficient plants fall early, so that carbohydrate production and translocation come to an early halt. Although the bolls become dry, they are not mature in the sense of having passed through the full process of development. Some bolls fail to open. Nelson (1949) reported that 67 per cent of the cotton fibers were mature in a crop produced on potassium-deficient soil, and that 80 per cent were mature in the crop produced on comparable potassium-fertilized soil. One therefore may speak more properly of the behavior of potassium-deficient cotton as "premature death" than as "early maturity."

Plant competition

Figure 7 shows the yield of different components of a uniformly seeded, mixed meadow that was fertilized with different quantities of potassium. As indicated by the relative responses of the clover and grass, the competitive position of the former was much better when the potassium supply was high than when it was low. This relative behavior seems to be generally characteristic of the legumes and

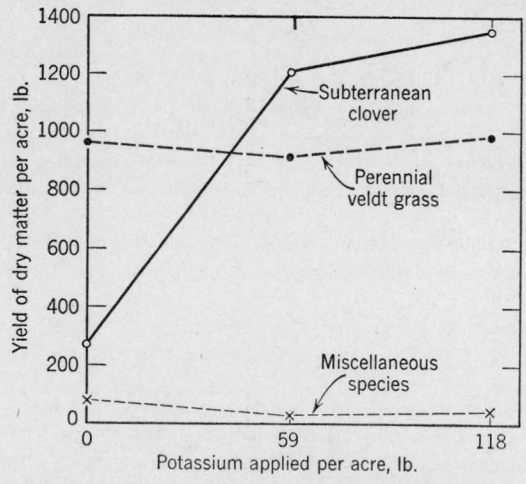

Fig. 7. Yield of botanical components of a mixed meadow with different applications of potassium fertilizer to a sandy soil in Australia. (Rossiter, 1947.)

grasses that are grown together in meadow mixtures. There are apparently two reasons for it. First, the soil supply of potassium is more nearly sufficient for maximum production of grass than legume when each is grown alone. Second, the difference between legume and grass grown alone may be exaggerated when they are grown together because of the effects of competition. The effects of competition for potassium evidently will be greatest when the potassium supply is smallest. Conversely, the effects of competition for factors other than potassium will be greatest when the potassium supply is ample for both crops. In the case represented by Fig. 7, the grass probably offered strong competition to the clover at the low potassium level by "robbing" the clover of potassium and thereby decreasing the yield without itself being much affected by the potassium deficiency. At high levels of potassium, where both species had enough potassium to produce essentially the maximum yield, the clover no doubt offered competition to the grass for the supply of growth factors other than potassium and thereby decreased the yield of grass. The competition offered by the clover on potassium-fertilized soil probably is responsible for the failure of potassium fertilization to increase the yield of grass.

LITERATURE CITED

Acker, W. (1932) Untersuchungen über die Wirkung der Kalidüngung auf den Bau und das mechanische Verhalten des Gerstenhalmes. Die Ernährung der Pflanze 28:401–403.

Alten, F., and G. Goeze. (1936) Der Einfluss der Düngung auf den Ertrag und die Güte der Flachsfasser. Die Ernährung der Pflanze 32:1–14.

Alten, F., and G. Goeze. (1937) Versuche über die Wirkung des Kaliums auf die Kohlensäureaufnahme von Weizenblättern. Die Ernährung der Pflanze 33:21–28.

Alten, F., G. Goeze, and H. Fischer. (1938) Mineralsalzernährung, Kohlensäureassimilation und Stickstoffhaushalt junger Weizenpflanzen. Die Ernährung der Pflanze 34:73–75.

Alten, F., and R. Gottwick. (1939) Untersuchungen über den Einfluss der Düngung auf das Wachstum und die Entwicklung der Sojabohne. Die Ernährung der Planze 35:277–284.

Anderson, M. S., Mary G. Keyes, and George W. Cromer. (1942) Soluble material of soils in relation to their classification and general fertility. U. S. Dept. Agr. Tech. Bul. 813.

Anderson, P. J., and T. R. Swanback. (1929) Report of the Tobacco Substation at Windsor for 1928. Connecticut (New Haven) Agr. Exp. Sta. Bul. 299.

Anderson, P. J., T. R. Swanback, O. E. Street, and others. (1930) Tobacco Substation at Windsor report for 1929. Connecticut (New Haven) Agr. Exp. Sta. Bul. 311.

Appling, Emory D., and Joel Giddens. (1954) Differences in sodium and potassium content of various parts of the cotton plant at four stages of growth. Soil Sci. 78:199–203.

Arland, Anton. (1931) Krankheitsbefall, Anfälligkeit, Pflanzenernährung und Winterfestigkeit in ihren Beziehungen untereinander und zur Transpiration. Wiss. Arch. f. Landw., Abt. A, Arch. f. Pflanzenbau 7:79–125.

Attoe, O. J. (1947) Potassium fixation and release in soils occurring under moist and drying conditions. Soil Sci. Soc. America Proc. (1946) 11:145–149.

Baker, K. G., and E. L. Mayton. (1944) A year-around grazing program for the alkaline soils of the black belt of Alabama. Jour. Amer. Soc. Agron. 36:740–748.

Barshad, Isaac. (1954) Cation exchange in micaceous minerals: II. Replaceability of ammonium and potassium from vermiculite, biotite, and montmorillonite. Soil Sci. 78:57–76.

Bolhuis, G. G. (1928) Kalidüngung und Nachtfrostgefahr. Landbouwkundig Tijdschrift 40, No. 475. (Abstracted by Taussig, Stefan. (1928) Die Ernährung der Pflanze 24:231.)

Bower, C. A., G. M. Browning, and R. A. Norton. (1945) Comparative effects of plowing and other methods of seedbed preparation on nutrient element deficiencies in corn. Soil Sci. Soc. America Proc. (1949) 9:142–146.

Bowling, J. D., and D. E. Brown. (1947) Role of potash in growth and nutrition of Maryland tobacco. U. S. Dept. Agr. Tech. Bul. 933.

Boysen, H. (1933) Kalidüngung und Nachtfrostgefahr. Die Ernährung der Pflanze 29:270.

Bray, R. H., and E. E. DeTurk. (1939) The release of potassium from nonreplaceable forms in Illinois soils. Soil Sci. Soc. America Proc. (1938) 3:101–106.

Bruns, Walter. (1935) Untersuchungen über Nährstoffaufnahme und Wasserhaushalt der Ackerbohne. Jour. f. Landw. 83:285–325.

Chaminade, Raymond. (1936) La rétrogradation du potassium dans les sols. Ann. agron. (N.S.) 6:818–830.

Chang, H. T., and W. E. Loomis. (1945) Effect of carbon dioxide on absorption of water and nutrients by roots. Plant Physiol. 20:221–232.

Denison, I. A., William H. Fry, and P. L. Gile. (1929) Alteration of muscovite and biotite in the soil. U. S. Dept. Agr. Tech. Bul. 128.

DeTurk, E. E., L. K. Wood, and R. H. Bray. (1943) Potash fixation in corn belt soils. Soil Sci. 55:1–12.

Eckstein, Oskar, Albert Bruno, and J. W. Turrentine. (1937) Potash Deficiency Symptoms. Verlagsgesellschaft für Ackerbau M.B.H., Berlin.

Eddy, A. A., and Cyril Hinshelwood. (1951) Alkali-metal ions in the metabolism of Bact. lactis aerogenes. II. Connexion with viability, growth rate and enzyme activity. Proc. Royal Soc. London 138B:228–237.

Eglits, Max. (1934) Die Empfänglichkeit des Winterroggens für Puccinia dispersa in Abhängigkeit von der Mineralsalzernährung. Die Ernährung der Pflanze 30:167.

Franck, Olle. (1931) Gödsling, mognadstid och kärnkvalitet. Nordisk Jordbrugsforskning 13:282–290.

Fraps, G. S. (1929) Relation of the water-soluble potash, the replaceable, and acid-soluble potash to the potash removed by crops in pot experiments. Texas Agr. Exp. Sta. Bul. 391.

Grim, Ralph E. (1953) Clay Mineralogy. McGraw-Hill Book Co., New York.

Grim, R. E., R. H. Bray, and W. F. Bradley. (1937) The mica in argillaceous sediments. Amer. Mineral. 22:813–829.

Hambidge, Gove (Editor). (1949) **Hunger Signs in Crops: A Symposium.** American Society of Agronomy and National Fertilizer Association, Washington, D. C.

Harmer, Paul M., and Erwin J. Benne. (1945) Sodium as a crop nutrient. **Soil Sci.** 60:137—148.

Hellriegel, H., H. Wilfarth, H. Römer, and G. Wimmer. (1898) Vegetationsversuche über den Kalibedarf einiger Pflanzen. **Arb. deut. Landw. Gesell.,** Heft 34.

Hoagland, D. R., and T. C. Broyer. (1936) General nature of the process of salt accumulation by roots with description of experimental methods. **Plant Physiol.** 11:471—507.

Hoffer, G. N., and R. H. Carr. (1923) Accumulation of aluminum and iron compounds in corn plants and its probable relation to rootrots. **Jour. Agr. Res.** 23:801—823.

Hoffer, G. N., and J. F. Trost. (1923) The accumulation of iron and aluminium compounds in corn plants and its probable relation to root rots. II. **Jour. Amer. Soc. Agron.** 15:323—331.

Holt, M. E., and N. J. Volk. (1945) Sodium as a plant nutrient and substitute for potassium. **Jour. Amer. Soc. Agron.** 37:821—827.

Illinois Agricultural Experiment Station. (1936) Potassium needs not always met by legume-lime system. In A year's progress in solving farm problems in Illinois. **Illinois Agr. Exp. Sta. 48th Ann. Rpt.,** pp. 35—36.

International Potash Institute. (1954) **Potassium Symposium.** International Potash Institute, Zurich.

Jeffries, C. D., J. A. Bonnet, and F. Abruña. (1953) The constituent minerals of some soils of Puerto Rico. **Puerto Rico Univ. Jour. Agr.** 37:114—139.

Kime, Chas. D., Jr. (1943) Leaching of potash from a sandy citrus soil of Florida. **Proc. Florida State Hort. Soc.** 56:43—48.

Lagatu, H., and L. Maume. (1932) Un cas d'absolue nécessité d'engrais potassique. **Le progrès agricole et viticole** 97:576—581.

Lardy, Henry A. (1951) The influence of inorganic ions on phosphorylation reactions. In McElroy, William D., and Bentley Glass (Editors). **Phosphorus Metabolism.** A symposium on the role of phosphorus in the metabolism of plants and animals. pp. 477—499. The Johns Hopkins Press, Baltimore.

Lawton, Kirk (1946) The influence of soil aeration on the growth and absorption of nutrients by corn plants. **Soil Sci. Soc. America Proc.** (1945) 10:263—268.

Lawton, Kirk, and R. L. Cook. (1954) Potassium in plant nutrition. **Adv. Agron.** 6:253—303.

Lee, Beatrice, and J. H. Priestley. (1924) The plant cuticle. I. Its structure, distribution, and function. **Ann. Bot.** 38:525—545.

Lehr, J. J. (1953) Sodium as a plant nutrient. **Jour. Sci. Food Agr.** 4:460—471.

Lipman, Jacob G., and Adrienne B. Conybeare. (1936) Preliminary note on the inventory and balance sheet of plant nutrients in the United States. **New Jersey Agr. Exp. Sta. Bul.** 607.

Luttkus, K., and R. Bötticher. (1939) Über die Ausscheidung von Aschenstoffen durch die Wurzeln. I. **Planta. Arch. f. wiss. Bot.** 29:325—340.

Macallum, A. B. (1905) On the distribution of potassium in animal and vegetable cells. **Jour. Physiol.** 32:95—128.

Maercker and Tacke. (1896) Über die Wirkung der Kalisalze auf verschiedenen Bodenarten. **Arb. deut. Landw.—Gesell.,** Heft 20.

Mann, C. E. T. (1924) The physiology of the nutrition of fruit trees. I. Some effects of calcium and potassium starvation. **Bristol Univ. Agr. Hort. Res. Sta. Ann. Rpt.** 1924:30—45.

McMurtrey, J. E., Jr. (1948) Visual symptoms of malnutrition in plants. In Kitchen, Herminie Broedel (Editor). **Diagnostic Techniques for Soils and Crops.** The American Potash Institute, Washington, D. C., pp. 231—289.

Mehlich, A., and J. Fielding Reed. (1946) The influence of degree of saturation, potassium level, and calcium additions on removal of calcium, magnesium, and potassium. **Soil Sci. Soc. America Proc.** (1945)   10:87—93.

Merwin, H. D., and Michael Peech. (1951) Exchangeability of soil potassium in the sand, silt, and clay fractions as influenced by the nature of the complementary exchangeable cation. **Soil Sci. Soc. America Proc.** (1950)   15:125—128.

Mohr, E. C. J., and F. A. Van Baren. (1954) **Tropical Soils.** Interscience Publishers, New York.

Moore, J. H., and W. H. Rankin. (1937) Influence of "rust" on quality and yield of cotton and the relation of potash applications to control. **North Carolina Agr. Exp. Sta. Bul.** 308.

Nelson, W. L. (1949) The effect of nitrogen, phosphorus, and potash on certain lint and seed properties of cotton. **Agron. Jour.** 41:289—293.

Parker, Frank W., J. Richard Adams, K. G. Clark, K. D. Jacob, and A. L. Mehring. (1946) Fertilizers and lime in the United States: resources, production, marketing, and use. **U. S. Dept. Agr. Misc. Publ.** 586.

Peech, Michael, and Richard Bradfield. (1943) The effect of lime and magnesia on the soil potassium and on the absorption of potassium by plants. **Soil Sci.** 55:37—48.

Penston, Norah L. (1931) Studies of the physiological importance of the mineral elements in plants. III. A study by microchemical methods of the distribution of potassium in the potato plant. **Ann. Bot.** 45:673—692.   •

Pierce, Elwood C., and C. O. Appleman. (1943) Rôle of ether soluble organic acids in the cation-anion balance in plants. **Plant Physiol.** 18:224—238.

Pirsson, Louis V., and Adolph Knopf. (1947) **Rocks and Rock Minerals.** 3rd Ed. John Wiley and Sons, New York.

Porter, C. L. (1927) A study of the fungous flora of the nodal tissues of the corn plant. **Phytopathology** 17:563—568.

Pratt, P. F. (1951) Potassium removal from Iowa soils by greenhouse and laboratory procedures. **Soil Sci.** 72:107—117.

Reitemeier, R. F. (1951) Soil potassium. **Adv. Agron.** 3:113—164.

Reitemeier, R. F. (1952) **Bibliography of literature on the release and fixation of native and fixed nonexchangeable potassium and ammonium of soils and silicate minerals.** (Multilithed). United States Dept. Agr., Agr. Res. Admin., Bur. Plant Industry, Soils, and Agr. Eng., Div. Soil Man. and Irrig. Agr., Plant Industry Station, Beltsville, Maryland.

Reitemeier, R. F., I. C. Brown, and R. S. Holmes. (1951) Release of native and fixed nonexchangeable potassium of soils containing hydrous mica. **United States Dept. Agr. Tech. Bul.** 1049.

Rohde, G. (1937) Die Bedeutung des Kaliums für die Wurzelentwicklung der Pflanze. **Die Ernährung der Pflanze** 33:65—73.

Rossiter, R. C. (1947) The effect of potassium on the growth of subterranean clover and other pasture plants on Crawley sand. **Australian Jour. Council Sci. Indust. Res.** 20:389—401.

Rouse, R. Dennis, and B. R. Bertramson. (1950) Potassium availability in several

Indiana soils: its nature and methods of evaluation. **Soil Sci. Soc. America Proc.** (1949) 14:113—123.

Russell, E. J. (1939) Fertilizers in modern agriculture. **Great Britain Min. Agr. Fisheries Bul.** 28, 3rd Ed.

Samuels, George, and Pablo Landrau, Jr. (1954) The influence of potassium on the yield and sucrose content of sugarcane. **Jour. Agr. Univ. Puerto Rico** 38:170—178.

Schachtschabel, Paul. (1937a) Aufnahme von nicht-austauschbarem Kali durch die Pflanzen. **Bodenkunde u. Pflanzenernährung** 3:107—133.

Schachtschabel, Paul. (1937b) Mikroskopische und röntgenographische Untersuchungen von Böden. **Bodenkunde u. Pflanzenernährung** 5:375—389.

Scheck, Helmut. (1953) Über den Einfluss des Kaliums auf den Kohlehydratstoffwechsel und auf die Carbohydrasen bei Kulturpflanzen. **Zeitschr. f. Pflanzenernähr., Düng., Bodenk.** 60:209—220.

Schmitz, G. W., and P. F. Pratt. (1953) Exchangeable and nonexchangeable potassium as indexes to yield increases and potassium absorption by corn in the greenhouse. **Soil Sci.** 76:345—353.

Scott, George T., and Hugh R. Hayward. (1953) The influence of temperature and illumination on the exchange of potassium ion in **Ulva lactuca. Biochim. Biophys. Acta** 12:401—404.

Sears, O. H. (1933) Following sweet clover potash increases corn yields. **Better Crops With Plant Food** 18, No. 6:5—6, 55—56.

Stauffer, R. S. (1942) Runoff, percolate and leaching losses from some Illinois soils. **Jour. Amer. Soc. Agron.** 34:830—835.

Stivers, Russell K., and A. J. Ohlrogge. (1952) Influence of phosphorus and potassium fertilization of two soil types on alfalfa yield, stand, and content of these elements. **Agron. Jour.** 44:618—621.

Thorne, Charles Embree. (1930) **The Maintenance of Soil Fertility.** Orange Judd Publishing Co., New York.

Turner, J. H., Jr. (1944) The effect of potash level on several characters in four strains of upland cotton which differ in foliage growth. **Jour. Amer. Soc. Agron.** 36:688—698.

Vogel, F. (1933) Topfvegetations-Vorversuche über Nährstoffmangel- und Wachstumserscheinungen auf drei verschiedenen Böden zu fünf Kohlarten. **Die Ernährung der Pflanze** 29:457—462.

Volk, N. J. (1934) The fixation of potash in difficultly available form in soils. **Soil Sci.** 37:267—287.

Volk, N. J. (1940) The effect of soil characteristics and winter legumes on the leaching of potassium below the 8-inch depth in some Alabama soils. **Jour. Amer. Soc. Agron.** 32:888—890.

Volk, N. J. (1942) Relation of exchangeable potassium in Alabama soils to needs of the cotton crop. **Jour. Amer. Soc. Agron.** 34:188—198.

Wall, Monroe E. (1940) The role of potassium in plants: III. Nitrogen and carbohydrate metabolism in potassium-deficient plants supplied with either nitrate or ammonium nitrogen. **Soil Sci.** 49:393—409.

Wallace, T. (1951) **The Diagnosis of Mineral Deficiencies in Plants by Visual Symptoms: A Colour Atlas and Guide.** His Majesty's Stationery Office, London.

Webster, George C., and J. E. Varner. (1954) Peptide-bond synthesis in higher plants. II. Studies on the mechanism of synthesis of γ-glutamylcysteine. **Arch. Biochem. Biophys.** 52:22—32.

Wiessmann, H. (1923) Ueber den Einfluss des Kaliums auf die Entwicklung der

Pflanzen und ihren morphologischen und anatomischen Bau bei besonderer Berücksichtigung der landwirtschaftlichen Kulturpflanzen. **Zeitschr. f. Pflanzenernähr. u.
Düng. 2A:1–79.**

Wilfarth, H., and G. Wimmer.   (1902)   Die Wirkung des Kaliums auf das Pflanzen-
leben nach Vegetationsversuchen mit Kartoffeln, Tabak, Buchweizen, Senf, Zichorien
und Hafer.   **Arb. deut. Landw. Gesell., Heft 68.**

Williams, C. B., S. K. Jackson, and H. B. Mann.   (1926)   Fertilizer experiments with
cotton.   **North Carolina Agr. Exp. Sta. Bul. 250.**

Williams, C. B., W. H. Rankin, and J. W. Hendricks.   (1942)   Soil fertility studies in
the Piedmont.   I. The effects of limestone and fertilizers in a 4-year rotation.
North Carolina Agr. Exp. Sta. Bul. 331.

INDEX

Acidity of soils (*see also* pH of soils)
  development, 137
  exchange, 128
  hydrolytic, 129
Active transport of ions by roots, 118
Aeration of soils (*see also* Air, Carbon dioxide, Oxygen)
  adaptation of plants to, 96
  diseases of plants and, 98
  evaluation of adequacy, 91
  nitrogen mineralization and, 195
  plant growth and, 91
  potassium availability and, 98, 304
  water availability and, 98
Aggregants, erosion of soils and, 14
  growth of plants in alkali soils and, 175
  nature of, 9
  use for evaluating soil structure effects, 10
  water infiltration and, 14
Aggregate analysis, 7
Aggregation of soils (*see* Structure of soils)
Air (*see also* Aeration of soils)
  composition in soils at different depths, 90
  composition of soil and atmospheric, 88
  composition of soil, validity of measurements, 93
  plant response to composition of, 92
  solubility in water, 94

Aluminum, exchangeable, 129
  toxicity in acid soils, 142
Amino acids, in plants, 222
  in soil hydrolysates, 184
  in soils, 183
Amino sugars in soil hydrolysates, 184
Ammonia volatilization from soils, 210
Ammonification, 188
Ammonium, fixation by soils, 185, 189, 203, 297
  in igneous rocks, 25
  in soil hydrolysates, 184
Anion-exchange properties of roots, 118
Antibiotics in soils, 30
Auxin in plants, nitrogen supply and, 225
  root and top growth of plants and supply of, 225
Azotobacter, 150, 212

Base-exchange capacity, 107
Bases in plants, estimation of proportionate content of, 122
Boron, pH of soils and availability of, 149
  toxicity in soils, 159

Calcium, concentration of, and growth of plants at different pH values, 145
  deficiency in acid soils, 146
  deficiency in alkali soils, 174

325

Calcium, deficiency in saline solutions, 168

degree of saturation and absorption by plants, 146

exchangeable in soils, 115

exchangeable and nonexchangeable in soils, 106

soil source used by plants, 104

Capillary rise of water, 66

Carbohydrate in plants, low-temperature injury and, 235

metabolism as affected by potassium supply, 311

Carbohydrate-nitrogen ratio, decomposition of organic materials and, 189

plant behavior and, 223

symbiotic nitrogen fixation and, 216

Carbon dioxide (see also Aeration of soils)

concentration in soil and atmospheric air, 88

concentration in soils and solubility of calcium phosphates, 98, 281

pH of soils and, 133, 138

plant growth and content in soil air, 92

production by soils, 89

solubility in water, 94

Carbon-nitrogen ratio, 189

Cation-exchange capacity, clay and organic matter interaction in relation to, 185

definition, 107

of clay minerals, 109

of mineral fraction of soils, 107

of organic fraction of soils, 107

of soil separates, 108

Cation-exchange properties of roots, 118, 281

Cation-exchange properties of soils, measurement and representation, 106

sources, 107

Cation-exchange reactions, equivalence, 112

rate, 114

reversibility, 113

Chemical composition of soils, 23

Chloride, succulence of plants and content of, 169

toxicity in saline soils, 168

Clay, amorphous components, 112

crystal structure, 109

formation, 18

minerals in, 20

nature of parent rock and, 21

stability of different kinds to weathering, 21

structure of soils and content of, 6

temperature and content in soils, 20

water supply and content in soils, 18

Clostridium, 212

Compaction of soils (see Structure of soils)

Competition among plants, nitrogen supply and, 237

pH of soils and, 153

phosphorus supply and, 280

potassium supply and, 318

Complementary-ion effects, absorption of bases by plants and, 121, 301

release of bases from exchangeable form and, 119

Denitrification, 189, 208

Diseases of plants, aeration of soils and, 98

nitrogen supply and, 236

pH of soils and, 151

phosphorus supply and, 279

potassium supply and, 315

Drying of soils, nitrogen availability and, 197

potassium availability and, 303

Electrical conductivity of soil extracts, 160

Energy concept of soil water (see Water, free energy of)

Evaporation (see Water, vapor loss from soils)

Evapotranspiration, components, 53

definition, 54

estimation from meteorological measurements, 54

fertility of soil and, 54, 78

free-water level in soil and, 54

optimum depth of free-water level and, 69

plant growth and, 54

water content of soil and, 55

Exchangeable and nonexchangeable
    bases, biological differentiation, 104
  chemical differentiation, 103
  isotopic differentiation, 104
  relative quantities, 106
Exchangeable bases, availability in acid
    soils, 144
  definition, 107
  estimation of bases in plants from,
    122
  plant nutrition and, 104, 118
  proportions in soils, 115
  release from exchangeable form, 119
  renewal, 116

Fallowing for water conservation, 51
Fiber, nitrogen supply and character-
    istics of, 225
  potassium supply and characteristics
    of, 313
Field capacity of soils for water, 47

Horizons of soils, 30
Hormones in soils, 29
Hydrogen, absorption by plants in
    competition with bases, 144
  electrovalent-covalent in soils, 131
  exchangeable in soils, 128
  hydrolytic in soils, 129, 131
  sources of titratable form in soils, 138
  titratable in soils, 128

Igneous rocks, 14, 15, 24
Illite, cation-exchange capacity, 109
  crystal structure, 110
  occurrence in soils, 20
  potassium in, 111, 113, 291, 293, 295
Infiltration, 13
Ions, absorption by plants, 118
  estimation of content in plants from
    content in soils, 122
  ratios versus quantities in relation to
    plant growth, 125
  selective absorption by plants, 122
  specific effects on plants in saline
    soils, 166
Iron, aeration of soils and availability
    of, 97
  pH of soils and availability of, 149

Isomorphous substitution, 111
Isotopes, calcium, 104
  carbon, 186
  nitrogen, 186, 201, 210, 238
  phosphorus, 259

Kaolinite, cation-exchange capacity, 109
  crystal structure, 109
  occurrence in soils, 20

Light, competition among plants for,
    240
Lignin, decomposition of organic ma-
    terials containing, 192
  in soils, 26
  reaction with ammonia, 185
  reaction with nitrous acid, 185
  reaction with protein, 184
Lime potential of soils, 136
Liming of soils, decomposition of or-
    ganic matter in soils and, 150
  nitrogen mineralization in soils as af-
    fected by, 150
  overliming injury, 269
  phosphorus availability and, 268
  phosphorus mineralization in soils as
    affected by, 150, 269
  plant growth and, 146, 149
  potassium availability and, 301
  prediction of needs, 132
Lithosphere, 14, 23
Lodging of plants, nitrogen supply and,
    229
  rootworm injury and, 230

Magnesium, deficiency in alkali soils,
    175
  exchangeable and nonexchangeable
    in soils, 106
  exchangeable in soils, 115
Manganese, aeration and availability of,
    97
  pH of soils and availability of, 150
  toxicity in acid soils, 143
Maturation of plants, nitrogen supply
    and, 230
  phosphorus supply and, 277
  potassium supply and, 317
Mechanical analysis, 3

Mechanical composition of soils (*see also* Separates of soils)
definition, 1
mechanical analysis, 3
nitrogen content and, 4, 181
phosphorus content and, 249
plant growth and, 1, 4, 33
porosity of soils and, 90
soil class designations, 3
texture of soils, 3
water availability to plants and, 4, 61
Microbial tissue in soils, 26
Mineralogical composition, of igneous rocks, 14
of sedimentary rocks, 14
of soils, 2, 14
plant growth and, 16
Moisture equivalent of soils, 48
Molybdenum availability, soil pH and, 149
Montmorillonite, cation-exchange capacity, 109
crystal structure, 109
occurrence in soils, 20
potassium fixation by, 298
Mulches, plant growth and, 52
soil temperature and, 52
water evaporation and, 52
water infiltration and, 14, 52
Mycorrhizae, 201, 281

Negative adsorption by soils, 162
Nitrate (*see also* Nitrogen mineralization)
aeration of soils and production of, 195
availability of nitrogen to plants as estimated from production of, 202
movement in soils, 205
pH of soils and production of, 150
plant growth and leaching loss of, 207
plant growth and production of, 25
poisoning of livestock by, 194
production in soils, 188
temperature and production of, 196
water supply and production of, 193
Nitric oxide, 208
Nitrification, 188

Nitrogen (*see also* Ammonia volatilization from soils, Ammonium, Nitrate, Nitric oxide, Nitrous acid, Nitrous oxide)
auxin content of plants and supply of, 225
availability to plants, 187
carbohydrate utilization in plants and supply of, 223
change in soil content with management practices, 219
competition among plants and supply of, 237
competition among plants for, 238
conservation in soil by cover crops, 207
content in crops, 205
content in soil organic matter, 183
content in soils, 179
content in soils in relation to land values, 30
content in soils with different management practices, 204
deficiency symptoms in plants, 222
diseases of plants and supply of, 236
erosion loss, 211
fiber strength and supply of, 225
fixation, combined nitrogen supply and, 212, 216, 238
nonsymbiotic, 150, 208, 212
symbiotic, 150, 214, 238
terminology of, 189
forms in plants, 221
forms in soils, 183
fruiting of plants and supply of, 227
function in plants, 221
gaseous, in waterlogged soils, 89
grain and straw growth and supply of, 227
immobilization, 187, 200
leaching loss of, 205
lodging of plants and supply of, 229
low-temperature injury to plants and supply of, 235
metabolism as affected by potassium supply, 311
microbiological oxidation, 187
microbiological reduction, 188, 208
mineralization, aeration of soil and, 195

Nitrogen (*see also* Ammonia volatilization from soils, Ammonium, Nitrate, Nitric oxide, Nitrous acid, Nitrous oxide)
  drying of soil and, 197
  freezing of soil and, 198
  mycorrhizae and, 201
  plant-growth effect on, 199
  seasonal effect on, 199
  soil pH and, 193
  substrate composition and, 189
  temperature and, 196
  total nitrogen of soils and, 189
  water supply and, 193
  plant growth in relation to content in soils, 25, 30, 202
  rainfall as source of, 218
  root growth and supply of, 225
  seasonal fluctuations in soils, 218
  stability in soils, 184
  sugar content of plants and supply of, 223
  tillering of plants and supply of, 230
  transfer from legume to nonlegume, 217, 238
Noncapillary pores in soils, 12
Nonsaline-alkali soils, 160, 163
Nitrous acid, 210
Nitrous oxide, 208

Organic matter, cation-exchange properties, 107
  chelation by, 113, 114
  decomposition in soils at different pH values, 150
  decomposition of soil, effect of added organic materials, 186
  estimation from organic carbon, 30
  estimation from organic nitrogen, 30
  microbial tissue as component of soil, 26
  movement in nonsaline-alkali soils, 163
  nature of soil, 26
  plant growth and, 27
  reaction with clay, 185
  toxins in soils, 27
Outer space of roots, 118
Oxygen, absorption by soils, 89
  adaptation of roots to external deficiency of, 96

Oxygen, concentration in soil and atmospheric air, 88
  diffusion rate in soils, 95
  diffusion rate in water and air, 94
  ferric phosphate dissolution and supply of, 98
  iron availability and supply of, 97
  manganese availability and supply of, 97
  solubility in water, 94
  temperature and root requirement for, 95

Partial sterilization of soils, 198
Passive permeation of roots by ions, 118
Penetrometer, 8
Permanent wilting point (*see* Water, availability to plants)
Permeability of soils, air, 8, 89
  sodium and, 173
  water, 8, 12, 45, 173
pH of soils, differences between supernatant solution and soil sediment, 134
  diseases of plants and, 151
  electrolyte content of soils and, 133
  fertilizers and, 139
  grazing of pastures and, 154
  iron pyrite and, 139
  junction-potential effects, 135
  measurement, 132
  nitrate production and, 133
  nutrient availability and (*see* Exchangeable bases, Liming of soils; *see also individual elements*)
  plant growth and, 140, 174
  range of values, 132
  soil-to-water ratio and, 132
  validity of measurements, 134
Phosphorus, absorption by plants from soils, 257
  availability to plants, 149, 257
  concentration and renewal in soil solution, 258
  content in crops, 250
  content in soils, 248
  deficiency symptoms in plants, 274
  diseases of plants and supply of, 279
  erosion losses, 251

Phosphorus, forms in plants, 271
  forms in soils, 252
  function in plants, 271
  growth stage and plant response to additions of, 278
  inorganic in soils, 252, 257
  isotopic exchange in soils, 259
  leaching losses of, 250
  maturation of plants and supply of, 277
  mineralization of organic, 150, 266, 269
  mineralogical forms in soils, 253
  organic in soils, 252, 256, 265
  pH of soils and availability of, 149, 268
  root growth and supply of, 275
  species differences in response to additions of, 280
Polysaccharides in soils, 26
Porosity of soils (see Permeability of soils)
Potassium, absorption by plants from exchangeable and nonexchangeable forms, 105, 292, 293, 300
  absorption by plants from soils, 292
  aeration and availability of, 304
  availability to plants, 292
  bonding in micaceous clay, 297
  carbohydrate metabolism and supply of, 311
  chemical forms in soils, 291
  competition among plants for, 240
  content in crops, 288
  content in soils, 287
  deficiency symptoms in plants, 308
  diseases of plants and supply of, 315
  distribution in plants, 306
  drying of soil and availability of, 303
  erosion losses, 290
  exchangeable and nonexchangeable in soils, 106, 291
  exchangeable in soils, 115
  exchangeable-nonexchangeable equilibrium, 293, 300, 303
  fiber characteristics and supply of, 313
  fixation, 203, 294, 295, 297, 299, 303
  forms in plants, 305
  forms in soils, 290

Potassium, function in plants, 305
  grain production and supply of, 313
  leaching losses, 289
  low-temperature injury to plants and supply of, 315
  maturation of plants and supply of, 317
  micaceous clay and availability of, 295
  mineralogical forms in soils, 290
  nitrogen metabolism and supply of, 311
  pH of soils and availability of, 301
  quality of plant products and supply of, 314
  release from nonexchangeable forms, 117
  root development and supply of, 313
  substitution by other cations, 307
  water utilization by plants and supply of, 309
Profile of soils, diagram of, 30
  nitrogen distribution in, 182
  nutrient availability in, 34
  phosphorus availability in, 251
  phosphorus distribution in, 249
  properties in relation to plant growth, 31
  type description, 31
Protein, decomposition of, 190
  in plants, 222
  in soils, 27, 183
  reaction with clays, 185
  reaction with lignin, 184

Reaction of soils (see pH of soils)
Redox potential of soils, 94
Rhizobium, 150, 215
River water, chemical composition of, 23
Roots, anion-exchange properties of, 118
  auxin in plants and growth of, 225
  cation-exchange properties of, 118
  differential extension among plants, 64
  drought resistance of plants and extension of, 64
  nitrogen supply and growth of, 225

Roots, phosphorus supply and growth of, 275
  potassium supply and growth of, 313
  structure of soils and growth of, 11, 14
  water availability and extension of, 62, 73
Rotation of crops, nitrogen availability and, 5, 153
  structure of soils and, 9

Saline soils, 160, 162
Saline-alkali soils, 160, 163
Salinity of soils, components of, 159
  distribution in soils and growth of plants, 170
  germination of seeds and, 83, 171
  ionic effects, 166
  plant growth and, 164
  tolerance of crops to, 169
  water availability and, 164
Salts (see Salinity of soils)
Saturation extract, 160
Sedimentary rocks, 14
Separates of soils (see also Mechanical composition of soils)
  cation-exchange capacity, 108
  chemical composition, 25, 249
  definition, 1
  mineralogical composition, 2, 15
  properties, 2
Site index, 32
Sod-bound condition, 186
Sodium, exchangeable and nonexchangeable in soils, 106
  exchangeable in soils, 115, 171
  nutritional effects in alkali soils, 174
  physical effects on soils, 172, 175
  potassium nutrition and supply of, 307
  removal from soils, 164
  saturation degree of different soils, 160
Soil class (see Mechanical composition of soils)
Soil conditioners (see Aggregants)
Soil-forming factors, 31
Soil solution and ion uptake by plants, 118
Soluble salts (see Salinity of soils)

Structure of soils, aggregate analysis and, 7
  bulk density and, 8
  characterization, 6
  cropping systems and, 9, 10
  deterioration with cropping, 8
  formation, 5
  infiltration and, 13
  measurement, 7
  nomenclature, 6
  organic matter and, 6, 8, 9, 14
  penetrometer measurements and, 8
  permeability and, 8, 13
  plant growth and, 9
  pore size and, 8, 12
  root development and, 11, 14
  seedling emergence and, 11
  sodium and, 172, 175
  stability, 5, 13
Succulence of plants, chloride supply and, 169
  diseases of plants and, 236
  nitrogen supply and, 224
Sugar content of plants and supply of nitrogen, 223

Temperature of soils, clay content of soils and, 20
  mulches and, 52
  nitrogen absorption by plants and, 196
  nitrogen content of soils and, 179
  nitrogen mineralization and, 196
  nitrogen supply and injury to plants at low values of, 235
  oxygen requirement of roots and, 95
  plant growth and, 197
  potassium supply and injury to plants at low values of, 315
Texture of soils (see Mechanical composition of soils)
Tillering and nitrogen supply, 230
Titration of acid soils and clays, 128
Total exchangeable bases defined, 107
Toxins in soils, 27, 98, 140, 159
Transpiration, 53

Vermiculite, cation-exchange capacity, 109
  potassium and, 297
Vitamins in soils, 29

Water, availability to plants, aeration
    of soils and, 57, 98
  carbohydrate translocation and, 73
  carbon dioxide assimilation and, 59
  critical period of, 76
  depth of free-water surface and, 66
  differentiation products in plants
    and, 71
  fertility of soils and, 78
  free energy and, 56, 57, 164
  grain and straw growth and, 73
  in soil profile, 34
  maturation of plants and, 75
  mechanical composition of soils
    and, 4, 61
  permanent wilting point and, 57
  plant growth and, 57
  responses indicative of, 60
  root and top growth and, 72
  root extension and, 62
  salinity of soils and, 164
  seed germination and, 70
  transpiration and, 59
  water absorption and, 57
  water level in soil and, 66
  available water capacity of soils, 57
  capillary rise in soils, 66
  clay content of soils and supply of,
    18
  fertility of soils and efficiency of
    utilization, 78
  field capacity of soils for, 47
  free energy of, basis for describing
    behavior in soils and plants, 39
    components, 41, 56
    freezing-point depression and, 42
    measurement, 42
    movement of water in soils and, 46
    plant growth and, 56, 161, 164

Water, free energy of, salinity of soils
    and, 161, 162, 164
    tensiometers and, 42
    units for expressing, 41
    vapor pressure and, 42
    water content of soils and, 43
    wetting and drying effects, 44
  movement in soils, field capacity and,
    47
    free energy and, 46
    movement of nitrate and, 205
    pore size and, 45
    potential gradient and, 45
  nitrogen content of plants and sup-
    ply of, 194
  nitrogen content of soils and supply
    of, 180
  nitrogen mineralization and supply
    of, 193
  potassium supply to plants and utili-
    zation of, 309
  removal of inhibitors by, 82
  vapor loss from soils (see also Evapo-
    transpiration), dry surface layer
    and, 50
    evaporation, 50
    fallowing and, 51
    mulches and, 52
    rainfall pattern and, 52
Waterlogged soils, adaptation of roots
    to conditions in, 96
  gases in, 89
  source of oxygen for plants in, 96
Weathering of rocks and minerals, 15,
    16, 18, 22
Weathering sequence of minerals, 22

Zinc availability at different pH values,
    150